Warning!

Violence and the Supernatural

The fictional worlds of Palladium Books® are violent, deadly and filled with supernatural monsters. Other-dimensional beings, often referred to as "demons," torment, stalk and prey on humans. Other alien life forms, monsters, gods and demigods, as well as magic, insanity, and war are all elements in these books.

Some parents may find the violence, magic and supernatural elements of the games inappropriate for young readers/players. We suggest parental discretion.

Please note that none of us at Palladium Books® condone or encourage the occult, the practice of magic, the use of drugs, or violence.

The Rifter® Number 40

Your guide to the Palladium Megaverse®!

First Printing – October, 2007

Copyright 2007 Palladium Books Inc.

Palladium Books®, Rifts®, The Rifter®, Coalition Wars®, RECON®, Nightbane®, Splicers®, Palladium Fantasy Role-Playing Game®, The Mechanoids®, The Mechanoid Invasion®, After the Bomb®, Phase World®, and Megaverse® are registered trademarks owned and licensed by Kevin Siembieda and Palladium Books Inc.

The slogan "A Megaverse of adventure – limited only by your imagination" and titles and names such as Dead Reign, Devil Muse, Rifts®: Promise of Power, Beyond the Supernatural, BTS-2, HU2, Chaos Earth, NEMA, MercTown, Merc Ops, Tome Grotesque, Beyond Arcanum, Naruni, Mechanoid Space, Dinosaur Swamp, Arzno, Lazlo, Victor Lazlo, Lazlo Agency, Lazlo Society, Heroes Unlimited, Powers Unlimited, Ninjas & Superspies, Aliens Unlimited, Mutant Underground, Mysteries of Magic, The Nursery, Hammer of the Forge, Hardware Unlimited, Gadgets Unlimited, Three Galaxies, Void Runners, Gramercy Island, Skraypers, Atorian Empire, Wormwood, Land of the Damned, The Citadel, The Palladium of Desires, Wolfen Wars, Wolfen, Wulfen, Cosmo-Knight, Cyber-Knight, Gargoyle Empire, Free Quebec, Xiticix, Xiticix Invasion, Fadetown, Siege on Tolkeen, Psyscape, Dweomer, ARCHIE-3, Northern Gun, Coalition States, Erin Tarn, Emperor Prosek, Splugorth, Splynncryth, Mega-Damage, Mega-Hero, Skelebot, SAMAS, Glitter Boy, Dog Boy, Dog Pack, Techno-Wizard, Ley Line Walker, Shifter, Bio-Wizardry, Psi-Stalker, Brodkil, Juicer, Crazy, 'Burbs, 'Borg, 'Bot, D-Bee, Chi-Town, Triax, NGR, and other names, titles, slogans, and likenesses of characters are trademarks owned by Kevin Siembieda and Palladium Books Inc.

Palladium Online **www.palladiumbooks.com**

The Rifter® #40 RPG sourcebook series is published by Palladium Books Inc., 12455 Universal Drive, Taylor, MI 48180. Printed in the USA.

Palladium Books® Presents:

THE RIFTER #40

BRANDT -97

Sourcebook and Guide to the Palladium Megaverse®

Coordinator & Editor in Chief: **Wayne Smith**

Editor: **Alex Marciniszyn**

Contributing Writers:
- **James M.G. Cannon**
- **Ed Emmer**
- **Carl Gleba**
- **S.E. Gibbons**
- **Josh Hilden**
- **Jason Marker**
- **John C. Philpott**
- **Jason Richards**
- **Joshua Sanford**
- **Kevin Siembieda**
- **Josh Sinsapaugh**

Interior Artists:
- **Nick Bradshaw**
- **Kent Burles**
- **Mark Dudley**
- **Comfort Deborah Love**
- **Allen Manning**
- **Brian Manning**
- **Mike Mumah**
- **Apollo Okamura**
- **Jeffrey Russell**
- **Adam Withers**

Cover Illustration: **Kevin Long**

Proofreader: **Julius Rosenstein**

Cover Logo Design: **Steve Edwards**

Credits Page Logo: **Niklas Brandt**

Typesetting: **Wayne Smith**

Keylining: **Kevin Siembieda**

Based on the RPG rules, characters,
concepts and Megaverse® created by **Kevin Siembieda**.

Special Thanks to all our contributors, writers and artists – and a special welcome on board to the artists and writers making their debut in this issue. Our apologies to anybody who got accidentally left out or their name misspelled.

– *Kevin Siembieda, 2007*

Contents – The Rifter® #40 – October, 2007

Page 6 – From the Desk of Kevin Siembieda

The Rifter® is 10 years old, and Publisher, Kevin Siembieda, reflects on what The Rifter® is all about – *a cosmic fanzine* – written for Palladium fans by Palladium fans. A forum to share ideas with other fans and have fun, and a chance to see your name in print. It is a vehicle created by Palladium for our fans by which fledgling writers and artists can test the waters, hone their skills and, perhaps, get discovered by the madmen at Palladium Books to go on to write full-fledged sourcebooks and games.

Ah, but it doesn't end there. Kevin reveals plans for **therifter.com** (should be up and running in October), and talks about the guy who has quietly kept The Rifter® running smoothly for ten years and counting, *Wayne Smith*.

Some Rifter® fun facts:

- The initial printing was 20,000 copies. It sold out in the first few months and we did a second printing of 5,000 copies. Today, the average printing is a modest 3,000-6,000 copies depending on the issue.

- *Jolly Blackburn*, a long time Palladium pal, did brand new, *Knights of the Dinner Table* comic strips for the first 12 issues or so before the workload became too much and he had to stop.

- *Apollo Okamura* is the only artist to contribute to EVERY issue of **The Rifter®**. He also got his *start* in **The Rifter®**.

- *Wayne Smith* has hand-picked every article in every issue of The Rifter®. Kevin Siembieda has pasted up every issue, #1-40, and handles the art direction.

- Issue #9½ was an elaborate *April Fool's Day joke* on Wayne Smith as well as a fun, bonus issue of **The Rifter®** for our fans. It is the only issue that is predominantly written by Palladium staff and professional writers. Wayne had no idea the issue was being produced until he was called into Kevin's office and asked to explain where this issue came from. The look on his face was priceless. The ruse was blown when Kevin started to laugh and Maryann started to take pictures.

- The cover to issue #10 is the *Simon Bisley* painting that was originally created as the cover to the **Teenage Mutant Ninja Turtles RPG, Second Edition**. However, the TMNT RPG was cancelled due to lack of interest by distributors and retailers. Rather than let this fantastic piece of art sit unseen, we used it as a cover on **The Rifter®**.

Page 7 – 10 Years of The Rifter®

Long time fan and Palladium writer, **Jason Richards** stretches back into the recesses of his memory to talk about the early days of Palladium online (predominately the efforts of Maryann Siembieda in those early days), and reminds us of the Palladium Mailing List (the PML), and many other fun memories and emotions, leading up to the launch of **The Rifter®**.

Thanks Jason, your recollections made all of us at the Palladium office smile, laugh and fondly remember some of the good ol' days. And you are right, **The Rifter®** continues to be a rare and wonderful vehicle for fans to unleash their imaginations and maybe realize a dream.

Page 8 – Palladium News

All the latest goings on, more about therifter.com, Palladium podcasts, downloadable adventures, and more.

The big news – Robotech® is back! Yep, Palladium Books has reacquired the Robotech® license and are busy planning a series of new RPGs and sourcebooks. Read the "official press release" on page 10. Oh, and to heap good news upon good news, we're shooting to have the first book out in time for Christmas 2007. Sing about that, Minmei.

Page 11 – Coming Attractions

The latest updates and descriptions of books currently in production or development.

Kevin Siembieda announced it first in a podcast interview and it has become one of the most talked about and anticipated releases for 2008: **Dead Reign**, Palladium's first ever "zombie RPG." And you get your first look at it inside this very issue of The Rifter® (starting on page 42).

The Minion War™ is off with a bang as fans go crazy over **Hades** and anxiously await **Dyval™, Dimensional Outbreak, Armageddon Unlimited™, Heroes of the Megaverse®**, and **Megaverse® in Flames**.

Rifts® and the Megaverse®, the Art of John Zeleznik is fabulous and available now, in three different versions.

Greeting cards, four Zeleznik prints, books delayed but not forgotten, and a list of 2008 releases round out this issues coming attractions.

Page 16 - The Palladium Fantasy RPG®

A Walk on the Wild Side – Barbarians, Part Two

John C. Philpott presents more interesting O.C.C.s, facts about barbarian society, stigmas, Hand to Hand: Wild, new Shamantic Chants, new skills, new abilities and more. Includes the Berserker O.C.C., Savage Warrior O.C.C., Native Tribesman O.C.C., and Wild Man O.C.C.

Ferocious and wild art by Brian and Allen Manning.

Page 38 – Beyond the Supernatural™

The Devil Muse

Josh Sinsapaugh whips up a delightfully wicked and vile creature for BTS-2.

Frightening illustration by Kent Burles.

Page 42 – Dead Reign™ – A preview of a new RPG

Your Guide to the Zombie Apocalypse

Josh Hilden and *Joshua Sanford* team up to give us the basic concept, setting, key types of zombies and even enough data for you to start playing! This game is gonna be awesome when it comes out Spring 2008.

Ghastly and gruesome art by Mike Mumah and Mark Dudley.

Page 55 – 2007 Christmas Surprise Package

Yep, it's that time of year again, when Palladium happily offers our annual Christmas Surprise Package or "Grag Bag." A fun way for us to dish out some Christmas cheer and for you to get a pile of gaming books, autographs and other fun stuff. Get all the details right here.

Page 57 – Rifts®, Palladium Fantasy®, and Others
Spell Books of the Megaverse®

S.E. Gibbons outdoes himself with this epic and wide-ranging look at how magic spell books are used across the Megaverse®. Suitable for any setting where magic and spell books may play a role. Presents all the whos, wheres, whys, hows, dangers, advantages and more behind spell books. We predict this is destined to be an instant classic.

Artwork by Kent Burles.

Page 69 – Rifts® Short Story
Circus! Circus!

Jason Marker gives us another poignant story in the Rifts Earth setting. Familiar characters and great personality makes this a joy to read.

Artwork by Mike Mumah.

Page 79 – Rifts® Adventure
The Spoils of War, Part One

Ed Emmer comes through with an epic adventure that puts players at odds with Coalition soldiers, pirates, slavers and demons, and pits them against the Xiticix and rival forces. It's all part of a quest for treasure and magic that starts at New Lazlo and leads to danger.

The player characters are mercs hired in the days shortly after the fall of Tolkeen to acquire secret plans somewhere in the Kingdom of Tolkeen. The journey takes many twists and turns on a wild ride of adventure, intrigue and surprises.

Includes new (optional) skills: Coalition Tactics, Lore: Xiticix and other source material like the TW Holo-Vid, the town of Lakeside, a new Xiticix hive, and much more.

Dynamic artwork by Comfort Deborah Love, Adam Withers and Nick Bradshaw.

Page 120 – The Hammer of the Forge™

Chapter 40: Some new twists and turns, vampires and a scary realm to explore and escape in this latest installment by James M.G. Cannon. Read and enjoy.

Artwork by Apollo Okamura.

Page 126 – Rifts®, Palladium Fantasy® & HU2™
Hades, Pits of Hell – Source material

Outtakes from *Carl Gleba's* **Dimension Book 10: Hades, Pits of Hell.** A handful of characters who had to be chopped out of the Hades book due to space limitations. Includes Warlord Thantu, leader of the Brass Guard II, as well as other Baal-Rogs on the team.

Demonic artwork by Jeffrey Russell.

The Theme for Issue 40

As is always the case with the October issue of the Rifter®, the theme is horror and things that go bump in the night. Hence, the zombies, Devil Muse, and array of demons and monsters, savage barbarians and undead cover. This issue also focuses on magic and adventure. And no, your eyes are not deceiving you,

this is an extra large issue with an additional 32 pages to celebrate **The Rifter's** ten year anniversary.

Another fun-filled issue designed to provoke your imagination, and inspire and motivate players and Game Masters alike to try new ideas and expand their gaming Megaverse®. When are you submitting your ideas?

The Cover

The cover was supposed to be a zombie-filled horror by Mike Mumah. Unfortunately, zombies attacked him before the piece was finished. While Mike and his wife managed to escape with their lives, Mike's cover got eaten. So we dipped into our archives and thought it would be nice to use the undead classic cover by *Kevin Long* for the original printing of **Rifts® World Book 4: Rifts® Africa.** We reversed the image to make the piece a bit different and new. Hey, it's a Long cover, always a crowd pleaser.

Optional and Unofficial Rules & Source Material

Please note that most of the material presented in **The Rifter®** is "unofficial" or "optional" rules and source material.

They are alternative ideas, homespun adventures and material mostly created by fellow gamers and fans like you, the reader. Things one can *elect* to include in one's own campaign or simply enjoy reading about. They are not "official" to the main games or world settings.

As for optional tables and adventures, if they sound cool or fun, use them. If they sound funky, too high-powered or inappropriate for your game, modify them or ignore them completely.

All the material in **The Rifter®** has been included for two reasons: One, because we thought it was imaginative and fun, and two, we thought it would stimulate your imagination with fun ideas and concepts that you can use (if you want to), or which might inspire you to create your own wonders.

www.palladiumbooks.com – Palladium Online

The Rifter® #41

- **Spoils of War conclusion.**
- **Material for *Heroes Unlimited*™.**
- **Material for *Rifts*®.**
- **Material for *Palladium Fantasy RPG*®.**
- **News and other developments.**
- **The next, epic chapter of *The Hammer of the Forge*™.**
- **Source material for the entire Palladium Megaverse®.**
- **Latest news and coming attractions.**
- **New contributors and fun. So please join us.**

Palladium Books® role-playing games ... infinite possibilities, limited only by your imagination™

From the Desk of Kevin Siembieda

Wow. Ten years of **The Rifter®**. I can hardly believe it until I look in the mirror and see all those silver hairs waving back at me. Ten years of giving fans, like you, a place where they can see their ideas published and shared by other gamers. Ten years of giving new writers a chance to test their mettle and artists to show off their craft. Ten years and 40 issues of **The Rifter®** offering alternative ideas and rules, realms of adventure, stories of horror and heroes, and hours of gaming fun.

The Rifter® is for the Fans

The cool thing about **The Rifter®** is that it is created for YOU, our fans. Not just as a quasi-magazine/sourcebook with game material, tips and adventures for your games, but as a vehicle – a voice – for YOU.

A place where *you* can get your ideas, stories, adventures and characters *published*. It's a way you can share your ideas and game creations with other gamers and see your name in print. Sadly, I think many people have forgotten that. I've actually had a few fans express a wish that they could send their game material to us and have it "posted or something where other fans could use it." That's what **The Rifter®** is for. It is an awesome way to reach other fans and see your name in lights . . . er, in print.

Send in your fan submissions!

Please, if you have some cool villains, a great adventure, optional rules, new magic spells or super abilities, or a hankering to write a short story (4-20 pages), write it up and send it in to **The Rifter®**! We are always looking for fun, cool source material to print.

We need material for everything: **Heroes Unlimited™, Ninjas and Superspies™, After the Bomb®, Palladium Fantasy RPG®, Nightbane®, Beyond the Supernatural™, Phase World®, Wormwood™,** and **Rifts®!**

The Rifter® Legacy

You can submit once and never again, or send in submissions for Wayne's consideration on a regular basis. **The Rifter®** is also an excellent vehicle for those of you with aspirations of becoming a professional artist or writer. **The Rifter®** has worked out great as a sort of talent show where we can find and cultivate new talent. The following artists and writers all got their start by contributing to **The Rifter®** and have gone on to illustrate and/or write for Palladium Books as freelance creators.

Adam Withers	Irvin Jackson
Apollo Okamura	Jason Marker
Brian & Allen Manning	Mark Oberle
Comfort Deborah Love	John Philpott
Nick Bradshaw	Jason Richards
Brandon Aten	Josh Sinsapaugh
Carl Gleba	Taylor White
Josh Hilden	. . . and others.

This makes **The Rifter®** sorta like Palladium's own *American Idol* except without the music, singing, competition, judges and television. Okay, it's nothing like *American Idol*, and even if it never leads to professional work in the game business, it's fun to see your work in print and seen by others.

If your fellow gamers have suggested you have great ideas and that you should send 'em in to Palladium, do it. It doesn't have to be a lot of material (4-20 pages of text can do the trick for writers, 6-10 photocopies of artwork can be enough for artists), we're looking for quality, new ideas and fun, not a polished masterpiece.

therifter.com

For those of you who might be *too chicken* to send in art samples or a short story or source material to see *print* in an "official" Palladium *publication*, how about submitting something to **therifter.com**?

You heard right, we're launching the **Rifter®** concept online. A place where Palladium gamers can post their favorite character(s), villain(s), monster(s), equipment(s), spell(s), adventure(s), house rules, short stories and a whole lot more for the whole world to read. We're calling it **therifter.com** because we want it to be an online resource created by YOU – Palladium fans – for other Palladium fans.

We will be keeping the printed material in **The Rifter®** separate from the material created and posted by the online community, so you'll get more unique material in two different mediums.

We only ask that you limit the source material and stories posted online to Palladium's Megaverse of role-playing games, keep the material suitable for ALL AGES, PG-13 (no gruesome gore, wild sex, decadence, gratuitous violence, etc.), and that you keep in mind that the whole idea behind **The Rifter®** (in any medium) is to share ideas and source material for role-playing games and to have FUN! Don't get snooty, no elitism, no cruel criticism, just have fun.

Use **The Rifter®** that is printed and **therifter.com** as places where YOU can support the worlds that haven't gotten too many sourcebooks in recent years, like **After the Bomb®**, **Nightbane®** and **Splicers®**, as well as fan favorites like **Rifts®, Heroes Unlimited™, Ninjas and Superspies™, the Palladium Fantasy RPG®**, and others.

The name is Smith . . .
Wayne Smith

We can't have a 10 year anniversary issue of **The Rifter®** without a tip of the hat and a thank you to *Wayne Smith*.

Wayne has been the Editor-in-Chief for all 10 years and 40 issues. He was handed the reins to **The Rifter®** when he was 22, and has grown up with the publication. Not only has he honed his own skills in editing and layout, but he's helped us discover many of the freelance writers Palladium uses today. Nice work, Wayne.

In addition to his duties as the *Editor-in-Chief* of **The Rifter®**, Wayne edits *all* of Palladium's RPG titles (as does Alex Marciniszyn), does all the typesetting, handles all the desk-top publishing (covers, advertisements, posters, prints, flyers, etc.), tweaks and fools around with artwork and various graphics, helps with marketing, does a great deal of the online work, is an idea guy, genius, and helps wherever he can. He's grown into a fine man who I'm proud to call my friend, and has become my right- (or is that left?) hand man at Palladium Books.

When I asked Wayne what he learned from his years at Palladium Books, he said with a chuckle: "It's hard to fight back when you're laughing." Unfortunately, I don't have a clue as to what that could possibly mean. That's my story and I'm sticking to it.

Happy 10 Year Anniversary, Wayne. May there be many more years of **The Rifter®** to come.

– Kevin Siembieda, 2007

10 Years of
The Rifter®

By Jason Richards

You know, a lot can happen in ten years. It spans three different terms of the presidency. Toddlers grow old enough to have sleep-overs where they stay up all night role-playing with their friends. A junior high kid can get through all of high school, college, *and* graduate school without too much in the way of academic gymnastics. We refer to eras in our country's history in such lengths of time. It has certainly been an *era* in Palladium Books' history. With this issue of *The Rifter®* completing the cycle of 10 years of publication, I think it's a good time to reflect. Hopefully my memory is good!

I remember when I first heard about the project that would come to be called *The Rifter*. The first people outside of Kevin's confidence to know about it were subscribers to a fan-run listserve that functioned as the unofficial online home of Palladium Books (so close to being official, in fact, that I recall Palladium giving a little money to the guy who ran it to help him out when his server needed upgrading). It was called, creatively enough, the Palladium Mailing List, or the PML. If you're a younger fan reading this, the thought of being a gamer without the Internet's vast wealth spread before you is probably as foreign and incomprehensible as trying to imagine a world where the Earth was still flat, but the 'net was young then, and Palladium's presence on it was even younger. "The list" was the only real interactive forum for Palladium fans to talk about the tricks and trades of the game, bounce around new ideas, and enjoy the community. The official online contact that we had with the company in those days was with then-Vice President, Maryann, who was one of what I would guess were 100 or more *active* members of the PML, in addition to an untold number of lurkers.

It's times like this that make me wish that I had backed up all of those thousands upon thousands of emails; hundreds every day over years, 95% of which were comments and critiques on someone or other's new bit of source material they had whipped up. We were, more than anything else, a community of amateur RPG designers and Game Masters, writing up new O.C.C.s, weapons, magic spells, combat rules, Morphus tables, or anything else you can imagine, and everyone rushed to get a word in on the day's new ideas. There were regular features like Nathan Taylor's "N.P.C. of the Week," and some large fan fiction projects like "Siege on Tolkeen." Netbooks were written, like one for "Hook, Line, and Sinker" adventures, and collaborative projects produced things like Coalition prison camps for *Rifts®*. And, of course, there were the common debates and discussions about things like whether or not a vampire could withstand a nuclear blast, and whether or not lasers really "kick" or make sound. In any case, it was lots of fun, and a great supportive environment for gamers of all stripes.

One day Maryann sent out a message saying that Palladium was going to take another stab at the periodicals market with an (almost) entirely fan-written, quarterly magazine designed to really cater to the fans. Needless to say, it created a stir, as we all imagined our endless catalogs of personal source material being published in something with the great Kevin Siembieda's name on the title page.

We all brushed up our best stuff to submit it, and for me that meant a pile of my favorite Techno-Wizardry creations that needed to be edited, fine-tuned, and run past some friends for a good vetting. As a pretty good example of how different things were then, I distinctly remember sending in my first submissions, not to a palladiumbooks.com email address, but to Maryann's personal AOL account. The Editor-in-Chief of this new undertaking was current Palladium fixture, Wayne Smith, who was then only a part-timer!

I don't envy those two for having to sort through that first wave of Unsolicited Manuscript forms and piles of years of accumulated material ranging from new super abilities, to entire adventures, to martial arts forms. Somehow they made sense of it all and put together the first issue. As I look through my copy of *The Rifter® #1*, I see familiar names from the days when Palladium barely had a website, and the Megaversal Bulletin Boards were in the distant future. Almost all of that first material came from members of the PML. The same is true for the first several *Rifters*, all of which featured material formed in the collective stew that was the Palladium Mailing List. From there the recognition of this sourcebook/magazine/newsletter/etc. grew and more and more fans began to get involved. Palladium marched on with another success to pile on their list of achievements.

Yes, ten years is a long time. I'm typing this up on a computer that is about ten times more powerful and a quarter the price of the family computer I worked on through the nights back then. I'll email this to the office late tonight without having to worry about waking anyone up with the screech of a modem establishing an extremely tenuous connection to my ISP. I nostalgically think about that 16 year old kid being so excited when he got word that Palladium was going to publish some of his writing. Ten years is, indeed, a long time.

If you can measure eras in tens of years, it's been an era of good times for Palladium fans. *The Rifter®* is an embodiment of that. If you have ever talked to me about Palladium, you've heard me say that it's a company that *really* cares about its fans. For Kevin and co. to give fans the chance to be published in something like *The Rifter* is a genuinely special thing. What's more, they are so encouraging of all of us taking that next step to push on with our writing and designing into something more than an idle hobby. I, for one, can vouch for that level of support. And for that reason, I've always loved *The Rifter* and what it represents. I hope that one day when I'm giving an interview on some national platform to talk about my hot new book, I'll have the chance to point to 1998 as the year that started it all, when I was given a shot by people I admired, who I now count as friends and colleagues.

Hopefully I haven't dragged this on too long, but I thought that this would be a good chance to pause and reflect on ten great years of fan imagination. May it be another ten years, at least.

Jason Richards, 2007

News————————

By Kevin Siembieda, the guy who should know

Robotech is back
and Palladium has it!

Yeah, it's official, Palladium has the license to produce **Robotech®** and **Robotech® the Shadow Chronicles** *role-playing games.*

These will be ALL NEW, pen and paper, role-playing games and sourcebooks for a new era of **Robotech®** role-playing fun.

Yes, we will use *some* of the artwork, text, and ideas from Palladium's famous **Robotech®** publications from the 1980s and 1990s, but EVERYTHING (much like what we did with *Rifts® Ultimate Edition*) will be rewritten, updated, tweaked, expanded upon, rules modified, and the whole kit and caboodle repackaged.

Apollo Okamura is working on the cover to the first book, **Robotech® The Shadow Chronicles RPG**, as well as doing some of the interior artwork. Meanwhile, we are lining up additional artists and writers for this and future **Robotech® RPG** titles, finishing the compiling of our research and gearing up for actual production. Other artists will include Palladium artists as well as other notable **Robotech®** artists like the Waltrips, Ben Dunn, maybe even Tommy Yune and others. We want the new **Robotech® RPG** products to be fun on every level.

See the price, 2007 release date and more specifics in the *Coming Attractions* section of this issue.

Mark Evans paintings for sale

Rifts® CCG paintings by Mark Evans as well as some of his other pieces of artwork are currently being offered on my, Kevin Siembieda's, *Ebay store* – **Kevin's Toys, Art & Collectibles** (web address: http://stores.ebay.com/kevinstoys-artandcollectibles). The paintings are extremely reasonably priced and a rare opportunity as Mark Evans has gone *completely digital* with his new works, meaning there is no original painting to sell.

The store primarily sells toys, some books and some artwork at set prices for immediate purchase. Most items are from my personal collection.

Kevin's Toys & Collectibles will soon host a number of **Palladium Art and Collectibles Auctions** starting at the end of September and continuing into December. These auctions will offer first printings and out of print Palladium RPG titles, original artwork, and other collectibles. We hosted two such auctions over the summer with good to excellent results. After cost, all money earned goes toward bankrolling Palladium RPG books and projects. Like the original artwork, many are one-of-a-kind or very few in number, rare, out of print and collectible. Most are from my private collection.

therifter.com

This Fall (October?), **The Rifter®** gets a sister website we will be calling **therifter.com** (hey, what else?).

The Rifter® sourcebook/magazine you are holding in your hands will continue to exist as a print publication. In fact, subscriptions are at an all time high and we encourage people to buy The Rifter® in stores or subscribe. Our plans are to keep The Rifter® going another 10 years (or longer)!

therifter.com is something completely different and separate, though it is being founded under the same principles – a forum where gamers can share their house rules, characters, adventures, and ideas. But material that is completely different than what appears in the *print* edition of **The Rifter®**.

It has been driving me crazy that Palladium fans seem to have forgotten that **The Rifter®** is supposed to be for *them*. A place where they can see their writing, stories, characters, adventures, etc. in print, read and shared by other fans. A slick "fanzine" and talent show. Maybe we made The Rifter® a little too slick, because a large number of people don't seem to feel comfortable sending their writing and art to the book.

My solution? **therifter.com** – an online forum where you can post your fan-based house rules, characters, adventures, monsters, villains, fan-fiction/short stories, etc. **We want material for ALL of Palladium's game lines** (with the exception of

Robotech®, sorry). Try to keep the material PG-13, *no conversion rules to other intellectual properties (i.e. no stats for Star Wars, Star Trek, Marvel Superheroes, etc.), and have fun, fun, fun!*

The website should be up and running sometime in October, 2007. We invite you to contribute, but please, also send other original (not stuff posted online) contributions to the *pen and paper edition* of **The Rifter**®. We are ALWAYS looking for fun source material, adventures, short stories, comic strips, cartoons, and artwork for this "fan" based publication.

Remember, the print edition of **The Rifter**® is also where we *scout and try new talent* – artists and writers – for work in our official game publications. **The Rifter**® is the place to not only get your fan work published, but a place to *catch our attention* for potential future recruitment on Palladium's role-playing game titles. **therifter.com** is the place to be silly, have fun, share ideas and adventures, get quick feedback, comments and criticism (hey, folks, be kind) and become a more active part of Palladium's expanding RPG online community.

Podcasts, podcasts everywhere

All of a sudden we're all podcast crazy here at Palladium Books. Podcasts are live or prerecorded audio interviews and such that are done on the internet and available for your listening pleasure online. Better yet, they can be downloaded to your iPod (hence the name "podcast"), saved and listened to anytime, anywhere. Cool, huh?

I recently did a two-hour podcast on the **Space Station Liberty** show on the **Talkshoe network** with *Robotech Master* and *Tommy Yune*, the writer behind the **Robotech**® **The Shadow Chronicles** animated movie and mover and shaker at Harmony Gold. It was a blast, and we revealed a lot of information about the upcoming **Robotech**® **role-playing game** line, the recently announced live action **Robotech**® *movie*, and other interesting topics.

I have also done a few podcast interviews at conventions over the last couple of years, but as the technology has grown, so too has the number of Palladium fans who have started their own "podcast shows" online.

Podcasts for Palladium fans by Palladium fans. The first one is *Matthew Daye's* **Gateway to the Megaverse**®. It airs "live" every Monday from 6:00 to 8:00 P.M. EST. and can be downloaded anytime thereafter. So far, guests have included me, *Kevin Siembieda* and freelance writers *Carl (Minion War) Gleba*, and *Brandon (Madhaven) Aten*. I'll be a regular guest, and numerous other Palladium creators and troublemakers will also be interviewed. All interviews are topical and fun, and questions from the audience provide an additional interactive element. Check it out at www.talkshoe.com/talkshoe/web/talkcast.jsp?masterId=50867&cmd=tc (web address).

I am working with *Chris Perrin* of *commondialogue* to set up a second, regular podcast Palladium show we're gonna call **Echoes from the Rifts**®. It will feature recorded interviews with me and many other Palladium creators and staff, as well as audio reviews of Palladium products, and other fun things. This is still a work in progress, but we are both pumped up about this show. We hope to have Echoes up sometime in October 2007.

Meanwhile, I'm having Thom and Wayne explore the possibilities of doing streaming video on the Palladium website (www.palladiumbooks.com). Actually, podcasts and videos have been something I've been talking about adding to the website for the last three years, but one failed venture with a website developer, the Crisis and our insane workload have prevented us from moving forward with it. Now, thanks to the dedication, friendship and hard work of Matthew Daye and Chris Perrin, we have podcasts in place.

More online fun is coming

Downloadable adventures is an entirely digital product that will provide gamers with a fully fleshed out adventure to play. We expect to offer a whole bunch of adventures for many (eventually, ALL our game lines) with 1-4 new ones being posted every month. As a "digital product" we'll be charging a nominal fee of $2-$3 per each downloadable adventure. Most will be adventures written by name writers like Gleba, Aten, White, Campbell, Richards, Siembieda and others. Some of the downloads will offer G.M. materials and aids, rather than an adventure. All of it will be fun and good.

Palladium Color Catalog Shipped to 18,000 gamers

You may be one of those getting a color catalog in the mail. If you get a second or third catalog, just pass it along to a friend or your local game store or game club. (A minor glitch in the system sent some folks two copies, a few three.)

If you want one of our FREE 40 page, 8 ½ x 11 color catalogs, just send us a letter or postcard requesting one (or more) and we'll send it right out. Make sure you include your current street address, and don't forget your apartment number.

Remember, Palladium role-playing games and sourcebooks are available at fine hobby and game stores across the country. *Please support your local stores.*

Annual X-Mas Grab Bag

Read all the details *elsewhere* in this issue and . . . season's greetings and good cheer from all of us at Palladium Books.

Margaret Hailey returns to Palladium

After a summer of working at Cedar Point Amusement Park (and seeing what the real world is like), our favorite intern has returned to school at U of M and giving Palladium Books a hand. She was a big help labeling the 19,000 Palladium Catalogs sent to gamers across the country, and we look forward to her smiling face and continuing support.

Jason Marker joins Palladium staff

Freelance writer, frequent contributor to **The Rifter**® and regular volunteer helper, Jason Marker, joins the Palladium staff. He is a welcomed edition to our crew and vows to help Palladium get new game books out on a faster basis.

Teresa is the new sales person

A full time job and other commitments have necessitated volunteer, Tony Falzon, to leave Palladium Books. His position as volunteer sales rep will be assumed by another long-time friend and sales wizard, Teresa. Welcome to the team.

ROBOTECH® RETURNS TO PALLADIUM BOOKS®

Ground-breaking series of role-playing games mark a triumphant comeback at the pioneering RPG publisher.

TAYLOR, MICHIGAN — It's official! **Palladium Books** and **Harmony Gold USA** are proud to announce a new license for pen-and-paper role-playing games and sourcebooks based on the *Robotech®* television series and its latest sequel, *Robotech® The Shadow Chronicles®*.

Palladium's *Robotech®* RPG, first published in 1986, was the game that introduced many gamers to the role-playing experience. "Palladium has a long tradition of working with Robotech and we are thrilled that they have this license again," said Tommy Yune, creative director at Harmony Gold and director of *Robotech® The Shadow Chronicles®*.

"We look forward to working with Tommy Yune and Harmony Gold to create a brand new series of RPG titles for the next era of Robotech gaming." said Kevin Siembieda, publisher and founder of Palladium Books. "It is our intention to make the upcoming new *Robotech®* and *Robotech® The Shadow Chronicles®* RPGs even more fun and exciting than the original RPG to please long-time gamers and enthrall a new generation of fans."

Robotech® made its debut in 1985 as a blockbuster animated television series that attracted an audience of all ages, from children to adults. The cutting-edge saga of war, love, and the indomitable human spirit spanned three epic generations of heroes battling to keep Earth safe from alien invaders. Robotechnology is the synthesis of human science and alien technology to create robotic vehicles, power armor, aircraft, and spacecraft to defend the Earth. Among the most famous of these mecha are the transformable *Cyclones, Veritech Fighters,* and *Shadow Fighters.*

Robotech® then blasted into the new millennium with the highly-anticipated continuation of the saga through *Robotech® The Shadow Chronicles®*, and the recent announcement that Tobey (*Spider-Man*) Maguire's production company and Warner Bros. Pictures had optioned the rights to produce *Robotech®* as a **live action** motion picture. Maguire is said to be considering the lead role. Palladium Books is aiming to release its first RPG, *Robotech® the Shadow Chronicles® Role-Playing Game*, in time for Christmas 2007.

ROBOTECH®
THE SHADOW CHRONICLES® RPG

The role-playing game will pick up where the DVD movie begins. The return of the Robotech Expeditionary Force, the separation of Rick Hunter and the SDF-3 from the rest of the fleet, and everything else that is part of the universe of *Robotech® The Shadow Chronicles®*.

- Written by *Robotech®* RPG creator Kevin Siembieda.
- Cover by veteran artist Apollo Okamura.
- Packed with detailed illustrations throughout.
- Comprehensive character, mecha, spacecraft, and vessel statistics and images.
- Mecha pilots and other fleet personnel Occupation Character Classes (O.C.C.).
- Additional background information and detail as space permits.
- Fast-playing RPG rules. Mega-Damage setting.
- Printed in popular manga size for easy portability.
- End of November release for holiday season (tentative).
- 192 pages – $16.95 retail – Cat. No. 550.
- Available in the U.S. and Canada only.

PALLADIUM BOOKS'
PLANS FOR ROBOTECH®

Here are the answers to frequently asked questions about Palladium's future Robotech plans:

- At this time, Palladium has no plans to reprint the past *Robotech®* role-playing games and sourcebooks in their original form. The upcoming RPG books will be new.
- Palladium will use some of the *best* artwork and text from the original games, but all of the new books will be substantially rewritten, expanded upon, and illustrated with much new artwork.
- The timeline will be brought into line with Harmony Gold's current Robotech continuity.
- Statistics will be adjusted and tweaked, rules will be modified and updated, and fan input will be taken into careful consideration.
- Much more attention will be devoted to *The Southern Cross* segment of the *Robotech®* saga.
- The current, but *evolving* plan is to release *Robotech®* RPGs and sourcebooks in the following order: *Robotech® The Shadow Chronicles® RPG*, a *New Generation/Invid* sourcebook, *The Macross Saga RPG*, and *Southern Cross* sourcebook followed by more sourcebooks for them all, rewritten and retold.
- **The manga size:** With the popularity of manga and anime, this compact format will pay homage to Robotech's Japanese origins. The games and sourcebooks will contain about 192-224 pages and will measure approximately 5 x 7 ½ inches. They will read front to back with art and text at a readable size, sell for $16.95 retail, and contain material that should appeal, not just to gamers, but to anyone who enjoys *Robotech®*.
- Other advantages of the manga size: Portable and easy to carry in a jacket pocket, backpack, etc. For collectors of manga, the game will fit conveniently on the shelf with their books. Furthermore, the format is expected to attract manga readers who have never played a role-playing game. Many first-time gamers discovered the genre with the original *Robotech® RPG* and sourcebooks in comic book stores.
- **Deluxe editions:** Palladium is also considering producing special "deluxe" printings of the new **Robotech®** role-playing games and sourcebooks in the traditional 8½ x 11 size with 160-224 pages (or more), featuring additional artwork, mecha transformation sequences, and details.
- Palladium has been conducting research for months in anticipation of the new *Robotech® RPG*, and is ready to dive into the production of the first of many, new *Robotech®* titles.

ABOUT PALLADIUM BOOKS

Palladium Books established itself as a pioneer in the implementation of a unified role-playing game system with *The Mechanoid Invasion®* in 1981. The company was also the first to introduce the perfect bound, trade paperback format to the RPG industry. Now in its third decade of operation, Palladium continues to be an innovator as one of the longest-surviving independent RPG publishers. Visit PalladiumBooks.com for more information.

ABOUT HARMONY GOLD

Harmony Gold has been active in the production, acquisition and distribution of quality programming worldwide since its inception in 1983, producing some of the television industry's classic and history-making programs. Visit HarmonyGold.com or Robotech.com for additional information.

Coming Attractions

Also by Kevin Siembieda, the guy who should know

Dead Reign

Zombies coming to Palladium in 2008

I don't know why everybody seems to love zombies, but they do. I casually mention it on a podcast and the next thing I know, there's a lot of excitement about this new title.

Your first look at Dead Reign is *in this very issue* **of The Rifter®!** Bear in mind that this article is just *part* of the story and setting, with suggestions for using existing rules to play right now. The final RPG will provide greater detail, specific O.C.C.s, a variety of zombies, dangers, challenges and butt-kicking action.

- S.D.C. setting.
- Zombies have taken over the world.
- Zombies control the cities. Humans hide in remote wilderness areas.
- Zombies and their evil lords capture and pen humans for food, torture and experimentation.
- Humankind fights to rescue those they can, and destroy as many of the abominations as they can.
- Is this the end of the world as we know it? Pick up a copy of Dead Reign and find out.
- Written by Josh Hilden and Joshua Sanford.
- Coming Spring 2008.

Minion War™ series off to an epic start

Rifts® Dimension Book 10: Hades

Fans have gone wild over **Hades, Pits of Hell,** the first book in the Minion War series.

This big, juicy, 224 page book is jam-packed with demons (new and old), Netherbeasts, Worms of Taut, the Demon Priest, information about Hades and maps, descriptions of key people and places, weird and deadly weapons, S.D.C. and M.D.C. stats, mention of the Palladium Fantasy RPG®, and much, much more.

- S.D.C./Hit Point stats for use in the Palladium Fantasy RPG® and Heroes Unlimited.
- Demon society and hierarchy.
- 30 demons and Sub-Demons described; expanded descriptions.
- Six completely new demons including the Soul Catcher, Death Demon, Demon Flies, and more.

- Demon High Priest O.C.C. for use as an NPC villain (new).
- Demon Bone Weapons and Soulmancy (new).
- Netherbeasts – demonic riding animals (new) – and monsters.
- Hades mapped and described.
- Encounter tables for almost every region.
- Weird plants, terrain, weather and phenomena.
- M.D.C. stats for those world settings.
- S.D.C. stats make the characters easy to use in any S.D.C. setting.
- World information and many adventure ideas.
- The Minion War series is unique, because EACH of the six titles works as a *stand-alone sourcebook* in and of itself, as well as being part of an epic *crossover series* that depicts the Hells of **Hades** and **Dyval™**, and then takes the War to **Phase World®, the Three Galaxies™,** the Earth of **Heroes Unlimited™** and **Rifts®** (as well as the **Palladium Fantasy RPG®** and others).
- Breathtaking artwork by Russell, Burles, and others.
- John Zeleznik cover painting.
- Written by Carl Gleba. Additional text by Kevin Siembieda.
- 224 pages – Cat. No. 872 – $22.95 retail.
- **Available now!**

Rifts® Dimension Book™ 11: Dyval™, Hell Unleashed – October

Dyval is the next book in the Minion War™ series and is the companion to **Hades.** It presents **Dyval,** the other Hell and arch-rival to the minions of Hades.

The Dyval Dimension Book™ is packed with more bizarre infernal beings, weird creatures, strange and horrible realms of Hell, new Dyvalians, Netherbeasts, monsters, magic, people, places and ideas by Carl Gleba.

- The hellish dimension of Dyval mapped and described.
- Deevils and monsters galore.
- Magic weapons and horrific war beasts.
- World information and adventure ideas.
- A stand-alone Dimension Book that is also the second step in an epic, five book adventure that spills across the Palladium Megaverse®.
- Artwork by Nick Bradshaw, Mike Mumah, and others.
- Cover painting by John Zeleznik.
- Written by Carl Gleba.
- 192 pages – Cat. No. 873 – $22.95 retail.
- Ships at the end of October, 2007.

Rifts® Dimension Book 12: Dimensional Outbreak™

The Minion War™ spills into **Phase World®, the city of Center** and the **Three Galaxies™.** The epic scale of the Minion War just got bigger and even the Worlds of Warlock, the Splugorth and Naruni are involved.

- Phase World's *Center* described and mapped. Four new levels, including the Gateland, Central Station, the Spaceport, Repo-Yards, Free Trade Zone, Warlock Market, notable merchants and places of business, and much more.
- Demon Knights, Star Slayers, demonic legions and more.
- Demonic spaceships, magic weapons and new horrors.
- Deevil fortifications and defenses.
- Space spell magic (new).
- Spaceships, power armor and other gear.
- The plot for conquering the Three Galaxies.
- A stand-alone Dimension Book that is also the third step in an epic, five book crossover that spills across the Palladium Megaverse®.
- Artwork by Apollo Okamura, Mike Mumah, and others.
- John Zeleznik cover painting.
- Written by Carl Gleba.
- 192 pages – Cat. No. 875 – $22.95 retail. November or December, 2007 release.

Armageddon Unlimited™

The Minion War™ in the *Heroes Unlimited*™ setting

The Minion War has rolled into countless dimensions with a roar, but not on *Heroes Unlimited*™ *Earth*. Here, the monsters of Dyval are working covertly behind the scenes, causing chaos and mayhem, and have brought Earth to the brink of global war. However, the demons' dimensional incursions have alerted super-heroes around the globe to their sinister presence and the heroes are mounting their own response. Can the heroes of Earth stop the demons' plans to plunge our world into Armageddon?!

- Superheroes vs demons!
- New Powers and Super Abilities.
- New Super Classes like the Heroic Hellion and the Demon Hunter, and variations on old classes like the Mystically Bestowed, Enchanted Weapon and Enchanted Object, only with a demonic twist!
- Notable Magic Guilds and their knowledge of the Minion War.

- The Deevils' plans to cause global Armageddon and create their own hellish version of Rifts Earth under their control.
- Notable Deevils, Anarchy Teams, and their henchmen.
- The Deevil Super Fortress mapped out and described, and the hellish minions who guard it.
- The Demons' response and their rival incursion into Earth.
- The Heroes' response – specific heroes locked in the greatest battle against evil the world has ever known.
- An optional, detailed time-line of events that have brought Earth to the brink of global annihilation. Game Masters can use the time-line to weave a long-term campaign or use it as background in their current games.
- The first Heroes of the Megaverse will make their grand appearance in the battle to save Earth!
- Written by the Head Minion, Carl Gleba.
- 160 pages – Cat. No. 527 – $18.95 retail. December, 2007, or January, 2008 release.

Rifts®/Phase World® Sourcebook: Heroes of the Megaverse®

War factions from the Hells, Hades and Dyval, have discovered the existence of a great mystic artifact that has been hidden and protected by the Cosmo-Knights of the Three Galaxies. And both sides want it.

The artifact is an ancient Rune Book that contains the names of the 2000 greatest heroes the Megaverse® has ever known. But it is more than a historical document, it is a magic item of unparalleled power.

According to legend, the tome has many great powers. One such power is that reading the name of any one person inscribed, while evoking the proper magic, will give the reader the knowledge and power of that great hero. And many are the powers of the 2000.

The artifact also has its dangers. It is said if the *List of Heroes*™ is wrested from the Cosmo-Knights and kept locked in the pits of Hell, then the Knights and all heroes of the Three Galaxies will lose hope and flounder. If the book is destroyed, it is said, the Cosmo-Knights will cease to exist within a generation and the forces of Chaos shall reign. Needless to say, the Lords of Hell, the Splugorth and many others who serve Chaos would do anything to get their hands on the *List of Heroes.*

Rumor also suggests that the artifact may hold clues to the location of the Cosmic Forge, perhaps in some sort of code or the memories of the heroes who can be evoked. And there are many other tales of cosmic power, healing and knowledge all associated with the book and the ghosts of the heroes named on its pages.

As circumstance would have it, the *List of Heroes* has fallen into the possession of the Player Characters. The question is, can they keep it safe from the forces of two Hells until it can be returned to the safekeeping of the Cosmo-Knights? Or will they misuse it for their own, personal gain? How will this scenario unfold? Who is on that list? Buy a copy, play out the scenario and find out.

Note: This is the Adventure Sourcebook that prints the names of everyone who purchased the *A Megaverse United*™ limited edition print. It is also likely to include the names of some winners from the *Heroes of the Megaverse® character contest* as fully statted out characters (heroes and villains).

- Minion War tie-in adventure sourcebook.
- Written by Kevin Siembieda.
- Illustrated by various Palladium heroes.
- 96 pages – Cat. No. 877 – $14.95 retail.
- Not yet scheduled. Shooting for December, 2007, release but might slip into early 2008.

Rifts® and the Megaverse®
The Art of John Zeleznik
– "Softcover" Edition

The book looks fantastic. The reproduction quality is impeccable, the color beautiful, the layout breathtaking, the commentaries by John Zeleznik fun and informative. And this beautiful book is only $22.95 – a steal for all you get.

- 50+ Zeleznik paintings are depicted.
- Dozens of color preliminary paintings.
- 200+ concept drawings.
- 15 years of artwork for Rifts® and other Palladium titles.
- High quality reproduction, and excellent paper quality.
- Paintings, artwork, cover and layout by John Zeleznik.
- Foreword by *Kevin Siembieda.* Introduction by *Zeleznik.*
- Softbound, 8 ½ x 11 inches. Color cover, glossy paper stock.
- 128 pages of full color – Cat. No. 2510 – $22.95 retail plus $6 for shipping in the USA, $10 to Canada, and $15 to all other countries for shipping. Available now.

Rifts® and the Megaverse®
New – "Hardcover" Edition

The book looks fantastic. The reproduction quality is impeccable, the color beautiful, the layout breathtaking, the commentaries by John Zeleznik fun and informative. And this beautiful, limited edition book is only $50.00 – we wanted to give those a chance who can't get a Masterwork Edition HC to still be able

to get a special, hardcover, coffee table edition. Perfect for Christmas.

- Only 300 copies.
- Each comes with a "printed" signature card signed by John Zeleznik and Kevin Siembieda.
- 50 Zeleznik paintings are depicted.
- Dozens of color preliminary paintings.
- More than 200 concept drawings.
- High quality reproduction, and excellent paper quality.
- Paintings, artwork, design and layout, all by John Zeleznik.
- Foreword by Kevin Siembieda. Introduction by Zeleznik.
- Hardcover, 8 ½ x 11 inches. Color cover, glossy paper stock.
- 128 pages of full color – Cat. No. 2510-HC – $50.00 retail plus $10 for shipping in the USA, $12 to Canada, and $20 to all other countries for shipping.
- Available now, for the first time.

Rifts® and the Megaverse®:
The Art of John Zeleznik
– Collector's *"Masterwork"* Edition

A great Christmas Gift! Rare and beautiful. Don't forget about the John Zeleznik Masterwork Edition that comes with an *original piece of artwork, one of Zeleznik's concept sketches.* It makes a wonderful birthday, anniversary or Christmas present ideal for the super-fan and collector.

- A truly one-of-a-kind collectible.
- Only 96 copies left (limited to 199 total).
- Color cover, different than the soft cover.
- Numbered and signed by *John Zeleznik* and *Kevin Siembieda.*
- 128 pages – quality color – Cat. No. 2510-CML – available only from Palladium Books and only while supplies last.
- *$125.00 each,* plus $15 for shipping in the USA, $20 to Canada, and $35 to all other countries for shipping. MUST be sent UPS, Priority Mail/Certified or some other way it can be tracked and is insured to arrive. Available now.
- Do not miss this extraordinary opportunity.

Four New Zeleznik Prints

Eleven years ago, in 1996, Palladium released a beautiful, six-plate, art portfolio called **RiftsworkZ™**. Signed and numbered by the artist, *John Zeleznik*, and limited to 2000 copies, they quickly sold out (originally sold for $40). The portfolios have since become collector's items that sell for $60-120+. Both the portfolio and individual art prints are expected to increase in value in the years to come.

Now, *for the first time ever,* four of the six prints are being released from Palladium's archives as individual prints. This is NOT a new printing, but one of the "overrun" printings originally created for the **RiftsworkZ™** portfolio in 1996. They are overruns that have been kept in storage for *more than a decade.* There are only between 100-140 of each of the four prints being offered. Available only while supplies last.

- Collector's item.
- Suitable for framing.
- Limited to less than 150 copies.
- 11x14 inches, printed on a light card stock.
- Available only online, directly from Palladium Books.
- Available on a first come, first served basis, while supplies last.
- Comes with a *Certificate of Authenticity* signed by Kevin Siembieda.
- $10.00 each, plus $5.00 for shipping (1-4 prints) in the USA – $7.00 to Canada, and $15.00 for shipping overseas. Shipped flat in a box.
- The prints are:
  Thor from Pantheons of the Megaverse® – Cat. No. PR802.

  Rifts® Japan™ Cat. No. PR803.

  Juicer Uprising™ – Cat. No. PR804.

  Coalition War Campaign™ – Cat. No. PR805.

Palladium Greeting Cards

Available now!

Some of you may be thinking, "Greeting Cards?" But they are awesome, unique, collectible, fun, in some cases funny, and reasonably priced.

They are the perfect surprise to send *fellow gamers,* as well as friends and family who enjoy *science fiction, fantasy, adventure, great artwork* and *comic books.*

When was the last time you saw a card that would appeal to a sci-fi or fantasy fan? Or a comic book inspired card that wasn't geared for a child?

Seldom. For some of you, NEVER. Well, here they are and you're going to love them.

Wouldn't it be nice to send a buddy a *birthday card* with John Zeleznik heroes on it, or Scott Johnson's Glitter Boy in flames? Wouldn't it be nice to send a J.R.R. Tolkien or fantasy fan *a card* with a Larry Elmore adventurer group? Or a soldier overseas, or a friend you haven't seen for a while a card with Dave Dorman's D-Bees that says *Thinking of you.* And just wait till you see the two humorous *Rifts® Christmas Cards.*

For gamers, the cards are not only amusing, attractive and cool, but they bring back fond memories of friends, games and adventure campaigns from days past.

For those who appreciate artwork, these cards are bigger and nicer than the little images on trading cards and CCGs. They are easy to display or hang on a wall, are more sturdy than prints, plus, the cards are probably collectible as we doubt Palladium will ever press more than a few thousand of each.

The color cards look great and serve a real purpose: To say hello, Thinking of You, Happy Birthday, Happy Holidays, and put a smile on the face of those you care about.

Reasonably Priced

$2.75 *for one card and envelope.*

$12.00 *for six cards* (one of each or all the same one) and envelopes.

Plus shipping and handling, of course. That makes your best deal buying them six or more at a time.

Shipped in a sturdy, cardboard envelope via First Class Mail or UPS.

Note: If these first cards sell well, others will follow. Kevin and Wayne already have a selection in mind for *Halloween* and additional *Christmas* season cards for the Fall.

Forget Hallmark! Make your Christmas and other occasions Palladium ones with *Palladium's Greeting Cards – you know you want to.*

Make Your 41 Cent Postage Stamps *Rifts*®

For those of you who haven't heard, Palladium has created **Rifts® postage stamps** depicting Scott Johnson's famous *Glitter Boy in Flames* illustration as a 41 cent stamp. You might think of these speciality stamps as "vanity stamps," like vanity license plates for your car. They cost more, but they are made to your specific design. They look great and Kevin Siembieda has been putting them on all of Palladium's mail since the postage went up to 41 cents.

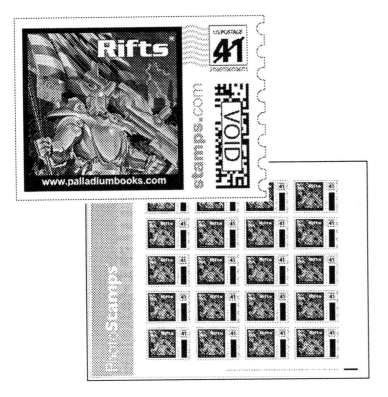

We thought they'd make a nice promotional item, but then we thought some of YOU might want to order Rifts® stamps too. We thought they'd be fun, and knew some of you would want them, but they are selling at a faster pace than we had imagined. We're glad you like them.

Regrettably, the stamps costs Palladium around $12 per sheet to create, so we have to sell them for $14.00 plus shipping and handling (around $3.11 First Class Mail). That means twenty, 41 cent stamps, with a *face value of $8.20,* cost you approximately **$17.11 per sheet**. Available only in sheets of 20 stamps. We're passing them on as cheaply as we can.

We don't think more than 300 sheets will ever be created, so this is a unique, fun collectible – or a fun way to surprise a friend – and they go great with the new *Palladium Greeting Cards.*

Cost: Rifts® 41 Cent Stamps ($8.20 in postage) – $17.11 per sheet ($14 for the sheet of stamps plus $3.11 for shipping, packaging and handling). Sold by the "sheet" of 20 stamps.

Catalog Number 2511

Must be shipped via *First Class Mail* or *UPS.* Not applicable for "Media Mail." Shipped in a sturdy card envelope. *Available now.* **Note:** If fans want to see stamps for other Palladium game lines, we may consider doing different/additional stamps in the future.

Delayed, but not forgotten

It has come to my attention that people assume books *rescheduled* or *delayed* for a long time (a year or more), and get removed from *product lists* or *Coming Soon reports,* are cancelled. That is not the case. They are simply delayed or put on hiatus until we can get back to them.

The main reason for such long delays is usually lack of time to do them right. Certain books, especially new role-playing games, take a long time to develop, play test, write and produce.

A long time as in 4-10 months. Although Palladium is getting healthier every day, we are still in fragile condition and we cannot afford to spend that kind of time on any one book, because it will delay many other titles we can produce more quickly. We need to focus on getting more product out, faster, without sacrificing quality. That means BIG projects have been temporarily shelved.

Ironically, these shelved projects are often our "pet projects," and we shelve them rather than rush them out and release an inferior incomplete product. Such pet projects include **Warpath: Urban Jungle™, Mechanoid Space™, BTS: Tome Grotesque™, BTS: Beyond Arcanum™, Wolfen War™** and various other Palladium Fantasy projects. I hope you understand the reason and believe me when I tell you that these delays pain *us* more than you. These are our babies, and we want to give them life!

So here is the latest on delayed, but not forgotten projects. Don't get too excited because further delays may ensue.

Warpath: Urban Jungle™ – Summer 2008. That's what we are shooting for. After *Robotech®,* **Warpath: Urban Jungle™** has been the most asked about and requested of announced titles. Certainly Warpath creator, Jeffry Scott Hansen has written his portion of the book and provided me with many notes, now I need to find the time to finish it and get the darn thing done and published.

For those of you not familiar with the title, it is a gritty, modern day role-playing game that deals with the secret war going on in the streets of our cities. Espionage, anti-terrorism, military and police combat that nobody knows about. The characters, the invisible agents – the spooks – who stop the worst acts of terror, crime and destruction before it happens, and put a quick end to those events when they occur.

Think 24 meets C.S.I. x 10, done Palladium style, and you start to get the idea. This will be Palladium's grittiest game ever and will not be suitable for young players.

Mechanoid Space™ RPG – Fall 2008 (tentative) – but it might slip into 2009. This project bringing new life to everybody's favorite villain, The Mechanoids®, is back on the schedule because of freelance writer, *Carl Gleba.* The project is just too epic and massive for me to do anytime soon by myself. Enter Carl Gleba, long time fan of The Mechanoids® and science fiction space games. Carl has offered to work on the RPG with me, even taking some parts over completely, and I said, "thank you, yes!" Carl's efforts should enable us to get Mechanoid Space™ published within the next year or two. Cool, eh?

Nightbane® sourcebook – Early 2008. I have a pair of freelancers putting the finishing touches on a Nightbane® sourcebook right now. We originally hoped to have the book out this Fall, but the writing took a bit longer than anticipated (hey, writing books means a lot of long hours and hard work). We might have been able to pound it out by the end of this year, but with the **Robotech® RPG** back and other books late, trying to do so is crazy. Look for it February or March.

Palladium Fantasy RPG® Sourcebooks – Throughout 2008. We had planned to release 2-4 Palladium Fantasy sourcebooks this Fall, but tumbling behind schedule and getting the Robotech® license later in the year than originally anticipated, we doubt we can get any Fantasy books out this Fall (maybe, but no promises). However, we WILL get several out in 2008. We love the Palladium Fantasy series (it's my personal favorite – KS) and intend to support it vigorously in the years to come.

Rifts® Lemuria – Spring or Summer 2008 (tentative). I didn't want to jinx this often started and stopped title so I haven't mentioned that we have a freelance writer working on it right now! No promises, but his outline and ideas sound excellent, let's see if he can pull it off. This is a tough assignment.

Tome Grotesque™ and **Beyond Arcanum™** are a pair of books that will take me a great deal of time to write, so they are in limbo. However, I hope that once Palladium is stronger and I have a good number of freelancer projects in the pipeline, I will be able to find the time to write them (maybe the end of 2008 or 2009). I need to write them both at the same time as much of the material goes hand in hand with each other.

Wolfen War™ and **various other Palladium Fantasy RPG® projects.** Various Palladium Fantasy titles are in development, but Wolfen War is not one of them. I just don't have the time right now. Sorry.

Lastly, let me answer the inevitable question of: *Why launch new game lines like the Palladium Zombie RPG Dead Reign, Warpath: Urban Jungle™ and even Robotech® when other announced products languish in development hell?*

The answers are simpler than you might think. **Dead Reign™, the Zombie RPG** is being done by a pair of new freelance writers and it is always smart to let the new guys cut their teeth on what they are most excited about. **Warpath: Urban Jungle™** *is* one of those languishing projects and I'm happy that we "should" be getting to it next Summer. **Robotech®** is fun, exciting and helpful to Palladium and its artists and writers on too many levels to even list here, and it's an old fave we're giving new life.

Also Coming in 2008

Robotech® New Generation (Invid)
Robotech® The Macross Saga
Robotech® Southern Cross

Rifts®/Minion War™: Megaverse® in Flames™
Rifts® Sourcebook: Shemarrian Nation™
Rifts® World Book: Triax™ 2
Rifts® World Book: Delta Blues
Rifts® World Book: Dark Woods™
Rifts® Federation of Magic™ 2: The Old Guard Rebellion

Phase World® Dimension Book: Fleets of the Three Galaxies
Chaos Earth™: First Responders

Mysteries of Magic™ for the Palladium Fantasy RPG®. May be a series of books, by Mark Hall.
Magic & Monsters™ for the Palladium Fantasy RPG®, by Randi Cartier.
Yin-Sloth Jungles™, Second Edition for the Palladium Fantasy RPG®. And more . . .

A Walk on the Wild Side

The Barbarians and Savages of the Palladium World

Part Two

By John C. Philpott

O.C.C.s of the Uncivilized World

The following O.C.C.s represent the people of the *barbaric* world in the same way the standard (main book) O.C.C.s represent those of the *civilized* world. These O.C.C.s include the Savage Warrior, the fearsome and chaotic Berserker, the Native Tribesman (a common barbarian clan member, the Vagabond/Peasant/Farmer of the barbarian cultures), and the instinctual, feral, Wild Man. Earlier "barbaric" O.C.C.s include the Barbarian Warrior and Barbarian Keeper from *Northern Hinterlands™* (collectively called "Barbarian" in this text), the Shaman O.C.C. from *Adventures on the High Seas™*, and the Were-Shaman from *Mount Nimro™*. Non-barbaric O.C.C.s that have "barbaric" wilderness tendencies, but which are still considered nominally "civilized," include the Ranger and Druid O.C.C.s from the *PFRPG®* main book. Each of these "barbaric" O.C.C.s is most comfortable in the wild, untamed world beyond the fringes of civilization, and finds the crowded streets of the big city as disconcerting or frightening as a common civilized peasant might find the wilderness beyond the farmlands.

Racial Notes

The barbarian cultures of the Palladium World are predominantly members of the so-called "monster" races (typically Orc, Ogre, Troll or Goblin/Hobgoblin), though barbaric members of the "beautiful" races (Humans, Elves, Dwarves, or even Gnomes) are known to exist, and can even be the largest percentage of the population in some barbarian cultures (such as in the Kiridin nations and the Northern Shipwrights). Note that while most tribes, clans, or nations are predominantly made up of a single race, more than one single-race tribe can fall under the same "Native Origins" classification (such as an all-Orc Agrarian tribe and an all-Human Agrarian tribe). Some of these predominant-race cultures occasionally have a relative handful of non-predominant-race members, such as an Orc tribe with a single Human member. Often these "token" members are orphans, runaways, slaves, or even abducted children who grew up in the culture. Other cultures are racially mixed, with two or three predominant races up to a whole mix of races. The Grassland Hordes (Horse Barbarians), for example, are famous for their racial tolerance and diversity, with Humans, Orcs, Ogres, and Coyles making up the primary races. The specifics of the individual tribe or culture of a player character or NPC are, as always, up to the G.M. and player.

Interactions Between Barbarian and Civilized People

To the "civilized" people of the Palladium World, the "barbaric" people are seen as wild and enigmatic, and often dangerous unknowns. While the wild Rangers are often looked at in an odd manner (who would willingly go into the unknowns of the wild?), they are still at least "civilized" to a degree. The Barbarians, Savages, and Tribesmen, however, are like "wild animals" and likely "beyond the hope of proper civilization" as far as the civilized man is concerned. When the growth of the civilized world leads it into contact with these people, the outcome is usually bad, with the stronger and more populous group almost invariably overcoming the weaker and smaller. On the rare chance that a power stalemate ensues, this sometimes will lead to a merging of cultures and ideas and result in a new combined culture (such as the fate of the Highlanders). However, the result of such meetings is rarely so peaceful.

To the "barbaric" peoples, on the other hand, the "civilized" urban people present an interesting oddity. They do "impossible" things (like build huge stone castles and cathedrals) and associate with fearsome men of magic the native would just as soon avoid. To the Tribesman or Barbarian/Savage, civilized people seem clumsy and childlike, crunching noisily through the landscape, inadvertently chasing away the game, and building impractically large and complex structures (like two-storey log cabins) that are often "impossible" to properly heat or cool in the local environment. Rangers are seen as a slight improvement (at least *they* have *some* clue how to behave in the wild), though they are still considered rather clumsy compared to a "proper" hunter-warrior.

The occasional appearance of a civilized person in a native people's cultural lands can be seen as an interesting oddity, or as a dire warning of dark things to come. How the native populace reacts to the stranger is often based on past experiences with "civilized" men (if any), and can vary from curious interest to open hostility. If the barbarian culture exists alongside many similar barbarian cultures (such as in Pre-Columbian America), the arrival of civilized people is typically treated like the arrival of another "tribe" or "nation," and sometimes weighed with the same threat level (high or low) as any other outside group – even if the newcomers are but the vanguard of the encroaching civilization. Many times this has led to underestimation of the civilized newcomers, which (like in the case of the Native American cultures) can prove a fatal mistake.

Such differences between barbaric and civilized people are further complicated by cultural dissimilarity and conflicting customs. Such seemingly odd and "uncivilized" customs as tattoos and body piercing or odd hair styles often add to the fearsome aspect of the clan/tribe/culture in the eyes of the civilized man. Direct cultural differences such as traditional gender roles, views on sex and religion, and other differing world views often add to the difficulty, giving one side the view that the other is "weak," "immoral," "godless," or creating other false assumptions – many of which lead only to violence.

In the end, the "barbaric" O.C.C.s represent people who (regardless of their race) wish to live out their lives in a way they understand. While worldviews vary from culture to culture, the average "tribe" values skill, bravery, and loyalty to the clan/tribe/culture as the cornerstones to a proper society. In many ways, this makes the "barbarian" no different from his "civilized" equivalent. However, it is often the little differences, and not the large similarities, that are apparent to both sides. From a role-playing perspective, the barbarian O.C.C.s offer an entirely new view of the Palladium World. Culture shock and misunderstanding can often make for great role-playing opportunities that can enrich or complicate (or both) the lives of all players and their characters.

Notes on the Barbarian Warrior and Barbarian Keeper

These O.C.C.s are described on pages 174 to 180 of the *Northern Hinterlands* sourcebook. The Barbarian Warrior (or "Noble Savage") is the common soldier of the barbarian clans – though there is certainly nothing common about them. As the clan/tribe's main warrior-hunters, the Barbarian Warriors are not only responsible for the safety and freedom of the clan, but are often the main source for feeding the tribe. The Barbarian is not just a warrior in the combat sense; they are linked to their environment, wholly at home in the wilds around them in a way few Rangers can match. Only the wilder Savage Warrior and feral Wild Man are more at home in the wild than these hardy people.

Like the Mercenary Warrior, the Barbarian Warrior is a tough fighter more than capable of handling himself in a fight. Yet, like the Ranger, the Barbarian knows also how to survive in the wild. Unlike the Ranger, however, the Barbarian has little to no understanding of the civilized world. While the Ranger is typically a civilized man who has forsaken the urban life for that of the wilderness scout/hunter, the Barbarian is a native of that wilderness. This makes the Barbarian better equipped to live in their native wilderness, but less equipped to live in other environs than the more "generalized" Ranger. A good analogy of the difference between the Ranger and Barbarian might be the difference between the American "Mountain Men" (fur traders and explorers) and the Native Americans in the "Old Northwest" of 1700s America. While the Mountain Men (like Daniel Boone) were well suited to life in the wild, they were still "clumsy, civilized outsiders" when compared with the Cherokee, Shawnee, and other Native American warriors they traded with and occasionally fought against.

The Barbarian Keeper, on the other hand, represents a legal or judicial "branch" of the tribe or a "cultural" storyteller or historian. Unlike the common villager (Tribesman), the Barbarian Keeper represents a select artist, intellectual, or civic leader. In many barbarian cultures the running of the tribe is divided between a "war council" of Barbarian and Savage Warriors and a "civic council" of Barbarian Keepers, Shaman, and Druids – with the Native Tribesmen simply doing what they're told.

Stigmas and New O.C.C. Options

Barbarian Stigmas (presented in the *Northern Hinterlands*™ sourcebook) represent the superstitions of a simple folk. Barbarian Warriors and Keepers develop several of these superstitions as their levels progress. However, before you choose your Barbarian's Stigma(s) you might ask whether the Stigma is based on a personal belief or a cultural taboo. Does your Barbarian hate the color red due to a personal aversion to the color, is it because his god(s) or spirits have deemed the color taboo, or is it because the color red is the color of a hated rival tribe? Does your Barbarian hold bears in such high esteem because he thinks they are noble beasts, because the bear is his personal totem (see Chant of Totem Communion below), or because the bear is the symbol of his tribe or god? This becomes a factor to consider if other player characters or NPCs from the Barbarian's home culture are encountered. If the Stigma is "personal," the other tribe members may not adhere to it, but if the Stigma is "tribal" then they might.

Another thing to consider is whether you wish to have Stigmas for your Barbarian at all. I (the author) did not include Stigmas in my new O.C.C.s (mostly due to the space concerns of reprinting a three-page percentile table). Since the concept of a tribal Stigma should affect all tribe members, all O.C.C.s from that tribe should have the Stigma (a tribe that will not eat goat meat should hold such a Stigma regardless of O.C.C. – even members of a "civilized" O.C.C. should hold to the Stigma). Be-

sides, barbaric cultures aren't the only ones to have Stigmas. Many modern "civilized" cultures forbid the eating of certain foods or working on certain days. Some cultures (civilized or savage) forbid the wearing of certain colors except by members of a certain rank or caste. For this reason you might not even want a Stigma for your Barbarian at all!

For these reasons I offer the following options for player characters and NPCs:

1. Non-barbaric O.C.C.s that do not have Stigmas (and barbaric O.C.C.s that do not have Stigmas, but are not presented in this article, such as the Druid, Shaman, and Were-Shaman), may select one or more Stigmas (one-for-one) in exchange for an equal number of new Secondary Skills.

2. Barbaric O.C.C.s presented in this article (Native Berserker, Native Tribeman, Savage Warrior, and Wild Man) may trade both the *Distrust and Fear of Magic and Magic Users* and *Aversion to Civilization* disadvantages under the Abilities, Notes, & Information section of the O.C.C. for a set of Stigmas exactly as described under the Barbarian Warrior O.C.C. (pages 175-178 of the *Northern Hinterlands*™ sourcebook).

3. The Barbarian Warrior or Barbarian Keeper O.C.C.s presented in the *Northern Hinterlands*™ sourcebook may exchange their Stigmas for the *Distrust and Fear of Magic and Magic Users* and *Aversion to Civilization* disadvantages exactly as described under the Abilities, Notes, & Information section of the Native Berserker O.C.C. below, but without any chance of entering a Berserker Rage.

Equestrian Skill O.C.C. Ability Note

In keeping with the barbaric nature of the Barbarian Warrior O.C.C. and the addition of the new Horsemanship: Barbarian skill in this article, it is strongly advised that the Equestrian Skill Special O.C.C. Ability for the Barbarian Warrior O.C.C. (page 178, *Northern Hinterlands™* sourcebook) be altered to change the ability from an equivalent skill of Horsemanship: Knight at +10% to an equivalent skill of Horsemanship: Barbarian at +10%.

Berserker O.C.C.

[**Author's Note**: This O.C.C. represents "true" Berserkers who have fully given themselves up to a life of Berserker combat – what you might call "professional" Berserkers. This O.C.C. and its Berserker Rage are not to be confused with Barbarian Warriors that possess the Berserker Fury O.C.C. Ability (page 178, *Northern Hinterlands™* sourcebook). The "true" Berserker Rage of the Berserker O.C.C. is an all-encompassing animalistic fury where the Berserker can not distinguish friend or foe, whereas the Berserker Fury of the Barbarian O.C.C. represents a lesser, more controlled fighting fury where aggression triumphs over self-concern, but not over cognitive sense.]

Of all the warriors in the Palladium World, perhaps none are as feared and loathed as the dreaded Berserkers. These fanatical and unconventional forces are the stuff of legends, and are known for charging, screaming, into battle and fighting to the last man. Berserkers are characterized by the *Berserker Rage* (or *Berserkergang*), an induced form of the semi-functional berserk insanity that turns the warriors into bloodthirsty killing machines who make no distinction between combatant and non-combatant or even foe and ally! Once induced into their Rage, Berserkers will charge into battle with a blood-curdling shriek and slash out at anything within reach. Berserkers in the Rage take on a feral, animalistic appearance to them as they rage, often drooling, grunting, slobbering, biting their shields, or speaking in tongues while they savagely lay into their enemies.

Many further add to their savage appearance by wearing body paint (war paint), tattoos, exotic body piercing and hairstyles, or dressing in animal skins. Some claim the name Berserker is derived from "bear sark" – literally "bear shirt" – due to the wearing of bear skins or wolf skins by Berserkers, while others say it comes from "bare sark" – bare shirt – from going into battle without armor or even a tunic. Rumors and documented cases of Berserkers drinking the blood of their victims, indulging in cannibalism, or drinking beer or mead from their victim's skulls, add to their feared reputation. The savage Rage and feared reputation of Berserkers makes them highly-effective shock troops, and they are often used as such by armies in a "disposable" manner: breaking apart formations and scattering armies so that a more conventional "mop up" force can be sent in to crush the scattered forces. This tactic is used often by the Wolfen Empire, who employs dedicated units of Coyle Berserkers specifically for this purpose. A group of Berserkers (at least 50) has a collective Horror Factor of 12 to opposing armies.

Once in the Rage, Berserkers will kill anything they can get their hands on. This includes enemies, non-combatants and allied forces alike. This indiscriminate behavior makes many commanders wary of employing Berserkers except in times of desperation (most "civilized" kingdoms will *never* openly employ Berserkers). Berserkers are also prone to Rage outside of combat, often being "set off" by alcohol, arguments, frustration, or competition. This has made unemployed Berserkers (those not actively in a combat situation) a very dangerous group and usually wholly unwelcome. Unemployed Berserker bands typically become roving bandits and marauders, and kings and commanders who once employed Berserkers often have to hunt down and kill the very same Berserkers after the fighting stops! This is another reason why many Berserker armies (mobs?) are often sent purposefully to their death on suicidal charges.

While Berserkers aren't necessarily always "barbarians" by birth, most (80%+) are from "barbaric" backgrounds and nearly all (90%+) are employed strictly by "barbaric" cultures, since "civilized" men typically want nothing to do with these brutal thugs. The much rarer "Urban Berserker" is known to exist, springing up in major cities or other "civilized" areas (most often in slums). While nearly every barbaric culture has been known to have used/employed Berserker (or Berserker-like) forces at one time or another, "true" (O.C.C.) Berserkers are most common to the Northern Shipwrights, from whom the name Berserker comes. Historically, the Dwarves may have claim to the first use of true Berserkers during the late stages of the Elf-Dwarf War (units they called "Loknar's Chosen"). These early Berserkers were typically fielded bearing the most chaotic and evil of Rune Weapons. To this day there are Dwarven Berserkers who lay claim to the "Loknar's Chosen" heritage, in spirit if not in fact, and many dream of a chance to get hold of one of the "Blood Blades of Loknar," as the evil Rune Weapons of the "Chosen" were called.

Berserkers are feared by all who have come in contact with them, and few of those unfortunate enough to have been on the receiving end of their Rage have lived to tell the tale. Even those who have fought *on the same side* as Berserkers rightfully fear and usually loathe these unconventional warriors – though they may consider them necessary evils, much like how modern conventional soldiers typically fear and loathe snipers and their distant, yet intimate form of killing. The Berserker character, whether native-born or urban, is typically a rough, dirty, and ill-mannered person with few, if any, social skills. Most are rude and selfish, taking what they want when they want it – by force if necessary. Most become mercenaries, bandits, or hired thugs when not actively serving in a combat environment, and the appearance of a Berserker (or worse yet, a group of Berserkers!) in an area is often taken as a sign of impending doom.

Berserkers typically dress simply and brutally, loving to enhance their already fearsome reputations through tattoos, body piercing, and wearing the bones and body parts of past victims. Most take the hate they receive from others in stride or (worse yet) try to convert the hatred into fear. The Berserkers' rough and violent lives mean that most die young and that few make friends outside of the "Berserker community," as it were. They feel most comfortable in the presence of fellow Berserkers or similarly savage and brutal Barbarian/Savage Warriors, Mercenaries, and Thieves/Assassins. Most Berserkers consider anyone less as weak and often treat them as prey. Their "edgy," rage-prone nature leads to many fatal conflicts among the

Berserkers, and among their companions. This is another reason why few non-Berserkers associate with them.

Being warriors by trade, the Berserkers are considered Men-at-Arms for purposes of determining S.D.C. and for armor penalties. Though most Berserkers wear no armor (since the "spirits of the Rage" will "protect them," and since wearing armor is considered a sign of weakness and cowardice among Berserkers), those few Berserkers who do wear armor prefer lightweight, less confining armor – Scale Mail at most.

Berserker Abilities, Notes, & Information

1. Berserker Rage! **The Source of the Berserkers' Power and Reputation:** The defining characteristic of Berserkers is their ability to go into a mindlessly aggressive bloodlust that turns them into killing machines. This is known as the Berserker Rage, or, in the language of the Northern Shipwrights, the *Berserkergang*. While in this Rage the Berserker ignores everything around him and concentrates on closing with the enemy forces and destroying them. The Berserker will ignore all pleas for help or mercy, all commands or suggestions (including "look out!" or similar warnings), and even his own pain and injury! All that matters is killing the enemy (and anyone or anything within reach, friend or foe alike). They will instinctively lash out to *kill* anyone within their reach. While in the rage they will *never* dodge or evade attacks, preferring simultaneous attacks (most Berserkers think that they are invulnerable to all attacks while in the Rage (not true!), a belief they like to instill in others – which only adds to their fearsome reputation).

Bonuses: The Berserker is +5 to strike, +10 to damage, and +3 to initiative while in the Rage, but dodges are impossible (will *never* attempt to dodge). Additionally, all skills are performed at a -10% penalty, communication is difficult (-25% to all communication attempts with the Berserker), and cognitive thought processes are limited (-2 to I.Q.). They gain one additional attack per melee while in the Rage and feel no pain or fear (any save vs pain or Horror Factor is an automatic success). Attacks are made with bare hands or hand-to-hand weapons (handheld bladed and blunt weapons are preferred to pole weapons), and ranged attacks are limited to thrown (targeting) attacks (no bows, guns, or other long-range weapons. These require more thought and patience to use than the Berserker typically possesses during Rage).

While within the Rage it is nearly impossible for the Berserker to discern between enemies, allies and even non-combatants. Players must roll an I.Q. check to identify the person as a friend or foe; remember to take into account the I.Q. loss; character gains a +1 bonus to identify friend or foe at 3rd, 7th, 11th, and 14th level. Additionally it is impossible for the Raging Berserker to know he is taking damage, though he will know something has "hit" him, and can turn and react to strikes. **G.M. Note:** In the case of a Raging Berserker player character, keep track of the character's S.D.C. and Hit Points for the player, but do not tell the player how much damage the character has taken, or even how badly injured the character is.

A Raging Berserker can lose up to the P.E. attribute number below zero Hit Points and still continue to fight as long as he is in the Rage, but will collapse into a coma after passing this point and quickly die without immediate medical attention. If a Berserker comes out of the Rage with zero or negative Hit Points, but less than the P.E. attribute number below zero (i.e. still able to fight while in the Rage), he will lapse into a coma as normal once the Rage has ended. The sight of bloody Berserkers stumbling out from a battlefield, their enemies dead around them, and then collapsing dead themselves is rather common.

Entering the Rage: There are several ways for a Berserker to enter the Rage. The first way is for the Berserker to purposefully induce the Rage in himself, the second is to have the Rage induced indirectly through outside sources (Shaman's chant or special potions), and the third is to have the Rage accidentally induced. The Rage can be self-induced if the Berserker character spends 1D4 minutes concentrating and/or performing some ceremony meant specifically to induce the Rage (during this "warm up" period, Berserkers are known for screaming, yelling, biting their shields, and other savage, animalistic acts). This self-induced Rage can be performed individually or in groups of Berserkers up to the size of an army if all the Berserkers chant/concentrate together in unison. The Rage can also be induced by others; a Shaman can induce all Berserkers within hearing and/or seeing distance by using the *Chant of the Berserker* (see below), or the Berserker can drink the mysterious *Berserker's Potion* (see below under the skill of the same name). Either of these methods will automatically induce the Rage in Berserkers, and may have some effects on non-Berserkers as well!

The Rage can also be accidentally induced. Any failed save vs Pain or Horror Factor has an 80% chance of inducing the Rage (on rolls of 81-00%, the Berserker reacts to the failure as standard). Engaging in mortal combat will automatically induce the Rage after 1D4 melees unless a saving throw vs Rage (12 or higher) is made by the Berserker (whether the Berserker attacks or is attacked), and engaging in any fierce physical competition (boxing, wrestling, horseplay, contact sports, etc.) results in the Berserker having to make a saving throw of 7 or higher to avoid the Rage (takes 1D4 minutes to take effect). Extreme anger or frustration similarly forces a save (10 or higher, add M.E. bonuses) to avoid Raging.

Saving Against Involuntary Rage: The Berserker may choose to resist involuntary Rage as described above. In all cases the character may add M.E. bonuses to the saving throw, and gains an additional +1 to save vs Rage at levels 3, 7, 12, and 15.

Ending the Rage is quite a bit more difficult than entering it. Once in the Rage, the Berserker will fight until everyone around him is dead, subdued, or fled/taken beyond the Berserker's notice. The Berserker will then slowly calm down over the next 3D4 melee rounds until the Rage ends – provided the Berserker is left alone and not hurt, prodded, taunted, or otherwise provoked (the Berserker *will* be looking for more "enemies" during this "cool down" period, so friends and foes alike look out!). The only way to prematurely end a Berserker's Rage is to kill the Berserker, knock the Berserker unconscious for one to three minutes (3D4 melee rounds), or subdue, stun, confine, or bind the Berserker until the Rage ends automatically after 3D4 melee rounds (if not provoked further). Regardless of the reason(s) why, once the Rage ends the Berserker will be physically, emotionally, and mentally exhausted. For the next 4D6 hours the Berserker (or any non-Berserker who enters the Rage due to a Berserker Chant or use of the Berserker Potion; see below) will be -5 to P.S., P.P., P.E., M.E., and Spd, and suffer a -5 to all combat actions and a -20% to all skills. More than likely, the Berserker will choose to sleep or otherwise remain inactive during this "recovery" time.

2. Native Tribal Abilities and Skills: [This section not applicable to Urban Berserkers.] All native-born Berserkers are inherently linked to their native lands and tribe, gaining a special link with their homeland and home people. This gives the Native Berserker certain skills and advantages when on their native soil. Roll once on (or select once from) the above Native Origins table to determine the character's homeland and origins.

Urban Berserkers: Alternately, the player can assume a Berserker of "civilized" background (a so-called Urban Berserker) and skip this step. The Urban Berserker loses the special *Native Skills* and the *Native Soil* bonuses (#3 below), but also doesn't suffer from the *Distrust of Magic* (#4 below) or the *Aversion to Civilization* (#5 below). The Urban Berserker character is also not limited on skill choices (e.g. can take the Streetwise skill at 1st level). Urban Berserkers are rare, accounting for only about 10% of all Berserkers.

3. Affinity to Native Soil: [This section not applicable to Urban Berserkers.] In keeping with the Native Berserker's deeply rooted attachment to his homeland, the character receives a +5% bonus on all Wilderness skills and on the skills of Prowl, Holistic Medicine, Camouflage, Detect Ambush, Detect Concealment, Track Humanoids, Surveillance, and Intelligence while in the familiar terrain of his "home territory." He receives a +2% on these skills when on similar (but not exact) territory, such as a desert Barbarian from the Sandy Desert of Baalgor visiting the Rocky Desert.

4. Distrust and Fear of Magic and Magic Users: [This section not applicable to Urban Berserkers.] Native-born Berserkers are naturally distrustful of men of magic. To them, dabbling in magic is often perceived as meddling with powers beyond human understanding or control. As a result, native Berserkers will automatically react to spellcasters, men of magic, or people who use flashy/showy Psionic abilities (like Psi-Sword) with suspicion. If the mage is operating within Barbarian lands, any foul deeds, crimes, or accidents will likely be blamed on the spellcaster. Necromancers, Witches, Wizards and Summoners are the most feared, though Diabolists, Mystics, and Mind Mages are certainly close seconds. Even Warlocks are universally feared, as they are tied into the most "horrifying and alien" aspects of the natural world and are considered "toys of creatures beyond their understanding." Most Berserkers from more wild backgrounds (the ones with fewer ties to the "civilized" world) fear and distrust Priests as well, as they are obviously involving themselves with powerful, untrustworthy gods and spirits.

In game terms this means the Native Berserker will react to any display of powerful and showy magic with fear as though it were a Horror Factor (save vs Horror Factor 10). A failed save vs Horror Factor will usually (90% chance) send the Berserker into Rage (see #1 above) and set him immediately to attacking with the desire to kill the magic user and any who stand in the way! The remaining 10% react to the failed Horror Factor as normal. This Horror Factor drops to 7 at third (3rd) level, 5 at fifth (5th) level, and disappears entirely at seventh (7th) level, though the distrust is likely to remain to some degree.

Note that Shaman, Were-Shaman, Hebalists, Druids, and similar "nature-oriented" O.C.C.s are excluded from this list of "feared" magic users, as these spell casters are more closely tied to the natural world, and are more readily "understandable" to the Native Berserker. Similarly, Psi-Mystics, Psi-Sensitives, Psi-Healers, and Major or Minor Psychics are considered acceptable as long as they avoid the use of "showy" or obviously arcane powers like Psi-Sword or Telekinesis. Also note that a clever magic user who is somehow able to convince the Native Berserker that he (the spellcaster) is one of these "acceptable" O.C.C.s can sometimes belay some of the distrust (at least until that fireball he throws proves otherwise). Some unscrupulous Witches have been known to take advantage of this and have led unwitting Berserkers down the road to disaster!

5. Aversion to Civilization: [This section not applicable to Urban Berserkers.] Being a child of the wilderness, the Native Berserker is as out of place in the busy, bustling streets of a major city as a pampered palace child would be in the untamed wilderness. All Native Berserkers have a natural dislike and distrust of the chaotic, crowded, smelly, and fast-paced world of urban life. Strangers are naturally something to be wary of (or potential victims), and to be surrounded by hundreds or thousands of strangers is a pretty harrowing experience to the Native Berserker! Many Berserkers refuse to even enter cities and some (such as the Horse Barbarians) despise cities so much that they are known to sack, loot, and burn cities just on general principle!

In game terms the Berserker who enters a city (or sufficiently large and/or crowded town) will be nervous, edgy, and jumpy. This leads to a penalty of -2 to all combat and initiative bonuses except dodge (they have a +2 to dodge!) as long as they remain inside the city. In addition, they are more prone to fear (-4 to save vs Horror Factor) and panic. For Berserkers, this panic almost invariably (80% chance) sends them into the Berserker Rage (#1 above), which might well prove unfortunate for the hapless citizens around them. These penalties (and the dodge bonus) are cut in half at fifth (5th) level and are eliminated completely at seventh (7th) level. Learning the ways of the city is difficult for the Native Berserker. As a result, the Streetwise skill can not be taken by the Native Berserker character until sixth (6th) level.

6. Bonuses: All Berserkers (native-born or urban) gain the following bonuses: +15 S.D.C., +2 to save vs Disease, +2 to save vs Pain, +1 to save vs Horror Factor at levels 1, 3, 5, 7, and 12, +1 to the P.S. attribute, and a +2 to the P.E. attribute.

7. Additional Special Abilities: Additionally, the Berserker O.C.C. gains the Battle Cry O.C.C. ability from the Barbarian Warrior O.C.C. (page 178, *Northern Hinterlands™* sourcebook), and may select one other of the Barbarian O.C.C. Special Abilities except for Berserker Fury or Equestrian Skill.

Berserker O.C.C. (Recommended for NPCs only)

Note: Due to the chaotic and indiscriminate nature of Berserkers, this O.C.C. is recommended for non-player characters or experienced role-players only. The presence of Berserkers in any party is likely to be a source of strife and difficulty and can prove dangerous to all characters involved.

Alignment: Anarchist, Miscreant, or Diabolic only! The very chaotic and bloodthirsty nature of the Berserker limits the character to these alignments, as no moral, ethical, or honorable person will ever be willing to act in such a mindlessly violent and indiscriminate way.

Racial Notes: Berserker warriors tend to be members of the so-called "monster" races, typically Orcs, Trolls, Ogres, Giants, Coyles, Quorian, Gossai, and Goblins/Hobgoblins. However, Human and Dwarven berserkers are rather common, and other humanoid Berserkers including Kobolds, Wolfen, Kankoran, and even rare Elves and Gnomes have been known to exist.

Attribute Requirements: P.E. 10. A high M.E., P.S., P.P., and Spd are helpful, but not required.

O.C.C. Skills:

Native Berserker:

Language: Native at 98% plus one additional language at +5%.

Climbing (+20%)

Prowl (+10%)

Land Navigation (+10%)

Wilderness Survival (+15%)

Identify Plants & Fruits (+5%)

Skin & Prepare Animal Hides (+5%)

Track & Trap Animals (+10%)

Track Humanoids (+10%)

Sign Language (Special: Native Tribal Sign Language ability. Cannot communicate with "civilized" Sign Language skill native to the civilized lands of Palladium, or with Barbarians/Savages/Tribesmen of other tribal origins.)

W.P.: Select three of choice.

Hand to Hand: Expert. The Berserker can upgrade to Hand to Hand: Martial Arts (or Assassin, if of an evil alignment) for the cost of one O.C.C. Related Skill. At the G.M.'s discretion, Hand to Hand: Wild (New!) may be selected for the cost of three O.C.C. Related Skills.

Urban Berserker:

Language: Native at 98% plus one additional language at +5%.

Climbing (+15%)

Escape Artist (+5%)

General Repair and Maintenance (+5%)

Land Navigation (+5%)

Prowl (+10%)

Recognize Weapon Quality (+10%)

Streetwise (+10%)

Wilderness Survival (+5%)

W.P.: Select three of choice.

Hand to Hand: Expert. The Berserker can upgrade to Hand to Hand: Martial Arts (or Assassin, if of an evil alignment) for the cost of one O.C.C. Related Skill. At the G.M.'s discretion, Hand to Hand: Wild (New!) may be selected for the cost of five O.C.C. Related Skills.

O.C.C. Related Skills: Select six (6) other skills of choice at level one, plus select two additional skills at levels three, six, nine, and twelve. All new skills start at level one proficiency.

Communications & Performing Arts: None.

Domestic: Any (+10%).

Espionage: Any (+10%).

Horsemanship: General, Exotic, or Barbarian (New!) only (+10%).

Medical: Any except Biology and Surgeon/Medical Doctor (Holistic Medicine +10%).

Military: Any except Heraldry (all at +10%).

Physical: Any (+5% where applicable).

Rogue: Any (Card Shark and Streetwise not available until level 6 or greater for "Native" Berserkers; "Urban Berserkers" get +10% to all Rogue skills).

Science: Math: Basic only.

Scholar, Noble, & Technical: Any (General Repair, Rope Works, and Sculpting & Whittling are at +10%).

W.P.: Any except Siege Weapons; prefer handheld bladed and blunt weapons.

Wilderness: Any (+15% for "native-born" Berserkers, no bonus for "Urban Berserkers").

Secondary Skills: The character also gets to select four (4) Secondary Skills from the previous list at level one, and two additional skills at levels two, four, six, eight, ten, and twelve. These are additional areas of knowledge that do not get the advantage of the bonus listed in the parentheses. All Secondary Skills start at the base skill level. Also, skills are limited (any, only, none) as previously indicated in the list.

Standard Equipment: *Native Berserker:* One set of tribal clothing (typically including pants, kilt, or loincloth, shirt or chest decorations, and leggings), fur/hide cape or cloak (typically of an animal killed and prepared by character), sandals, boots or moccasins, war paints and/or simple body ornamentation (shells, feathers, claws, etc.), crude knapsack or backpack, 1D4 small sacks, one large sack, water skin, flint and tinder box, fishing line and hooks, 1D4 simple snares, set of skinning/tanning knives (typically flint, obsidian, or copper), and 50 feet (15 m) of rope.

Urban Berserker: One set of clothing (typically simple peasant garb), cloak or cape, boots, war paints or simple body ornamentation/piercing (optional), backpack, 1D4 small sacks, one large sack, water skin, flint and tinder box, fishing line and hooks, 1D4 simple snares, and 50 feet (15 m) of rope.

Armor: Starts with none. Berserkers tend not to wear armor, considering it a sign of weakness or lack of faith in the spirits that grant them their power. If armor is worn it will almost always be of a light, natural type that permits mobility and stealth.

Weapons: A utility knife (often of stone; 1D6 S.D.C.), small hatchet or tomahawk (often of stone; 1D6 S.D.C.), and two additional weapons of choice reflecting the character's Weapon Proficiencies. Favorite weapons typically include clubs/maces (typically spiked), axes, hammers, spears, and heavy swords.

Money: Starts with 3D6x10 gold (Urban Berserkers) or equivalent value in barter (trade) items such as skins or precious metal ores or raw (uncut) gems (Native Berserker). Additional money will come from payment for services rendered, animal hides, parts, and meat, and booty. Berserkers are often hired by warlords and the military as shock troops and mercenaries. They are sometimes also hired as native scouts or guides – often against rival tribes or common enemies. Pay can be excellent for an experienced Berserker (assuming the Berserker lives long enough and is familiar enough with the value of currency not to be taken advantage of by unscrupulous merchants, etc.), and can vary from 50-100 gold for simple tasks to as much as 300-1000 gold for dangerous missions or military assignments.

Savage Warrior O.C.C.

Barbaric even by barbarian standards, the Savage Warrior is even closer to the animalistic nature of humans' (or other races') past. The Savage, like the Barbarian, is close to nature and dislikes "civilized" life. The main difference is a matter of degrees, as the Savage Warrior is even less civilized than the Barbarian. Savages tend to be found in places totally (or at least mostly) untouched by the encroachment of the "civilized" world. As a result, they are better suited to the wilderness than even the Barbarian, though they are far more disturbed by urban life and suffer greater penalties for visiting the cities. Only the feral Wild Man is less "civilized." However, the Savage Warrior usually does have a certain measure of "civility" and morality, as most are very protective of their family/clan/tribe and way of life. They tend to be even more resistant to change than the Barbarian or native Tribesman as a result of this. As warriors, the Savages are considered Men-at-Arms for purposes of determining S.D.C. and for armor penalties (though most prefer lightweight, less confining armor, Scale Mail at most).

Like the Barbarian, the Savage Warrior is a warrior-hunter in tune with the natural world around them. They live close to the wild world and disdain any civilization beyond that of small villages. Often the difference between Barbarian and Savage is a matter of perception. For game purposes the Savage O.C.C. is assumed to be closer to the wild environment (greater Wilderness skill) yet farther from civilization (greater penalties from visiting the "civilized" world). Since the Barbarian is often seen as a more "civilized" (or "noble") being than the Savage Warrior, the Barbarian is often referred to as the "Noble Savage." In general, "Barbaric" cultures that have more contact with the "civilized" world (such as the Northern Shipwrights and Horse Barbarians) tend to be populated more by Barbarians, while the more hidden, remote cultures (such as the Jungle Savages or Swamp Men) tend to be populated more by Savage Warriors. The Savage Warrior gains the following abilities and penalties to reflect their "uncivilized" lifestyle and world view.

Savage Warrior Abilities, Notes, & Information

1. Native Tribal Abilities and Skills: All Savage Warriors are inherently linked to their native lands and tribe, gaining a special link with their homeland and home people. This gives them certain skills and advantages when on their native soil. Roll once on the above Native Origins table (or select one) to determine the character's homeland and origins.

2. Affinity to Native Soil: The Savage has a deeply rooted attachment to his homeland. Often, the Savage is so attuned to his environment that all native animals consider the character to be a part of the natural surroundings as much as any other ani-

mal. As a result, birds and insects continue chirping, frogs, toads, and other amphibians continue their calls, and animals do not run in fear as the character passes if the character is not actively hunting (somehow the animals know). If the Savage *is* hunting, then the animals will react normally, assuming Prowl is successful. Because of this "oneness" with his surroundings, the character receives a +20% bonus on Prowl and +15% on all other Wilderness skills and on the skills of Holistic Medicine, Camouflage, Detect Ambush, Detect Concealment, Track Humanoids, Surveillance, and Intelligence while in the familiar terrain of his "home territory." He receives +5% on these skills when on similar (but not exact) territory (such as a desert Savage from the Sandy Desert of Baalgor visiting the Rocky Desert), but suffers a *penalty* of -5% to all of these skills when in completely unfamiliar territory (such as a Desert Savage in the Yin-Sloth Jungles).

3. Weather Divination: Savage Warriors live close to the land and at the mercy of the weather in a way "civilized" people do not. As a result, they have grown to understand the way of the weather, including recognizing the "signs" that nature gives to indicate incoming changes. This ability is not mystical, divination, or scientific, but rather relies on recognizing wind direction and speed, cloud features, the natural behavior of animals and plant life, and other natural signs as indications of the coming weather. This often relies on knowledge handed down through the clan or tribe for generations. On a successful skill roll, the character can predict the general trend of the upcoming weather for the next 72 hours (three days). This will include precipitation (type and severity; low, moderate, high, extreme), wind direction and strength, approximate relative temperature (cold, temperate, hot), and a basic idea about how long the weather trend will last (to within 2D4 hours). Long-term (seasonal) weather can be predicted starting at level 6 at half the percentile level. This "long term" prediction is simple, such as "it will be a cold/warm (or wet/dry) winter," or modifiers like "expect a good/poor harvest," or "hunting will be difficult this fall." Furthermore (at 6th level or higher), serious disasters (such as earthquakes, hurricanes, etc.) can be predicted 1D4 days in advance for long-term storms/disasters (such as hurricanes), or 2D4 hours in advance for short-term storms/disasters (tornadoes or earthquakes). This does not include Ley Line Storms. All Savage characters, regardless of level, will immediately and automatically recognize a weather event as a natural event, or as "unnatural" weather (such as weather coming from magic or divine interference). The base ability is 30%, +5% per level of experience.

4. Distrust and Fear of Magic/Magic Users: Exactly as described above for the Native Berserker O.C.C., but without any chance of entering a Berserker Rage. Additionally, the penalties are higher: the Savage Warrior will react to any display of powerful and showy magic as though it were a Horror Factor of 14. This Horror Factor drops to 10 at third (3rd) level, 7 at fifth (5th) level, 5 at seventh (7th) level and disappears entirely at tenth (10th) level, though the distrust is likely to remain to some degree.

5. Aversion to Civilization: Exactly as described above for the Native Berserker O.C.C., but without any chance of entering a Berserker Rage. Additionally, the penalties for being in an urban environment are -4 to all combat and initiative bonuses except dodge (they have a +4 to dodge!) as long as they remain inside the city. In addition, they are more prone to fear (-6 to save vs Horror Factor) and panic. These penalties (and the dodge bonus) are cut in half at fifth (5th) level, cut in half a second time at seventh (7th) level (so ¼ the original penalty), and are eliminated completely at tenth (10th) level. Learning the ways of the city is difficult for the Savage Warrior. As a result, the Streetwise skill can not be taken by the Savage Warrior character until eighth (8th) level.

6. Increased Psionic Potential: Due to the Savage's close link to nature, inherit psionics are likely. Rather than using the chart on page 21 of the PFRPG® main book, roll percentile on the following table to determine Savage Psionics:

01-20: Major Psionics.

21-50: Minor Psionics.

51-00: No Psionics.

Psionics granted are exactly as described under the Random Psionics section of the PFRPG main book, page 21. Typical powers include Sixth Sense, Sense Evil, Sense Magic, Commune with Animals, Mind Block, Bio-Regeneration, Resist Fatigue, Impervious to Cold, Impervious to Fire, Impervious to Poison/Toxin, Nightvision, Resist Fatigue, Resist Hunger, Resist Thirst, Summon Inner Strength, and Telekinetic Leap.

7. Bonuses: All Savage Warrior characters receive the following bonuses: +15 S.D.C., +3 to save vs Disease, +2 to save vs Horror Factor at level 1 (with an additional bonus of +1 to save vs Horror Factor at levels 3, 5, 7, and 12), and a +2 to the P.E. attribute.

8. Additional Special Abilities: Additionally, the Savage Warrior O.C.C. may select two of the Barbarian O.C.C. Special Abilities (page 178, *Northern Hinterlands™* sourcebook).

Savage Warrior O.C.C.

Alignment: Any, though most tend to be of Anarchist, Aberrant, or Miscreant alignment. Elven, Dwarven, Gnomic, and Kankoran Savages tend towards Scrupulous or Unprincipled, while the so-called "monster" races tend towards Anarchist and Evil.

Racial Notes: Savage Warriors, even more so than Barbarians, tend to be members of the so-called "monster" races, typically Orcs, Goblins/Hobgoblins, Trolls, Ogres, Troglodytes, Giants and Coyles (and the enigmatic Kankoran). However, Human savages are rather common, and other humanoid Savages, including Elves, Dwarves, Wolfen, and even Gnomes, have been known to exist.

Attribute Requirements: M.E. 10 & P.E. 12. A high P.S. and P.P. are helpful, but not required.

O.C.C. Skills:

Language: Native at 98% only.

Climb/Scale Walls (+25%)

Prowl (+15%)

Land Navigation (+20%)

Wilderness Survival (+20%)

Identify Plants & Fruits (+15%)

Skin & Prepare Animal Hides (+15%)

Track & Trap Animals (+20%)

Track Humanoids (+15%)

Sign Language (+10%) (Special: Native Tribal Sign Language ability. Cannot communicate with "civilized" Sign

Language skill native to the civilized lands of Palladium, or with Barbarians/Savages/Tribesmen of other tribal origins.)

W.P.: Select two of choice.

Hand to Hand: Expert. The Savage can upgrade to Hand to Hand Martial Arts (or Assassin, if of an evil alignment) for the cost of one O.C.C. Related Skill. At the G.M.'s discretion, Hand to Hand: Wild (New!) may be selected for the cost of two O.C.C. Related Skills. Regardless of Hand to Hand selection, the Savage still fights in an unorthodox and instinctual way that will result in a penalty for any "civilized" opponent who has not fought a Savage or similar O.C.C. before. The unfamiliar opponent suffers a one-time penalty of -1 on all combat rolls for the first encounter (after this first encounter the penalties no longer apply and the character is assumed "experienced" against such savage combat).

O.C.C. Related Skills: Select six (6) other skills of choice at level one, plus select two additional skills at levels three, six, nine, and twelve. All new skills start at level one proficiency.

Communications & Performing Arts: None.

Domestic: Any (+10%).

Espionage: Any (+10%).

Horsemanship: General, Exotic, or Barbarian (New!) only (+10%).

Medical: Any except Biology and Surgeon/Medical Doctor (Holistic Medicine only +10%).

Military: Any except Heraldry (all at +10%).

Physical: Any (+5% where applicable).

Rogue: Any (Streetwise is not available until level 8 or greater).

Science: Math: Basic only.

Scholar, Noble, & Technical: Any (General Repair, Rope Works, and Sculpting & Whittling are at +10%).

W.P.: Any except Siege Weapons.

Wilderness: Any (+15%).

Secondary Skills: The character also gets to select four (4) Secondary Skills from the previous list at level one, and two additional skills at levels two, four, six, eight, ten, and twelve. These are additional areas of knowledge that do not get the advantage of the bonus listed in the parentheses. All Secondary Skills start at the base skill level. Also, skills are limited (any, only, none) as previously indicated in the list.

Standard Equipment: One set of tribal clothing (typically including pants, kilt, or loincloth, shirt or chest decorations, and leggings), fur/hide cape or cloak (typically of animal killed and prepared by character), sandals, boots or moccasins, war paints and/or simple body ornamentation (shells, feathers, claws, etc.), 1D6 small sacks, one large sack, water skin, flint and tinder box, fishing line and hooks, 1D4 simple snares, set of skinning/tanning knives (typically flint, obsidian, or copper), and 50 feet (15 m) of rope. Typically travels light and prefers to live off of the land.

Armor: None to start. Savages tend to prefer light, natural armors that permit mobility and stealth, and many wear no armor at all, often considering it a sign of weakness (the Kankoran are notorious in this regard).

Weapons: A utility knife (usually of stone; 1D6 S.D.C.), small hatchet or tomahawk (usually of stone; 1D6 S.D.C.), and two additional weapons of choice reflecting the character's Weapon Proficiencies. Favorite weapons typically include clubs, axes, spears, bows, and staves.

Money: Starts with 1D6x10 gold in barter (trade) items such as skins or precious metal ores or raw (uncut) gems. Additional money will come from payment for services rendered, animal hides, parts, and meat, and booty. Savage Warriors are sometimes hired by merchants, wealthy travelers, and the military as native scouts or guides often against rival tribes or common enemies. However, many consider Savages to be too unpredictable, and as a result, usually prefer to hire Rangers or Barbarians. Pay can be excellent for an experienced Savage (assuming the Savage is familiar enough with the value of currency not to be taken advantage of by unscrupulous merchants, etc.), and can vary from 30-80 gold for simple tasks to as much as 200-800 gold for dangerous missions or military assignments.

Native Tribesman O.C.C.

[Author's Note: This O.C.C. is essentially the same as the first edition Nomadic Tribesman O.C.C. detailed on page 29 of the *Yin-Sloth Jungles*™ sourcebook of the first edition of the **Palladium Fantasy RPG®**, but represents not just jungle nomads but tribesmen from all "barbaric" cultures, whether nomadic gatherers or sedentary farmers. Unlike the Barbarian Keeper O.C.C. from the *Northern Hinterlands*™ sourcebook, the Native Tribesman holds no real distinct authoritative or cultural position in the tribe and is instead more a "peasant" than a "noble."]

The Native Tribesman is the basic member of the barbaric tribe, clan, or village much in the way that the Vagabond/Peasant/Farmer is the basic member of the urbanized world. These are the common people of the tribe – the farmers, herders, gatherers, and basic workers who perform the day-to-day tasks that keep the tribe/clan/village running. In many barbarian cultures there is a distinct gender division, with the males being the hunter-warriors (Barbarian or Savage Warrior) and females or "weak" males being the gatherer-farmers (Tribesmen) or civic leaders (Barbarian Keepers). In other cultures the distinction is based on ability, family background, or even divided equally between members of the clan/tribe. Most cultures tend to take a pragmatically survival-based view, letting the members perform the task they are best suited to.

Regardless of cultural divisions, the Native Tribesman is a stout and hardy person who can survive in the wild as well as (or even better than) the best-trained "civilized" person (Ranger). They are used to the day-to-day difficulty of life in the wild and take such difficulty in stride, growing and adapting as necessary to changing conditions rather than attempting to manipulate the world to suit them. Like the Barbarian and Savage Warrior, the Native Tribesmen deplore and fear the civilized urban world, much preferring the relative simplicity of the natural world.

The Native Tribesman is, much like the Vagabond/Peasant/Farmer of the civilized world, the common person of the barbaric cultures. Like the Vagabond/Peasant/Farmer O.C.C., the Tribesman character is likely to be the person unwittingly dragged into a life of adventure. Most Tribesmen are more than content to continue their lives in the tribe/clan/village of their birth and leave the adventurous life to the Barbarian and Savage Warrior. This does not mean they are weak, however, and many would-be marauders have suffered greatly at the hands of "common" Tribesmen. Note that Native Tribesmen are considered *non*-Men-at-Arms for purposes of determining S.D.C. and for armor penalties (most prefer lightweight, less confining armor, Scale Mail at most).

All Native Tribesmen gain the following abilities and penalties to reflect their "uncivilized" lifestyle and world view.

Native Tribesman Abilities, Notes, & Information

1. Native Tribal Abilities and Skills: All Tribesmen are inherently linked to their native lands and tribe, gaining a special link with their homeland and home people. This gives them certain skills and advantages when on their native soil. Roll once on the above Native Origins table (or select one) to determine the character's homeland and origins.

2. Affinity to Native Soil: In keeping with the Tribesman's deeply rooted attachment to their homeland, the character receives a +10% bonus on all Wilderness skills and on the skills of Prowl, Holistic Medicine, Camouflage, Detect Ambush, Detect Concealment, Track Humanoids, Surveillance, and Intelligence while in the familiar terrain of their "home territory." They receive a +5% on these skills when on similar (but not exact) territory, such as a desert Tribesman from the Sandy Desert of Baalgor visiting the Rocky Desert.

3. Weather Divination: Exactly as described above under the Savage Warrior O.C.C. but the base ability is 20%, +5% per level of experience.

4. Distrust and Fear of Magic/Magic Users: Exactly as described above under the Native Berserker O.C.C., but without any chance of entering a Berserker Rage.

5. Aversion to Civilization: Exactly as described above under the Native Berserker O.C.C., but without any chance of entering a Berserker Rage.

6. Bonuses: All Native Tribesman characters receive the following bonuses: +5 S.D.C., +2 to save vs Disease, and +1 to save vs Horror Factor at levels 1, 5, 8, and 15.

7. Additional Special Abilities: Additionally, the Native Tribesman O.C.C. may select one of the Barbarian O.C.C. Special Abilities from among numbers 2-6 (page 178, *Northern Hinterlands™* sourcebook).

Native Tribesman O.C.C.

Alignment: Any, though tend to be of Scrupulous, Unprincipled, Anarchist, or Aberrant alignment. Elven, Dwarven, Gnomic, and Kankoran Tribesmen tend towards Scrupulous or Unprincipled while the so-called "monster" races tend towards Anarchist and Evil.

Racial Notes: Tribesmen tend to be members of the so-called "monster" races, typically Orcs, Goblins/Hobgoblins, Trolls, Ogres, Giants, Troglodytes, and Coyles (and the enigmatic Kankoran). However, Human Tribesmen are rather common, and other humanoid Tribesmen, including Elves, Dwarves, Wolfen, and even Gnomes, have been known to exist.

Attribute Requirements: P.E. 10. A high M.E., P.S., and P.P. are helpful, but not required.

O.C.C. Skills:

Language: Native at 98% plus one additional language at +5%.

Animal Husbandry (+10%)

Climb/Scale Walls (+15%)

Prowl (+10%)

Land Navigation (+5%)

Wilderness Survival (+15%)

Identify Plants & Fruits (+20%)

Skin & Prepare Animal Hides (+15%)

Track & Trap Animals (+15%)

Sign Language (+5%) (Special: Native Tribal Sign Language ability. Cannot communicate with "civilized" Sign Language skill native to the civilized lands of Palladium, or with Barbarians/Savages/Tribesmen of other tribal origins.

W.P.: Select two of choice.

Hand to Hand: Basic. The Tribesman can upgrade to Hand to Hand: Expert for the cost of one O.C.C. Related Skill or Hand to Hand: Martial Arts (or Assassin, if of an evil alignment) for the cost of two O.C.C. Related Skills. At the G.M.'s discretion, Hand to Hand: Wild (New!) may be selected for the cost of five (5) O.C.C. Related Skills.

O.C.C. Related Skills: Select ten (10) other skills of choice at level one, plus select two additional skills at levels three, six, nine, and twelve. All new skills start at level one proficiency.

Communications & Performing Arts: None.

Domestic: Any (+10%).

Espionage: None.

Horsemanship: General, Exotic, or Barbarian (New!) only (+10%).

Medical: Any except Biology and Surgeon/Medical Doctor (Brewing and Holistic Medicine are at +10%).

Military: Camouflage, Falconry, and Surveillance only (Camouflage at +10%).

Physical: Any (+5% where applicable).

Rogue: Any (Card Shark and Streetwise not available until level 6 or greater).

Science: Math: Basic only.

Scholar, Noble, & Technical: Any (General Repair, Rope Works, and Sculpting & Whittling are at +10%).

W.P.: Any except Siege Weapons.

Wilderness: Any (+15%).

Secondary Skills: The character also gets to select six (6) Secondary Skills from the previous list at level one, and two additional skills at levels two, four, six, eight, ten, and twelve. These are additional areas of knowledge that do not get the advantage of the bonus listed in the parentheses. All Secondary Skills start at the base skill level. Also, skills are limited (any, only, none) as previously indicated in the list.

Standard Equipment: One set of tribal clothing (typically including pants, kilt, or loincloth, shirt or chest decorations, and leggings), fur/hide cape or cloak (typically of animal killed and prepared by character), sandals, boots or moccasins, war paints and/or simple body ornamentation (shells, feathers, claws, etc.), crude knapsack, 1D4 small sacks, one large sack, water skin, flint and tinder box, fishing line and hooks, 1D4 simple snares, set of skinning/tanning knives (typically flint, obsidian, or copper), and 50 feet (15 m) of rope.

Armor: Starts with soft leather (A.R. 10, S.D.C. 20). Tribesmen tend to prefer light, natural armors that permit mobility and stealth, and many wear no armor at all, often considering it a sign of weakness (the Kankoran are notorious in this regard).

Weapons: A utility knife (often of stone; 1D6 S.D.C.), small hatchet or tomahawk (often of stone; 1D6 S.D.C.), and two additional weapons of choice reflecting the character's Weapon Proficiencies. Favorite weapons typically include clubs, axes, spears, bows, and staves.

Money: Starts with 2D6x10 gold in barter (trade) items such as skins or precious metal ores or raw (uncut) gems. Additional money will come from payment for services rendered, animal hides, parts, and meat, and booty. Tribemen are often hired by merchants, wealthy travelers, and the military as native scouts or guides often against rival tribes or common enemies. Pay can be excellent for an experienced Tribesman (assuming the Tribesman is familiar enough with the value of currency not to be taken advantage of by unscrupulous merchants, etc.), and can vary from 30-80 gold for simple tasks to as much as 100-700 gold for dangerous missions or military assignments.

Wild Man O.C.C.

Hearkening back to the days of our animalistic origins, the feral Wild Man is more animal than man. Living deep in the recesses of the wilderness, the Wild Man has no sense of his "human" (or other racial) origins, living from day to day in an instinctual need to survive. Earth legends are full of stories about wild, untamed humans who have forgotten (or never learned of) their humanity: Tarzan being raised by apes, Mowgli from Kipling's *The Jungle Book*, wild Enkidu of the Gilgamesh legend, and Romulus and Remus of Roman myth being suckled by a she-wolf. Even some modern, eyewitness accounts of "Wild Men" appear, such as the "Wild Boy of Aveyon" in Seventeenth Century France or the recent case of Romania's "Wild Boy" Traian Caldarar, who lived alone as a child in the wilderness for three years! The Palladium World is no different, having many legends of "Wild Men"; feral, animalistic men (and other races) who act and think like animals and have no identity as "men" (or other races). These Wild Men typically avoid contact with sentient beings (like a wild animal would), though are occasionally "brought back into society" and "domesticated" to a point.

The Wild Man differs from the Barbarian and Savage in that the Wild Man has no knowledge of himself as a "sentient" being. Wild Men are purely feral and instinctual, living in the wilderness without speech, shelter, or typically even clothing! They live only to survive, hunting and gathering and scavenging like a wild animal would. Wild Men never live in "tribes" or "communities," except in the case of the Wild Men raised by communal animals (like wolves or apes). Wild Men are occasionally spotted running naked through the wilderness, sometimes sneaking into human camps to steal food or useful tools. Few Wild Men learn how to manufacture tools (beyond the most simple use of a stick or rock), but many can "learn through imitation" how to use a simple manufactured tool or weapon (like an axe, mace, or spear). The wearing of clothing or ornamentation is typically due to imitation as well, though Wild Men from colder climates occasionally learn to wear skins or furs.

Wild Men, due to their feral nature, gain incredible skill in the wild and a savage, instinctual fighting style (Hand to Hand: Wild). This wild nature, however, confines the scope of their ability and limits the skills they can take to a relative handful. Language, in particular, is difficult for a Wild Man, even if partially civilized. It will always require two skill selections (and 3rd level of experience or higher) to take a Language skill. Sign Language can be taken for one skill selection, but still only at third level or higher. In addition, Wild Men find it almost impossible to succeed outside of the wild unless fully "civilized," and even then will retain a great degree of their wild nature. Even the most "re-civilized" of Wild Men are prone to bouts of feral behavior in times of panic or stress, and may revert to their wild nature under such circumstances (roll a saving throw of 12 or higher plus M.E. bonuses, if any).

The difficulty of life in the wild has made the Wild Man a strong survivor with a plethora of special abilities, which are often lost when a Wild Man becomes "civilized." Wild Men are considered Men-at-Arms for purposes of determining S.D.C. and for armor penalties, though most do not wear armor (or even clothes). Those who do wear armor (exceedingly rare) prefer lightweight, less confining armor like Leather (Scale Mail at most).

Wild Man Abilities, Notes, & Information

1. Natural Abilities and Skills: All Wild Men are linked to their native lands in a way no other sentient beings are. In fact, the feral Wild Man is as much a native animal as the birds and squirrels around him! Wild Men live completely as a part of their native world. This gives them certain skills and advantages when on their native soil. Roll once on the above Native Origins table (or select one) to determine the character's homeland, but *do not* give the character the associated skills (special abilities like resistance or weakness to hot/cold, bonuses to save, and attribute bonuses still apply, however).

2. Affinity to Native Soil: Like the Tribesman and Savage, the Wild Man has a deeply rooted attachment to his home environment. However, the Wild Man is so attuned to his environment that all other native animals consider the character to be a part of the natural surroundings as much as any native animal. As a result, birds and insects continue chirping, frogs, toads, and other amphibians continue their calls, and animals do not run in fear as the character passes if the character is not actively hunting (somehow the animals know). If the Wild Man *is* hunting then the animals will react normally, assuming Prowl is successful. Because of this "oneness" with his surroundings, the character receives a +30% bonus on Prowl and +25% on all other Wilderness skills (plus on the skills of Holistic Medicine, Camouflage, Detect Ambush, Detect Concealment, Track Humanoids, Surveillance, and Intelligence) while in the familiar terrain of his "home territory." He receives +5% on these skills when on similar (but not exact) territory (such as a desert Wild Man from the Sandy Desert of Baalgor visiting the Rocky Desert), but suffers a *penalty* of –10% to all of these skills when in completely unfamiliar territory (such as a Desert Wild Man in the Yin-Sloth Jungles).

3. Wild Background: All Wild Men live a feral, instinctual lifestyle. However, how they came to live in the wild varies. Some were "civilized" men who got lost in the wilderness at a young age, having to fend for themselves, while others were raised since childhood by wild animals. Most of the latter became "wild" at a young age, but may have some vestigial "flashes" of memory from their earlier "civilized" lives. Those raised by animals will typically think of themselves as being an animal of that type (e.g. Wild Men raised by gorillas consider themselves to be gorillas). To determine a Wild Man's background, roll once (or choose from) the following list.

Roll Percentiles (%) or Choose Once from the Following List:

01-30%: Lost as an infant, raised by animals: Like *Tarzan* or *Romulus and Remus,* this character was raised from an early age by member(s) of an animal species. Often this species is a primate or other human-like creature, but not always. The character has no recollection of humans and will likely think of him/herself as one of the species that raised him/her. For this reason, these Wild Men are the most difficult to "bring back in" to human society. If humans (or humanoids) are encountered by this character he will likely react like any other member of "his" species would (typically fleeing). However, the longer the exposure to humans, the more likely the character is to find something oddly familiar about these unusual beings.

As a seeming "member" of the animal race that raised them, Wild Men of this type gain some bonuses and abilities similar to their "foster parents." These bonuses are the same

28

as received by the Were-Shaman (page 49 of the *Mount Nimro™* sourcebook; choose the most accurate fit – e.g. a Wild Man raised by Wolves will use the "Canine" bonuses, etc.). As a result, many "re-civilized" Wild Men of this type become Were-Shaman after their "reintroduction" into humanity (Primary Totem is *always* that of the animal type that raised them). If this happens the character (upon "multi-classing" into the Were-Shaman O.C.C.) may, at the G.M.'s discretion, spend four of his O.C.C. Related Skill selections to "keep" the Hand to Hand: Wild skill (Hand to Hand will remain "frozen" at the current skill level until the Wild Man-turned-Were-Shaman reaches the equivalent level as a Were-Shaman).

Regardless of reeducation, other members of the "parent" species will instinctively consider the character to be "one of them" and react accordingly. Similarly, the character will consider himself one of that species (even if reintroduced to his "humanity") and will not harm or kill another member of the parent species (unless evil!) except accidentally in "natural" pecking-order or territorial conflicts. Only a truly Diabolic Wild Man (or Diabolic former Wild Man if multi-classed) will eat a member of his former species (they consider it cannibalism)!

31-70%: Lost at a young age, raised by animal(s): Same as above, but the character was initially lost as a small child. The main difference is that the character will most likely retain some memory of his time as a "human." As a result, he will have a natural curiosity towards humans (or humanoids) and will be more inclined to approach them. These characters are typically easier to "reintroduce" into humanity than those lost as infants. Like the lost infants above, these characters consider themselves to be members of the "parent" species and gain the Were-Shaman bonuses and multi-classing "ease" to Were-Shaman O.C.C. as with the above lost infants.

71-85%: Lost at a young age, lived alone in the wilderness: Like *Enkidu* or the *Wild Boy of Aveyon*, this character was lost as a young child, but had to fend for himself, since no animals chose to raise him. As a result, the character is hardy and independent, gaining a +2 bonus to P.E. and an additional +5% to all Wilderness and wilderness "related" skills. This character may be curious about humans, or may shun them as "competition" infringing on his "territory." The character will have been a child when "lost," since an infant would never survive on its own, and so will likely have some recollection of being a "Human" even if faint.

86-00%: Lost as an adolescent or adult, but suffered from some form of memory loss: Among the rarest and most unique of Wild Men are those who were older and fully cognizant of their humanity before being "lost." They were lost, cast, or fled into the wilderness and have (in their struggle to survive) forgotten their humanity completely, or perhaps suffered a total memory loss (amnesia) before finding themselves in the woods. Either way, their earlier "humanity" is lost; they have reverted to a feral, wild state with little to no conscious recollection of their "humanity."

Depending on his age when "lost," the character *may* retain some (multi-classed) level in another O.C.C. that was forgotten, but still there, buried away. If the character's memory is "restored" he will revert to this original O.C.C., though his conscious and subconscious recollection of his "feral" state will remain as a "Wild Man O.C.C." frozen at his last level. For the case of such memory loss, the character's original O.C.C. should be created and the Wild Man O.C.C. written up as though it were the "new" O.C.C. after multi-classing (see "Multiple O.C.C.s," *Adventures on the High Seas™*, page 10, for rules on multi-classing). Note that all magic and Super psionic powers will be "forgotten" while in this wild state.

If the character was lost at a younger age (too young to have an "O.C.C."), then he will likely have some subconscious knowledge of life in the "human" world. This case opens up the Wild Man's O.C.C. Related and Secondary Skills to skills not normally available to the Wild Man O.C.C., such as "Animal Husbandry" or "Play Musical Instrument." The player and the G.M. should discuss which skills will be allowed, keeping in mind the limitations that life in the feral Wild Man state would present.

Author's Note: The "Multi-classing" option offers an interesting adventure scenario for a one-on-one single player session, where the player character is somehow "lost" and has reverted to a feral state. The player's character will "multi-class" to the Wild Man O.C.C., freezing the original O.C.C. (note the character must live the "feral" life for at least three years before this happens). He will then remain a "Wild Man," likely totally forgetting his humanity and former life/O.C.C. in an instinctual need to survive (all magic and Super psionic powers forgotten). Should he "rediscover" his humanity, he has the option of reverting to the original O.C.C. or choosing a new (third) O.C.C. (Note: the character must spend at least three years or achieve five levels of experience in the feral Wild Man state, in addition to the three years needed to "become" a Wild Man, or he will completely lose the "Wild Man" O.C.C. levels and all bonuses and skills associated with the Wild Man O.C.C.).

4. Weather Divination: Exactly as described above for the Savage Warrior O.C.C., but at a base skill level of 40%, +5% per level of experience. In addition, the prediction of coming disasters begins at level 1, but long term weather prediction is impossible (Wild Men do not think that far ahead). The Wild Man will react to coming weather like any animal, with a sense of acceptance for weather changes and a sense of fear and panic for disaster.

5. Distrust and Fear of Magic/Magic Users: Exactly as described under the Native Berserker O.C.C., but without any chance of entering a Berserker Rage, and extends to all mystical characters, including Shaman, Druids, flashy psionic displays, and any obvious display of super-human abilities.

6. Aversion to Civilization: Exactly as described above for the Native Berserker O.C.C., but without any chance of entering a Berserker Rage. Additionally, the penalties for being in an urban environment are -6 to all combat and initiative bonuses except dodge (they have a +6 to dodge!) as long as they remain inside the city. In addition, they are more prone to fear (-8 to save vs Horror Factor) and panic. These penalties (and the dodge bonus) are cut in half at fifth (5th) level, cut in half a second time at seventh (7th) level (so ¼ the original penalty), and are eliminated completely at tenth (10th) level. Learning the ways of the city is difficult for the Wild Man. As a result, the Streetwise skill can never be taken by the Wild Man character.

7. Increased Psionic Potential and Special Psionic Abilities: Due to the Wild Man's close link to nature, inherent psionics are likely. Rather than using the chart on page 21 of the PFRPG main book, roll percentiles on the following table to determine Wild Man Psionics:

01-40: Major Psionics.

41-70: Minor Psionics.

71-00: No Psionics.

Psionics granted are exactly as described under the Random Psionics section of the PFRPG main book, page 21. Typical powers include Sixth Sense, Sense Evil, Sense Magic, Commune with Animals, Mind Block, Bio-Regeneration, Resist Fatigue, Impervious to Cold, Impervious to Fire, Impervious to Poison/Toxin, Nightvision, Resist Fatigue, Resist Hunger, Resist Thirst, Summon Inner Strength, and Telekinetic Leap.

Empathic Communication: (Sensitive power unique to the Wild Man O.C.C. and not available to non-Wild Man characters.) In addition to the above increased psionic potential, all Wild Men have the special ability of Empathic Communication.

Range: 100 foot (30.5 m) area.

Duration: Two minutes per level of experience.

I.S.P.: None, innate ability of the Wild Man.

Saving Throw: Standard; a save vs Empathic Communications will allow a character to "shield" his true emotional intentions, but only if the character knows to do so. Otherwise, he will unwittingly project his true emotional "intentions."

Empathic Communication is an odd ability that seems to be unique to the feral Wild Man and many wild, undomesticated animals. This odd ability is a sort of combination between Empathy and two-way Telepathy, wherein the Wild Man is able to project or receive emotional impressions. These impressions convey a simple emotional "feeling" of the current mood and/or desires of the character. In the projective sense, the Wild Man can send a simple emotional impression to let others know his current mood or basic needs. All within range who do not attempt to "shut out" the impression (by consciously saving or by having a Mind Block up) will receive the emotional impression as though it were shouted aloud to them. These are simple emotional impressions such as "curious," "suspicious," "friendly," "hungry," "in pain," "angry" (at the characters or at some outside event), "happy/content," or "malevolent." The Wild Man will automatically send ("shout") these emotional impressions to anything within range unless he purposefully suppresses these impressions. Note that the impressions are always true; the Wild Man cannot "lie," or send false emotional impressions (for example, a Wild Man that is actively seeking to harm or attack someone/something can *not* project an impression of "friendly" good will, only his true feelings and intentions).

Wild Men are also attuned to picking up the empathic projections given off by every living thing. All living things involuntarily project their emotional desires about them (which may be the basis for being able to "read" someone). Unless the character is aware of this and takes steps to suppress these empathic projections (by Mind Block or a conscious effort to "save"), the Wild Man will be able to read his emotional mood and desires. These projected desires are exactly as described in the Wild Man's "projected" impressions: simple desires like "curious," "hungry," and so on. In this way the Wild Man will know of a person's "true" intentions (for example, a Western slaver who is trying to "act friendly" to lure the Wild Man out into the open for capture will unwittingly "project" his true intention of "hostility," letting the Wild Man know to be wary). If an outside character has Empathy and Telepathy, a simple form of two-way communications with the Wild Man may be possible. The conversation will be an interesting mix of emotional impressions and simple, one-to-three word sentences (many psychics describe the process as similar to having a conversation with a small child). The specifics of the conversation are dependent upon the role-playing situation.

8. "Civilizing" Wild Men: Wild Man characters generally avoid and distrust most other humans, though some do retain some vestigial curiosity for those "strange beings" who seem so familiar. Wild Men are occasionally "civilized" by others, typically by some of the wilder Savage tribes. Some, however, are discovered by "civilized" men, and brought back to civilization – sometimes to be "reeducated" by well meaning Samaritans, but sometimes to be put on display in freak-shows or worse, gladiatorial arenas. Full "reeducation" requires 5D6 months of continual attention and education and results in a change of O.C.C. for the Wild Man. Whenever the Wild Man is fully "reeducated" he loses his "wild" nature, and must change to a new O.C.C., which is typically based on the environment in which he was reeducated. Those reeducated in barbaric tribes typically become Native Tribesmen or Barbarian/Savage Warriors, while those raised in "civilization" typically become Vagabonds, Thieves, or Soldiers/Mercenary Warriors. Note that those raised by animals often become Were-Shaman with a primary totem of the animal species that raised them.

To determine the success of a reeducation attempt, add the "teacher's" I.Q. and M.A. to the Wild Man's I.Q. and M.E. and roll that sum total or less on percentile dice. If the roll is successful, the Wild Man is fully civilized; if unsuccessful (or if the training is incomplete), the Wild Man becomes "partially" reeducated. "Partial reeducation" is really nothing more than a new life experience for the Wild Man, though it may affect the character's instinctual nature (causes the Hand to Hand: Wild combat skill to "freeze").

9. Bonuses: All Wild Man characters receive the following bonuses: +20 S.D.C., +3 to save vs Disease, +1 to the P.S. attribute, and a +3 to the P.E. attribute.

10. Additional Special Abilities: Additionally, the Wild Man O.C.C. gains the Battle Cry O.C.C. ability from the Barbarian Warrior O.C.C. (page 178, *Northern Hinterlands*™ sourcebook) and may select two other of the Barbarian O.C.C. Special Abilities except for the Equestrian Skill.

Wild Man O.C.C.

(Recommended as an N.P.C. only)

Alignment: Always start out as Anarchist. Any sense of alignment, ethics, or morality must come later, and typically must be taught to them.

Racial Notes: Wild Men tend to be members of the so-called "monster" races, typically Orcs, Goblins/Hobgoblins, Trolls, Ogres, Giants and Coyles (and the enigmatic Kankoran). However, Human Wild Men are rather common and other humanoid Wild Men, including Elves, Dwarves, and even Gnomes, have been known to exist.

Attribute Requirements: P.E. 12. A high P.S. and P.P. are helpful, but not required.

O.C.C. Skills:

Language: *None!* Can not learn a language until 3rd level or higher (even then it requires 2 skill selections).

Climb/Scale Walls (+25%)

Prowl (+15%)

Land Navigation (+20%)

Wilderness Survival (+20%)

Identify Plants & Fruits (+15%)

Skin & Prepare Animal Hides (+15%)

Track & Trap Animals (+20%)

Track Humanoids (+15%)

Hand to Hand: Wild (New!). Can not be changed or substituted.

O.C.C. Related Skills: Select six (6) other skills of choice at level one, plus select two additional skills at levels three, six, nine, and twelve. All new skills start at level one proficiency.

Communications & Performing Arts: Sign Language only, and may choose other Languages at a cost of two skill selections each (must be 3rd level or higher to take any, including Sing Language).

Domestic: Any (+10%; but only Fishing may be chosen at first level).

Espionage: Detect Ambush, Detect Concealment & Traps, Escape Artist, and Tracking only (+10%).

Horsemanship: None at first level. General, Barbarian (New! – costs 2 skill slots) or Exotic at 3rd level.

Medical: Holistic Medicine only (+10%).

Military: None.

Physical: Any except Hand to Hand, Boxing, Wrestling, or Juggling; skills are considered "feral" equivalents of the learned skill (+5% where applicable).

Rogue: Any except Card Shark and Streetwise.

Science: Math: Basic only.

Scholar, Noble, & Technical: General Repair and Sculpting/Whittling only (and see Communications, above, for notes on Languages).

W.P.: Any (only W.P. Blunt may be chosen at 1st level).

Wilderness: Any except Boat Building and Carpentry (+15%).

Secondary Skills: The character also gets to select four (4) Secondary Skills from the previous list at level one, and two additional skills at levels two, four, six, eight, ten, and twelve. These are additional areas of knowledge that do not get the advantage of the bonus listed in the parentheses. All Secondary Skills start at the base skill level. Also, skills are limited (any, only, none) as previously indicated in the list.

Standard Equipment: None to start (all equipment must be acquired in play). Simple furs may be allowed for Wild Man characters from cold origins.

Armor: None to start. "Civilized" Wild Men tend to prefer light, natural armors that permit mobility and stealth, and most wear no armor at all, often considering it binding and unnatural.

Weapons: Only a simple wood club or stick (if desired) may be taken to start.

Money: Starts with none. Money will come from payment for services rendered, animal hides, parts and meat, and booty. "Civilized" (or partially civilized) Wild Men are sometimes hired by merchants, wealthy travelers, and the military as native scouts or guides. However, many consider them to be too unpredictable, and as a result, usually prefer to hire Rangers or Barbarians. Pay can be excellent for an experienced "re-civilized" Wild Man (assuming the Wild Man is familiar enough with the value of currency not to be taken advantage of by unscrupulous merchants, etc.), and can vary from 30-80 gold for simple tasks to as much as 200-800 gold for dangerous missions or military assignments.

Amazons

The legendary Amazons were (are?) a tribe of barbarian warrior women who reportedly lived in the Palladium World in years long past. These legends, which typically place the Amazons in the Yin-Sloth Jungles, the Old Kingdom, or the Land of the Damned, speak of entire Amazon tribes led by fearsome woman-warriors and populated by submissive males. Scholars constantly debate whether the Amazons actually did or do exist. The legends claim the Amazons to be tall and powerful (and often beautiful) women and generally refer to them as being particularly skilled with the bow (some legends speak of these as "longbows," though many scholars assume that they would be, in fact, composite bows, whose range and deadliness mirrors that of the longbow). Some of these legends even claim that the bow-wielding women warriors would amputate their right breast in order to allow for more room for the drawing of the bowstring, and therefore allow better use of the bow! While legends persist, no documented proof of Amazon tribes has yet come to light, though eyewitness reports of Amazon tribes continue to surface.

Whether the fierce Amazons are real or mythical remains to be settled; however, theories continue to surface and speculation abounds. Some scholars point to documented cases of matriarchal tribes and races (such as the Eandroth) as the source for the legends, while others assume it comes from memories of Elven female archers and longbow troops. Some sightings have also been linked to travels by male sailors to the Island of Lemaria. The *Tristine Chronicles* are conspicuously quiet on the subject. Whatever the case, the spotting of Amazons and the occasional appearance of a woman warrior claiming Amazon heritage continue to fuel the argument. In the context of role-playing, I leave the existence of true Amazons entirely up to the Game Master and/or the players. If they "exist" in your game, Amazon player characters and NPCs will generally be Barbarians, Savage Warriors, or Longbowmen by O.C.C. (or "Composite Bowmen," see W.P. Composite Bow for details), with the specifics of the character and culture of the Amazon "tribes" being left up to the player and/or G.M. to decide.

New Skills, Weapons and Chants

New Skills

The following new skills should be added to the PFRPG® skills list in order to reflect the addition of barbaric cultures to the Palladium World.

Domestic:

Tattooing: (Note: May also be taken as a Scholar/Technical (Art) Skill.) This skill indicates proficiency in the design and creation of decorative tattoos and skin art, either as decoration/ornamentation or for religious, ceremonial, or status/position reasons. Tattooing as an art form varies from culture to culture, and ranges from primitive black scars to intricate and colorful full body designs. Tattoo art is created in a variety of ways; tapping ink/pigment into the skin with blades, rubbing ink/ash/dye into cuts made by blades, injection into the skin using a needle, etc. Regardless of the method of creation, Tattoos always result in a permanent design or picture in the character's skin. While tattooing is mostly practiced by "barbaric" cultures (particularly in the south of the continent), tattoos have recently become all the rage with Byzantium sailors (who, it is assumed, picked up the habit from the south island natives they have met), a fad that has begun to spread to other sailors around the Palladium World and even some gladiators, warriors, rogues, or other landlubbers. **Base Skill:** 35% +5% per additional level of experience. **Note:** This skill does *not* include the creation of Danzi Spirit Tattoos or Atlantean "Magic Tattoos," which are unique and mystical in nature. Only decorative, non-mystical tattoos can be created using this skill.

Horsemanship:

Camelry: (Note: May also be taken as a Domestic/Cultural Skill) Effectively "Horsemanship" for camels and other desert animals, this skill indicates extensive training and experience riding and caring for such animals. While anyone with the Horsemanship: Exotic or even Horsemanship: General skill can be assumed to have some fundamental idea on how to control a camel (with a little specific training), this skill goes a step further, giving the skill holder the ability to raise and care for the camels (etc.), use selective breeding to enhance the herd, and, most importantly, understands the proper use of such animals in combat, including how to take advantage of their unique abilities in arid conditions. This includes all of the abilities and bonuses listed under the Horsemanship skill category and the Horsemanship: General skill, pages 52-53, PFRPG® main book, but applies to Camels, Draybacks, Silonar, and similar desert/arid mounts. It also includes the understanding necessary to make the best tactical/strategic use of such animals, crossing vast stretches of seemingly impassable desert terrain no horse could survive, quickly and with no logistics train, and delivering surprise attacks to unguarded flanks that non-desert-experienced commanders may have overlooked. The Desert Nomads make great use of such tactics, catching their enemies off guard or making swift escapes across lands their horse-riding foes can not cross. **Base Skill:** 35/25% +5% per additional level of experience. **Note:** Camels themselves do not officially exist in the **Palladium Fantasy RPG®**, but Game Masters may certainly include them in their campaigns.

Horsemanship: Barbarian: The Barbarian Horseman is a strong and hardy warrior every bit as attuned to combat from horseback as a Knight or Palladin. The Barbarian Horseman usually comes from a horse-based culture where the children learn to ride and live on horseback from an early age (much like the Mongols or Lakota Sioux of Earth). The Barbarian Horseman is totally comfortable on horseback, often thinking and behaving as though he and the horse were, in fact, "one" being. Rather than riding the huge War Horses favored by "civilized" Knights, however, the Barbarian Horseman prefers the small, quick, and hardy wild "ponies" that inhabit the wilds of the Palladium World. These wild ponies (more like the Appaloosa and Arabian horses of Earth than the tiny Shetland "children's" ponies) are quick, fast, agile, and tough. Unlike the large, powerful warhorses of the Knights and Palladins (which require large quantities of a rich diet of oats and grains to function), the wild ponies can survive on wild grasses and a relative handful of grains per day. As a result, the Barbarian Horsemen and their hardy ponies can travel lightly, covering great stretches of ground and inhospitable areas difficult for the civilized cavalry.

In addition to the proper care and husbandry of the ponies, the Barbarian Horseman knows the capabilities of these steeds and the limits of the steeds' endurance. As a result, a Barbarian Horseman will typically take more than one pony with him on a long ride (typically as many as five), switching horses mid-gallop to ease the burden of the individual mounts and increase the overall speed and distance traveled. This has the added bonus of allowing the Barbarian Horseman to have one or more "fresh" mounts available for combat. The barbarian will know each of his steeds with the intimate knowledge of a father, and likely even helped to birth the horse as a foal. The barbarian will know the abilities and limits of the animal and will be able to push the steed to the peak of its potential without exceeding its limits. Barbarian Horsemen typically perform incredible stunts and tricks on horseback, for both combat and recreation. Many clans hold periodic contests of horsemanship or horseback games with honor and possible prizes available for the winners. Horse Barbarians typically also use their herds for milk animals and even food. As a result, the Barbarian Horseman likely can sustain himself on mare's milk and light travel rations while traveling through the worst of lands. [*Author's Note:* For more information on these "ponies," see their description on page 206 of the *Palladium Book of Monsters & Animals, 2nd ed.*]

In combat, the Barbarian Horseman is to be respected and feared. Even though their steeds are small and unarmored, the Barbarian Horsemen are a fierce, capable, and organized force. Highly-mobile and well-coordinated corps of barbarian horseback bowman have been known to employ fast, organized, and devastating attacks using the speed and mobility of their steeds and the range and deadliness of their feared composite horse bows to stage blitzkrieg-like assaults. Excellent use of flank attacks, envelopments, and hit-and-run tactics have, in the past, proved enough to defeat even the largest of armies. Whole armies of mounted Knights have been devastated by these seemingly small and under-equipped horsemen. Corps of Long Bowmen have likewise been slaughtered by armies of horse barbarians who have used their superior range and speed to hammer the Longbow corps, charging in from beyond Longbow range to deliver deadly volleys before withdrawing back out of reach. In addition to their organization and deadly accuracy, the horse barbarians have also made excellent use of their multiple-horse philosophy both to conceal their numbers and exaggerate their size, and to keep their horses fresh and ready.

Like the Horsemanship skills listed on pages 52 and 53 of the PFRPG® Main Book, a character with the Horsemanship: Barbarian skill is familiar with all of the basic care, breeding and husbandry skills described under Horsemanship on page 52 of the main book. **Base Skill:** 45%/35% +5% per level of experience.

Combat: All bonuses are in addition to other combat skills, Weapon Proficiencies, or attribute bonuses. Applies to the rider, not the horse. The rider gains a combat advantage from the height and speed of being mounted.

- +1 initiative when on horseback.
- +3 to roll with fall or impact when knocked from a horse.
- +2 to parry and +4 to dodge while on horseback.
- Inflicts +1D6 to damage when on horseback.
- Horse Archery & Targeting: Can use thrown weapons from horseback with no penalties for speed and movement, and can use small bows (short bows, crossbows, or the feared composite horse bow) from horseback at only ½ the normal penalties for speed and movement. If the W.P. Composite Bow skill is also known, no penalties are suffered for the use of short bows or composite bows from horseback.
- Charge Attack: Unlike the standard "knightly" charge attack, this attack involves charging *past* the opponent and attacking them with hand weapons, thrown spears, or bows as the rider passes. The attacking rider must roll under the second percentile number to avoid being dismounted. Charge attack counts as two attacks and does +2D6 damage.
- Charging Jump: Similar to the charge attack, but the rider jumps off of the horse to attack or body block/tackle his opponent. Does a Critical Strike to the intended victim on a successful strike and knocks the victim prone if the victim fails a roll with impact. Roll under the second percentile number. Rider must also roll successfully with impact (12 or higher) or suffer 1D4 damage. This tactic can also be used on another rider to dismount him. Note that a successful simultaneous strike against the attacking rider with a piercing weapon (spear, sword point, pole arm, etc.) will be a Critical Strike (x2 damage) against the jumping rider.
- Horseback Acrobatics: The Barbarian Horseman was likely raised on horseback and feels as comfortable on a horse as walking on the ground. As a result, the character can perform any number of acrobatic flips, leaps, and mounts/dismounts even while at a full gallop. The character can (on a successful modified strike roll of 7 or higher) vault onto or off of horseback (strike roll increases to 10 for slow moving horse (walk, trot, etc.) and increases to 12 for fast movement (canter, gallop, etc.)). Also, the character can "slide down" to the flanks (sides) of the horse and remain "hanging" there. This move is useful for shielding yourself behind the horse for either protection or concealment. These maneuvers require a successful roll of the second percentile number. In addition, if the character also knows the Acrobatics, Gymnastics, or Tumbling

skills, variations of the skill-provided abilities and maneuvers can be performed while on horseback (using that ability's percentile number) at no penalty.

- Horse Attack: This indicates that the rider is skilled enough to remain mounted while he attacks and has his horse rearing or kicking in simultaneous attack (roll under the second percentile number). Damage from the kick of the horse will vary with the size and breed of the animal; generally 1D6+2 from the front legs (for the ponies favored by the barbarians) and 2D6+4 from the rear legs.

Medical:

Create Berserker Potion: This skill encompasses the creation of the mysterious *Berserker Potion*, a toxic and hallucinogenic substance that brings out the aggressive, violent nature in people. This potion is used primarily as a method of inducing the Berserker Rage in Berserkers (see description under the Berserker O.C.C.), or occasionally in others. Known only to a very select few, this skill is very limited. [G.M.s, don't just let players arbitrarily take this skill; it should ideally be limited to Shaman, Were-Shaman, Druids, Witches, or the Barbaric O.C.C.s.]

Berserker Potion Effects: This potion causes the person who drinks a dose (roughly one ounce of the Potion) to fall into a violent, hallucination-plagued delirium that tends to bring out the darkest parts of the human (or non-human) psyche. Berserkers who drink it will automatically enter into the Berserker Rage (as stated under the O.C.C. description) 1D4 melees after drinking it, with the following additional bonuses/penalties, which last until the potion's effects subside in 1D4 hours: +2 P.S., +2 P.E., +1D6 temporary S.D.C., -10% to all skills, -2 I.Q., -1 M.E., communication is impossible. At the end of the 1D4 hours, the potion wears off and the effects (and Rage) end automatically. In addition, the Berserker loses 1D6 Hit Points (not S.D.C.!) due to the toxic nature of the potion (save vs Lethal Poison for half damage; damage can be healed or restored as normal).

Non-Berserkers who drink the Berserker Potion are likewise affected by the potion (1D4 hours duration), taking the 1D6 Hit Points of damage and rolling on the following chart to determine the effects the potion has on them:

Non-Berserker Potion Effects; Roll Percentiles (%):

01-40%: Enters into a Berserker Rage (exactly as described under the Berserker O.C.C. description above) with the standard Berserker bonuses and penalties.

41-60%: Enters into a Berserker Rage with all the standard bonuses/penalties for the O.C.C., *plus* the additional bonuses/penalties described above for the Berserker who takes the potion!

61-85%: Falls into a mindless delirium, completely detached from the world around them. For the duration of the potion's effects, the character suffers -25% to all skills, can not control any abilities/magic/psionics (though abilities may "go off" by themselves), suffers -1D6 to I.Q., M.E., and M.A., gains +1 to P.S. and P.E., gains +1D6 S.D.C., and will find all communication with others and all combat actions except dodge impossible.

86-00%: Same as the mindless delirium above, but has a "bad trip" with horrible, terrifying hallucinations that seem utterly real. The character will scream and run blindly in terror

(possibly running headlong off a cliff or into a dangerous situation) and will strike out to *kill* anyone who gets close, thinking them a horrible monster. At the end of the duration, the character must save vs insanity or suffer from a random insanity (page 26, PFRPG®).

The effects (and all bonuses and penalties) from the potion end after 1D4 hours. When this duration ends, the character (Berserker or otherwise) will suffer from bad after-effects, including headache, stomach trauma, and blurred vision (-2 on all combat bonuses, -5% on all skills, and will be irritable and moody). These effects last for the next 2D6 hours.

Due to the dangerous nature of the Berserker Potion, its manufacture, possession, use, and distribution have been banned by all major civilized nations and by most uncivilized cultures except in times of emergency (penalties can include flogging for first-time offenders and banishment or torture/death for repeat offenders!). Some Western Nobles secretly experiment with the potion (though even this is rare), and some Mercenary Warriors or bandits have been known to keep a dose around "just in case."

A one-ounce dose of the Berserker Potion costs 3D6x1000 gold pieces on the black market. Multiple-dose usage of the potion is highly dangerous, as each additional dose taken simultaneously results in a progressive doubling of the penalties suffered and damage taken (2D6 Hit Points of damage for two doses, 4D6 for three, 8D6 for four, etc.) with no new bonuses. If the save vs lethal poison is failed for a three-dose use or more, the character will fall unconscious for the duration of the effects (1D4 hours) and must make a second save vs lethal poison or fall into a potentially fatal coma. The taking of multiple doses is therefore *never* done deliberately by sane or rational people.

Base Skill Level: 25% +4% per additional level of experience. If the Use/Recognize Poison skill is also known, the character receives a one-time bonus of +5% to the Create Berserker Potion skill. The Chemistry skill likewise adds a one-time +10% bonus.

Weapon Proficiencies:

W.P. Composite (Horse) Bow: This W.P. involves skill in the use and maintenance of the famous barbarian composite bow. The Composite (or horse) bow is a recurved bow constructed from composite layers of wood, horn, sinew, and other materials, which gives it damage comparable to that of the longbow and superior range. This skill is essentially the same as the W.P. Archery skill described on page 59 of the PFRPG® main book, but deals only with the specific use of the composite (horse) bow. Composite bows have a nominal effective range of 820 feet (250 m) and do 2D6 damage per arrow. In addition to rate of fire and strike/parry bonuses, this W.P. also allows the composite bow to be used from horseback with all penalties due to movement reduced by half. If the character with the W.P. Composite Bow skill also has the Horsemanship: Barbarian skill, all penalties for using the bow on horseback are eliminated (full bonuses). See Horsemanship: Barbarian and the description of the composite bow for more information. [*Author's Note:* At the G.M.'s discretion, a "Composite Bowman O.C.C." can be created using the Long Bowman O.C.C. (PFRPG® main book, pages 83-85) as a template. Merely substitute "Composite Bow" in the place of "Longbow." Note that the Composite Bowman

O.C.C. does *not* gain skill in the use of the longbow, nor does the Long Bowman O.C.C. gain skill in the use of the composite bow; these are two separate skills and two separate O.C.C.s.]

Wilderness:

Construct Stone Tools & Weapons: (Note: Can also be taken as a Domestic or Scholar/Technical skill.) This skill entails the construction of simple stone or wood tools and weapons, from simple axes to intricate spear and arrow points (depending on the technological abilities of the character's home tribe/culture). This character not only knows how to chip the stone into usable shapes and edges, but also knows how to attach the blade to the shaft of a spear or arrow or handle of an axe/club (assuming high enough cultural tech level). If an Archery skill is also known, the character can attach fletching (feather guide fins) to arrow shafts. Non-stone items can also be used, such as shell or bone. Preferred stones include flint and obsidian for bladed/edged weapons (obsidian blades do +1 damage due to sharpness, as chipped obsidian is sharper than even good steel) and hard, indigenous rock like granite for blunt weapons. Note that stone blades must be regularly re-chipped to preserve sharpness (-1 damage penalty per week without such maintenance), and blades will have to be replaced every 1D6 months as they wear down. Bladed stone weapons also have difficulty penetrating metal armor (treat as if the A.R. of the armor were two points higher against the stone blade) and will require immediate "sharpening" after they strike such metal (-1 damage per 4 strikes to metal). **Construction Times for Stone Tools/Weapons:** Simple stone clubs require 1D4 hours to construct; arrowheads require 2D6+20 minutes each, while the mounting takes 2D6 minutes and the fletching 2D6+10 minutes; knife blades and spear/hoe/axe heads require 3D6+30 minutes each and mounting takes 2D6 minutes; stone swords are not practical, though wooden "paddles" with stone blades placed along the side edges ("Maquahuilts") take 2D6+20 minutes per blade (typically six or eight) to construct, while the "paddle" requires 1D6 hours to construct (requires Carpentry skill). **Base Skill Level:** 30% +5% per additional level of experience. If the Carpentry skill is also known, the character receives a one-time bonus of +5% to the Construct Stone Tools & Weapons skill for the construction of wooden "hafts" or similar items only.

New Hand to Hand

Hand to Hand: Wild: Wild Hand to Hand is an instinctual form of combat based on the built-in need to survive. The combat style is not "taught" or "learned," but rather grows out of the Wild fighter's own instinctual reactions to dangerous situations. Rather than formal stances and fighting techniques, Wild hand to hand combat involves the character simply "reacting" to the stress of combat and attacking with whatever seems appropriate for the moment: overhead raps, wild punches, elbows, kicks, biting, whatever works! This savage fighting style is therefore unpredictable and difficult to counter using traditional "trained" combat styles. Hand to Hand: Wild is automatically known by all Wild Man O.C.C. characters and by some Savage Warriors or other "barbaric" O.C.C.s, though it can also be (optionally) known by "wild" mutant characters from the **After the Bomb®** or **Heroes Unlimited™** settings (at a cost of four skill selections).

Hand to Hand Note: Hand to Hand: Wild, due to its instinctual and untrained nature, can *not* be formally learned as a martial art. Instead it is a manifestation of a person's *instinctual* need to fight to survive. As such, it is not a formal *style*, but rather a reactive form of instinctual combat, much like how a wild animal will bite, claw, charge, kick, etc. in an effort to kill prey/rivals or defend itself against predators. For this reason, *any* attempt to formalize this fighting style will be unsuccessful. In addition, the "practitioner" of Hand to Hand: Wild *can not* learn any formalized or trained combat style. *Any form* of formalized combat training (Hand to Hand or otherwise) taken by the Hand to Hand: Wild fighter will supercede Hand to Hand: Wild, causing the character to *permanently lose* his skill in Hand to Hand: Wild, regardless of the level of proficiency attained in Hand to Hand: Wild. Even taking the Physical skills of Boxing or Wrestling (or a "quasi" fighting style like Tai Chi or similar exercises) will result in this loss. In addition, becoming overly civilized will result in the loss of the Hand to Hand: Wild skill. If the character doesn't spend *at least one week out of every two months* living in the wilderness (away from civilization), he will lose the Hand to Hand: Wild skill. This "week" does not have to be continuous: a few hours spent in the wilderness every day or so will suffice, so long as the minimum total "week" (168 hours) is spent.

Level

1. Starts with two attacks per melee round. +3 to roll with punch/fall/impact. +1 on initiative. Opponents unfamiliar with fighting against a Hand to Hand: Wild opponent are -2 to strike/parry/dodge against this character.
2. +2 to parry and dodge, +2 to strike, +2 damage.
3. Tripping leg hook, power punch, elbow, knee, kick attack (no formal "style," just whatever works).
4. One additional attack per melee round.
5. Leap Attack (Critical Strike) and Body Block/Tackle. Critical Strike or Knockout from behind.
6. Critical Strike on an unmodified 18, 19, or 20.
7. Backflip, additional +3 damage.
8. One additional attack per melee round.
9. An additional +3 damage, +2 to pull punch.
10. Body throw/flip and an additional +2 on initiative.
11. Knockout/stun on an unmodified 18, 19, or 20.
12. An additional +2 to parry/dodge.
13. Automatic Dodge.
14. One additional attack per melee round.
15. Death Blow on a roll of a Natural 20 (if desired).

New Weapons

Atlatl: One of the earliest tools known to many stone-age cultures is the Atlatl. In its simplest form the Atlatl is a short stick or carved horn/bone with one end curving around and notched or hollowed out into a cupped groove. The blunt end of a throwing spear or javelin is placed into this groove and the spear is held up on top of the Atlatl. The user then uses the Atlatl to "fling" the spear, but holds onto the Atlatl, using it for extra leverage and throwing arm length. An Atlatl will add 20 feet (6.1 m) of range and +1 damage to any thrown short spear or

+50 feet (15 m) range and +1 damage to any thrown javelin. The Atlatl will not work with long spears, tridents, pikes, or pole arms, as these weapons are too heavy and cumbersome. Note that the use of the Atlatl is covered by the W.P. Targeting skill.

Composite Bow (sometimes called the horse bow): The feared composite bow, made famous by the horse barbarians, is a re-curved, multi-material short bow that rivals (some say surpasses) the famed long bow in range and deadliness. The composite horse bow of the horse barbarians combines several layers of strong, flexible wood with strips of horn, sinew, or other non-wooden materials bound by strong, natural glues (hence "composite"; compound materials used). These multiple layers give the bow strength, power, and rigidity. On top of that, the bow is greatly re-curved to a point that the bow is concave rather than convex when unstrung. Great strength is necessary just to string it (P.S. 16 or higher). Once strung, the composite bow delivers extreme power and long range (range is superior to even the long bow), but is no larger than a standard short bow, allowing its use from horseback or from a kneeling position. Although usually associated with the horse barbarians, the composite bow is popular with many "barbaric" peoples, including many Agrarian tribes and the Desert Nomads. The composite bow has an effective range of about 820 feet (250 m) and does 2D6 damage per arrow.

Maquahuilt (or Bladed War-Club): The brutal Maquahuilt is a paddle-shaped war club used by many barbaric warriors of the Yin-Sloth Jungles (particularly the Mazeca). The Maquahuilt in its simplest form is a wooden "paddle" with a long handle (grip) and a flat, rectangular head. The two opposite side edges of the head are fitted with six to twelve opposing "blades" of stone (typically obsidian) in a wicked, "saw-tooth" arrangement, and is used in a hacking/clubbing or slashing manner, much like a non-pointed chopping sword or axe. Maquahuilts are the principle weapon of the warriors of the Yin-Sloth Jungles, and Jungle Savages often hold their Maquahuilts to the same level of esteem that Knights hold their swords to or Long Bowmen their bows. Many warriors "customize" their Maquahuilts with intricate carvings, paint, feathers, or other decorations, and enchanted Maquahuilts are known to exist. Maquahuilts are usually 36-48 inches long (91-122 cm) end-to-end, weigh about 3-5 pounds (1-3 kg, roughly), and do 2D6 damage with a chopping/slashing attack. Though used in a manner similar to a sword or axe, they are really war-clubs of sorts and require either W.P. Blunt or W.P. Axe (with some specific training or practice with the Maquahuilt) in order to use properly.

New Shamanic Chants

These new shamanic chants are available for the Shaman O.C.C. detailed in PFRPG® Book #3: *Adventures on the High Seas*™ (page 38):

Chant of the Berserker

Range: 20 foot (6 m) radius or within sight and/or hearing for Berserker O.C.C. characters.
Duration: Special; chant takes 10 minutes, effects vary.
P.P.E.: 70

Saving Throw: Standard; Berserkers have a -5 penalty to save.

The little-known, dangerous, and often forbidden Chant of the Berserker is a passionate, energetic, and all-consuming ceremony that allows the Shaman to connect him- or herself and the participants of the ceremony to the deepest, darkest, most violent aspects of their psyche. This psychological "plunge" into the dark (often aided by the use of harsh hallucinogens such as the Berserker Potion) connects the Shaman and the participants with their darker, animal aspects, driving them into a killing (Berserker) Rage! The dark nature of this chant (as well as the possibility that the Shaman will be "overtaken" by the chant himself) has resulted in a Stigma attachment to this chant: most Shaman (75%) will *never* use this chant except in the most dire of circumstances (unless evil or insane!).

As the chant digs its way into the minds of the participants, it drives them into a mindlessly violent state that induces the Rage. Willing participants are automatically affected (including the Shaman himself, if "willing") while unwilling or hesitant participants can save vs magic to resist the violent desires (most Shaman (90%) are "unwilling" to enter the Rage themselves). If the save is successful, the unwilling character is not affected, but will probably be in a dark, angry, and/or depressed mood for the next 1D4 hours. Willing participants, or those who fail their saving throws, are driven immediately into the Berserker Rage as defined above in the Berserker O.C.C. (exactly as described under the O.C.C. description). True Berserkers (Berserker O.C.C.) will also receive an additional bonus of +2 to strike, +2 to damage, and +1D6 additional *temporary* S.D.C. This Rage will continue until the fight is done or the participant is dead (see Berserker Rage description for more details). If the Shaman fails his/her saving throw he/she will Rage as well, joining the melee. If the Shaman is killed, this has no effect on the other participants (the Rage has already been initiated, the magic has already been done). If the Berserker Potion is used as well, its effects will be cumulative with the Chant's effects (see Berserker Potion description; non-Berserkers gain the +2 strike and damage bonus and +1D6 temporary Hit Points (like for the true Berserkers) in this case).

Chant of Totem Communion

Range: Self or other(s) by Touch (one additional recipient at 3rd, 6th, 9th, 12th, and 15th level of experience).
Duration: The dream-like "Communion" typically lasts about one hour; effects of the first ("finding") chant last 48 hours per experience level of the Shaman, and the effects of all subsequent ("reconnecting") chants last 24 hours per experience level of the Shaman. The duration is doubled if a Were-Shaman of 5th level or above is participating in the chant.
P.P.E.: 100 P.P.E. for initial "finding" ceremony, 70 P.P.E. for subsequent "reconnecting" chants.
Saving Throw: Standard for others, none for the Shaman.
Note: This chant *will not* affect Were-Shaman characters, since they are already fully in touch with their "Totem natures." Were-Shaman characters gain no bonuses or abilities from this chant.

The Chant of Totem Communion is unique among the chants in that it draws power from the animal Totem of the recipient. In this way it is closely linked with the focus of the Were-Shaman (see O.C.C., page 47, PFRPG® Book 10, *Mount Nimro*™). As a

result, the addition of a Were-Shaman of 5th level or higher to the ceremony will enhance the communion process and double the duration of the chant's effects! In this chant the Shaman and/or one or more recipients are sent into a dreamlike trance, wherein they encounter (and commune with) the spirit of their animal Totem.

The first time a recipient joins the chant and enters the dream-trance (called the "finding" dream), the Totem spirit will "introduce" the recipient to the Totem nature within them, and the recipient will henceforth forever "know" and "be joined to" their Totem animal (this Totem animal will be a specific species, such as "Black Bear" or "Red-Tailed Hawk," and not the general "Fish," "Canine," etc., as is the case for the Were- Shaman O.C.C.). The recipient may also experience a period during the dream-trance where they "become" their Totem animal for a time, living and experiencing life as a member of that species and often "forgetting" their humanity for a while. This dream-trance lasts about one hour, but may feel like several hours or even days to the recipient. Note that this specific species is the character's *unique* and *permanent* Totem, no "secondary" Totems (unless the character "multi-classes" to the Were-Shaman O.C.C., in which case this primary Totem remains their primary Totem (as the general animal "type" this time) for the Were-Shaman O.C.C., with secondary Totems chosen later as dictated under that O.C.C. description).

The result of this "finding" dream is that, for the next 48 hours per level of the chanting Shaman (double this duration if a Were-Shaman of 5th level or above is present for the ceremony), the recipient gains both the Animal Totem bonuses listed under

Special O.C.C. Abilities #1 for the Were-Shaman O.C.C. (page 49 of the *Mount Nimro™* sourcebook), and the Empathic Rapport abilities (#2) beginning on the same page. None of the other abilities are gained, only the Totem bonuses/skills and the Empathic Rapport. [Note: Choose the most accurate fit for the totem, e.g. "Rattlesnake" Totems use the "Reptile" bonuses, etc.] Once the duration has ended, all of these abilities and bonuses will vanish, though the recipient will completely remember the experience and will always feel a "connection" with the appropriate Totem animal.

Each additional time this chant is experienced by the recipient after the initial "finding" chant (must wait at least one full moon (month) between chants), the recipient, who now "knows" his Totem animal, will re-enter the dream-trance and again commune with his Totem spirit. These "reconnecting" dreams return the recipient to the connected state of mind he had with his Totem after the finding dream, once again giving him the bonuses from and Empathic Rapport with the Totem animal. The bonuses and abilities received during these reconnecting dreams last for 24 hours per experience level of the chanting Shaman (double this duration if a Were-Shaman of 5th level or above participates in the chant). All recipients must wait one full moon (month) between reconnection chants (30 days from the end of the previous chant's bonuses/abilities duration) or the dream-trance will not be achieved and no bonuses or abilities will be gained.

Note to G.M.s: The Totem Chant offers an excellent opportunity for role-playing and characterization. Player characters will get an opportunity to discover "new" aspects of their characters that may become a life-changing experience for the character and will offer new role-playing opportunities for the player. Totem animals should be carefully selected by the G.M. *and* player to "fit" the character, as this animal is now a *permanent* representation of the character. Typically, the imagined "personality" of the animal is more important than the player's *desired* Totem: just because the *player* likes wolves doesn't necessarily mean that the wolf is the *character's* ideal Totem. Disposition and O.C.C. are often the governing factors, with aggressive or athletic characters or Men-at-Arms typically leaning towards "predatory" animals (hawks, wolves, jaguars, etc.) while clever, wise, or learned characters (like men of magic) tend towards animals thought of as clever or wise (owls, ravens, turtles, etc.), for example. Also note that the location of the ceremony and/or the character's homeland will be a major factor in determining the specific species of the Totem animal. While being from or experiencing the chant in the Northern Wilderness might lead to a mountain lion Totem, the Yin-Sloth Jungles might lead instead to a Jaguar or Tiger Totem and the Old Kingdom to a Lion or Leopard Totem. Remember that the first "finding" chant species will be the one and only Totem for all future "rediscoveries," so choose wisely.

Chant of Oneness with the Wilderness Spirits

Range: 20 foot (6 m) radius.

Duration: 24 hours per experience level of the Shaman.

P.P.E.: 35

Saving Throw: Not applicable to those who want the blessing.

With this enchantment the Shaman leads the participants in a ceremony that lets them commune with the spirits of the natural world, seeking unity and balance with the natural forces about them. When the ceremony is completed, all willing participants (within the 20 foot area) feel a sense of connection and "oneness" with the natural world, gaining a bonus of +10% to all Wilderness skills (including Wilderness "related" skills, as defined under the Native Origins section of the Savage Warrior O.C.C. above) for the duration of the chant's magic (24 hours per experience level of the Shaman). This chant must be performed deep within the wild (minimum 10 miles (16 km) from any town or city; small tribal villages are acceptable) where no urban influence is felt. Virgin wilderness is ideal.

Berserker & Wild Man	Native Tribesman
1 0,000 – 2,400	1 0,000 – 1,900
2 2,401 – 4,800	2 1,901 – 3,800
3 4,801 – 9,600	3 3,801 – 7,600
4 9,601 – 17,000	4 7,601 – 12,000
5 17,001 – 28,000	5 12,001 – 20,000
6 28,001 – 38,000	6 20,001 – 30,000
7 38,001 – 53,000	7 30,001 – 45,000
8 53,001 – 75,000	8 45,001 – 55,000
9 75,001 – 100,000	9 55,001 – 75,000
10 100,001 – 140,000	10 75,001 – 110,000
11 140,001 – 190,000	11 110,001 – 140,000
12 190,001 – 240,000	12 140,001 – 180,000
13 240,001 – 290,000	13 180,001 – 240,000
14 290,001 – 350,000	14 240,001 – 300,000
15 350,001 – 410,000	15 300,001 – 350,000

Savage Warrior

1 0,000 – 2,300
2 2,301 – 4,600
3 4,601 – 9,200
4 9,201 – 18,400
5 18,401 – 26,500
6 26,501 – 36,600
7 36,601 – 51,700
8 51,701 – 71,800
9 71,801 – 96,900
10 96,901 – 137,000
11 137,001 – 188,100
12 188,101 – 229,200
13 229,201 – 279,300
14 279,301 – 340,400
15 340,401 – 400,000

The Devil Muse

An Optional New Monster for Beyond the Supernatural™

By Josh Sinsapaugh

Michael was crying for the third time that night, bawling on the basement floor of some dilapidated building on the outskirts of Quarryville. He had just finished driving a piece of rebar through a human skull when the shakes came over him again, sending him to his knees and into another hysterical fit.

Get up. Get up you worthless piece of crap, the voice spat. *Get up. We had a deal.* Michael mouthed the word "no" a few times, unable to bring himself to say it, tears and lack of will-power holding him back. He punched the dirt and cried some more, hoping the voice would go away. *Stop your blubbering and get up.* The voice never went away when he wanted it to. *Stand up and finish what you started.*

Rising to his feet, Michael did just that, completing the macabre work of art that the voice had commissioned. Constructed out of bits of corpses strung together with rusty rebar, it was a grisly spectacle, his sin made physical. The voice spoke again, and he obeyed. He grabbed the sprayer, and began to apply urethane to the construct, preserving it in all of its unholy glory. When he was done, he dropped to his knees again and began to sob – it was too much to bear.

"I can't do this anymore!" he cried aloud in a hoarse whisper. "It's not worth it, you freak! It was never worth it!"

Has the lil' baby grown a backbone? the voice taunted, cold and emotionless. *I should think not, worthless dregs like you don't have willpower. Do they?*

"I'm not a worthless dreg..." Michael began.

You just dug up two corpses that have been buried for over one hundred fifty years. That doesn't sound like the work of a worthwhile citizen to me. No, it sounds like the handiwork of a loathsome dreg.

"You made me..."

Damn right, I made you. You were nothing before I found you.

"No, you made me dig up those bodies," Michael cried, still in a hoarse whisper.

Pssh, Michael! I only suggested it. You were the one with the shovel.

"I only did it because you threatened to take my gift away, like you always do."

And well I should. It almost seemed as if the voice was laughing. *A blubbering little tart like you hardly deserves the talent that I provide...*

"I had my own talent!" This time it was Michael who cut the voice off. "I was already a great artist before you came along!"

Now now, Michael, you know that isn't true, the voice lied. *Before I came along, you were nothing, and if I leave, you will be nothing once again. In fact... don't interrupt me!* The voice cut off Michael even before he could speak. *In fact, you were*

nothing more than an outcast high school art student before I came along. You couldn't get a girl, and you had no friends. I have provided you with both.

"I didn't need you for that."

Liar.

"Shut up!" he whimpered weakly, knowing full well that the voice was beginning to speak the truth, or at least a version of it.

Besides, you can't turn back now, the voice mocked. *You've already taken a life.*

"I didn't take anybody's life."

Hmm... yes, my mistake. Michael dreaded what came next. *You didn't kill those urban explorers who found one of your Death Arts in that abandoned cement factory. It was Veronica and Lisa who did it, right?*

"Shut up!"

Your two biggest fans, they killed those boys, didn't they? The voice sounded almost singsong now. *And then, they chucked the bodies down into that old sewer. They did it all for you, didn't they? They love your work, and they love you. They would do <u>anything</u> for you. In fact, they have, haven't they?*

"Shut up!"

What's wrong?

"Shut up!"

What, don't you love them?

Michael couldn't answer.

I thought as much.

"Just shut up, I'm going now," Michael whispered as he rose to his feet. "Where do you want me to hide this one?" He gripped the new piece of Death Art, awaiting the voice's reply.

There is an old house in Fish Creek, deep in the woods, the voice answered. *Bury it there, in what remains of the basement. You sure as hell had better not defy me again. Do you understand?*

"Yes."

Yes, what?

"Yes, Master."

Very good... The voice seemed to be fading, like it always did when it decided to leave Michael alone for a few days. *Now hurry up, you have deadlines to meet. Those album covers won't draw themselves...*

Imagine all the artists who ever existed or will exist. There are normal people who can draw, paint, sculpt, or what have you. Then there are artists who seem to have a natural knack for giving ideas life via drawing, painting, or some other visible medium – many of whom fall under the Genius/Natural P.C.C. A select few are artists who truly stand out, rising above even the other naturals to a position of prominence that sometimes seems to grant them immortality. Some of these artists are, or were, true masters of their craft, while others (an unknown number) were/are the pathetic pawns and victims of the **Devil Muse**.

The Devil Muse is an insidious supernatural being that seeks out *already skilled* artists (in game terms, a Genius P.C.C. who excels in art) and offers them glory in exchange for their "assistance." Of course, the monstrosity rarely makes it clear what exactly it means by "assistance." Most people know better than to make deals with mysterious voices whispering from dark places, thus the creature usually passes over good or strong willed artists in favor of those that are depressed, evil, stupid, vulnerable or downright weak. Unfortunately for the vile horror, this means that it has to pass over some truly skilled artists, lest it expose itself to those mortals who hunt its kind. Luckily for the Devil Muse, artists who feel dejected or misunderstood are not hard to come by – especially in the Twenty-First Century – and thus the creature usually has an ample supply of potential pawns to choose from.

The results of the pact manifest immediately, and the artist's skills increase by leaps and bounds the moment he agrees to a partnership with the Devil Muse. Yesterday, he may have been a misunderstood but skilled art student, today he is a veritable prodigy, well on his way to being celebrated by the artistic community; the transition is that simple. Or is it? What about that "assistance" that his or her supernatural patron mentioned? Most don't bother with such details and push it into the back of their minds, believing that they got something for nothing. After all, that voice that suddenly spoke from the darkness is silent now, and the budding artist has more important things to worry about.

It is weeks, months, or even years later before the artist hears from the Devil Muse again. Usually, the artist finds himself diligently at work, when a voice suddenly rattles in his head: *time to start paying your debt.* The voice then begins to lay out its plans, instructing the artist to make artwork that is truly perverse and macabre, ranging from paintings made with human blood and gore, to modern art sculptures constructed out of human remains (dug up from a graveyard or snatched from a morgue at first, gathered "fresh" later). Those who refuse are met with a frightening threat from their patron: *serve me as you promised, or I shall leave you and take* all of your talent *with me as payment.* Most realize that the Devil Muse is not bluffing, or simply do not want to take the chance. Those who think the monster is bluffing and refuse will see their natural aptitude for art leave them forever, though their former supernatural partner usually stays behind to taunt the artist as he or she is flung into misery and almost inevitable suicide.

The macabre artwork created via the Devil Muse's instruction is often made in secret, hidden away in a basement, attic, or in some other place where it will be hard to come by. This is both due to the nature of the artwork (the artist sure as hell does not want to get caught), and because the fiendish being wills it to be so, as its existence depends on it. Unbeknownst to the artist, when he creates such "Death Art," a portion of his supernatural patron's essence is instilled into the piece, providing the being with a *permanent anchor* to this plane of existence. Once a piece of Death Art is created, it is impossible to kill the Devil Muse via normal means. Only destroying the macabre art that the fiend commissioned will render it vulnerable to expulsion from our dimension, hence the true reason such art is often hidden away where few can get at it. Anyone who does find the "art" and sees it for what it is (i.e. that it is made out of blood and/or human remains) will be marked for death by the Devil Muse, an order the artist-slave readily follows under threat of losing his or her talent.

The Death Art that has been commissioned by the Devil Muse is sometimes guarded by foolish fans of the artist-slave. These fans are either totally obsessed with the artist (or his work), or are members of one of the so-called "sub-cultures" that center around darkness and the occult. In the latter case, such a fan usually goes beyond what is acceptable in his or her sub-culture of choice, and is thus viewed as a dangerous radical by his or her own peers. They may even feel betrayed or misunderstood by their friends (who they believe should understand them), and are thus easy pickings for the Devil Muse and its artist-slave. The minion-fans will also assist the artist in digging up dead bodies, committing murders, creating macabre artwork, and may even take the fall for the artist. The Devil Muse might even request that a minion-fan please its artist-slave sexually, which either placates the artist or causes him or her to become more distraught (after all, many artist-slaves hate what they are doing and definitely do not want others helping them in any way, let alone *that* way).

Further complicating matters, many Devil Muses are not satisfied with a single piece of Death Art, and will have their hapless pawn create up to three pieces, scattering their essence across the city, county, state, country, or even world! In such situations, all three pieces must be sought out and destroyed before the vile creature can be destroyed. Worse yet, the Devil Muse can always have its pawn create a replacement piece if one of its Death Art pieces is destroyed, and often instructs its artist-slave to create several (sometimes hundreds of) decoy pieces, both to throw off any would-be adversaries, and to simply torment the artist by having him or her create more perverse artwork. Truly crafty (and rare) Devil Muses have even gone so far as to break tradition and have their pawns create one or more Death Art pieces that are not so obvious, so that the piece may be hidden in plain sight in a museum or gallery, protected by unwitting security guards and hi-tech security systems. A scant few have even managed to have the Death Art that their essence is bound to installed in the Metropolitan Museum of Art in New York City and the Louvre in Paris!

As one might expect, unless the artist was already a depraved individual, his enslavement by the Devil Muse is a harrowing experience. Many are driven insane and separate themselves from what they do for the monster, leading two separates lives: the talented artist, and the man or woman who is *forced* to do the Devil's bidding. Some of those who become insane go a step further and develop *Dissociative Identity Disorder* (also known as *Multiple Personality Disorder*), with two or more identities (personalities) occupying one fragmented mind. Those who aren't driven insane either slowly twist into being truly evil people, or become outrageously depressed, to the point that they either commit suicide or that the quality of their artwork (ironically) improves. All who are enslaved, regardless of how the Devil Muse's presence affects them emotionally, slowly waste away physically as the fiend feeds on their life force energy, driving them toward an inevitable death. Those who are freed or free themselves from the Devil Muse's grasp often commit suicide due to their loss of talent. Many choose to live instead, however, either starting their life over or seeking out a new supernatural master to provide them with direction.

Despite what one might think, a Devil Muse that has lost an artist-slave is neither influenced directly nor negatively impacted. The pieces of Death Art that its former pawn created are still valid, and will remain linked to the fiend until it wills otherwise. This means that even without its helper, the malignant being is still firmly entrenched in this world. Thus, the Devil Muse needs only to find another pawn to continue its devilish work where the last one left off. In fact, the malevolent fiend may abandon a current artist-slave for a more promising victim (or simply for the hell of it) at the drop of a hat and does so without emotion or care. To this creature, humans are as discardable as a snot-covered tissue, and worth about the same.

The Devil Muse is an ethereal energy being, and is invisible in its natural state. Thus, only those who can see the invisible and/or spirits can see what the fiend looks like. When not enslaving an artist, the creature appears to be a three-foot (0.9 m) long, black strand of ectoplasm. The creature floats and twists through the air like an eel in the sea, and will dart from person to person in search of a suitable "host" (the energy being may be confused with the more common Possessing Entity at first glance). Those that are enslaving an artist have a similar appearance, though they are six feet (1.8 m) long, and continually spiral around their victims. Furthermore, those that have a slave will manifest a dozen sub-strands/tentacles of ectoplasm (1 foot/0.3 m long each), which will be caressing the artist at all times – often in a suggestive manner as if to humiliate the pawn. Artists who are enslaved by a Devil Muse will never be able to see what their supernatural master looks like, and will falsely assume that the creature leaves them for extended periods of time (i.e. when it is not speaking to them).

The Devil Muse – Supernatural Energy Being

Alignment: Aberrant (10%), Miscreant (50%), and Diabolic (40%).

Attributes: I.Q. 16+1D4, M.E. 2D6, M.A. 18+2D4, Spd 50 (35 mph/56 km), all other attributes are inapplicable.

Hit Points: 2D6x10+20, no S.D.C. or A.R., and can only be damaged by magic and psionics, or affected via an Exorcism.

Discorporation: Only those who can see the invisible or see spirits can see the Devil Muse discorporate. When destroyed, the energy being seems to evaporate, fading away as if it never existed.

Threat Level: x4; Haunter and Cruel Prankster (supernatural energy being/Entity).

Horror Factor: 12

Size: Three feet (0.9 m) long when independent, six feet (1.8 m) long when enslaving an artist.

Weight: Not applicable to energy beings.

Average Life Span: Unknown, probably immortal.

P.P.E.: 1D6+1

Natural Abilities: An energy being, the Devil Muse is naturally invisible and intangible, able to pass through solid objects with ease, and is impervious to physical and energy attacks. The monster can also hover and fly at a speed of 35 mph (56 km).

Imbue Artistic Genius with Additional Talent (special): The Devil Muse seeks out a Genius P.C.C. who excels in one or more of the following Occupational Skills: *Art, Masonry, Photography,* and/or *Whittling & Sculpting* (though those with the skill *Art* are overwhelmingly preferred), and pro-

poses a pact: greater skill for unspecified assistance. If the Genius P.C.C. agrees to the pact, the Devil Muse imbues a portion of its essence into the artist, increasing the already excellent Occupational Skill by +30% (on top of the +30% that the skill has from the Genius P.C.C.). Once a pact is made and the talent imbued, the Devil Muse typically stays with the artist, spiraling around him or her, though it will occasionally travel away from him or her in order to scout ahead or contact its fanatic-pawns (if any). **Note:** The Devil Muse can only imbue talent/its essence into one artist at a time.

Rob Artistic Genius of Talent (special): Two weeks after the Devil Muse imbues the Genius P.C.C. with additional talent, the influence of the supernatural Entity over the character's artistic abilities becomes permanent. Should the Devil Muse die or leave (i.e. "pull" its essence from) the Genius P.C.C., the character will see his artistic skills disappear altogether (i.e. drop to 0%), never again to return to their former level of talent (even their level of talent *before* making a pact with the Devil Muse!). The Devil Muse usually waits several weeks, months, or even years, and then asks the artist to do its dirty work, threatening to rob him of his talent if the artist refuses. Effectively, the artist is made a slave to the supernatural Entity's wishes as long as he wants to keep his talent. *If the Devil Muse leaves the artist or is banished/destroyed before the initial two weeks are up*, then the artist is not negatively affected, save for the loss of the +30% provided by the pact with the supernatural energy being.

Create "Death Art" Anchor (special): Two weeks after the Devil Muse imbues the Genius P.C.C. with additional talent, the malignant fiend can have its artist-slave create a "Death Art" anchor. The Death Art is a work of art created using human blood, gore, or remains, and then imbued with a portion of the Devil Muse's essence. Once the macabre work of art is created, the fiend is *permanently anchored* to our plane of existence, and thus cannot be banished or destroyed via any means until each and every piece of Death Art is destroyed (the Devil Muse can maintain three at a time, and can always have its pawn create more if one is destroyed). The monstrous energy being automatically senses the status of each of its Death Arts (fine, being attacked, or destroyed), though it cannot pinpoint where the piece is (which means it will have no idea where it is if moved without its knowledge). Most Devil Muses have their artist-slaves hide their Death Art in attics, abandoned buildings, basements, or other hard to reach locations. **Note:** The Autistic Psychic Savant P.C.C., Diviner P.C.C., Psychic Sensitive P.C.C. and Psychic Medium P.C.C. can all recognize a Death Art for what it is: the anchor of a Devil Muse. Anyone else only sees a macabre and disturbing piece of art, and may not realize that it is tied to the Devil Muse without a successful roll on *Lore: Entities & Ghosts* or *Streetwise: Weird*. A Diviner can locate a Death Art anchor through Psychic Dowsing, with a bonus of +10%.

A Devil Muse can also choose to abandon a Death Art at any time, for whatever reason. If the fiend does so, it cannot re-instill its essence into the piece; a new Death Art needs to be created to replace the abandoned one. All "active" Death Art Anchors must be within ten miles (16 km) of the Devil Muse, unless the artist who created the art is still alive and linked to the Entity (in which case there is no maximum range). Death Arts can be destroyed via normal means, though fire usually works best in order to insure that the anchor is destroyed in a timely fashion (plus, it is difficult to stop the destructive force of fire once it has started). The Devil Muse, even with Telekinesis, cannot create a Death Art by itself, and requires an artist-slave to do its dirty work.

Sap Life Energy (special): After the Devil Muse has been with its artist-slave for over a year, the malignant energy being can begin to feed on the artist's life force. The artist permanently loses up to 1D4 H.P. a year, and one P.E. point every five years! It is important to note that the Devil Muse will not kill the artist by sapping his energy, and will stop feeding should the artist approach death's door. The evil Entity gains no sustenance from sapping the life out of its victim, and only does so in order to torment the poor soul.

Knows All Languages: Magically understands and speaks all languages at 90%; communicates via Telepathy. Those that have been active in the World of Man for several years learn to read the Native Language of the region in which they are active at 50%.

Vulnerabilities: Normally, Exorcism, magic, and psionic attacks can destroy the Devil Muse. However, if the Devil Muse has had a Death Art created, it is firmly anchored in our world, immune from all attacks until the macabre work of art(s) is destroyed. Devil Muses can only exist in our world for a week at a time, unless the Entity makes a pact with an artist or has a Death Art to use as an anchor.

R.C.C. Skills or Equivalents: The equivalent (i.e. knowledge) of Art, Masonry, Photography, and Whittling & Sculpting, all at 98% (all considered to be Occupational Skills). Basic Math 85%, Land Navigation 70%, Streetwise 60%, and Streetwise: Weird 45%. Skills do not increase with experience.

Equivalent Level of Experience: 1D6+2

Attacks per Melee: Three, by means of psionics only.

Damage: By psionics only, the Devil Muse can, of course, command its artist-slave and his or her loyal fans (if any) to attack.

R.C.C. Bonuses: +2 on initiative, +2 on all Perception Rolls, +1 to dodge, +10 to save versus Horror Factor, and is impervious to possession.

Magic: None.

Psionics: Needs a 10 or higher to save versus psionic attack. I.S.P. base is 50. The Devil Muse *is not* a psychic vampire, and thus cannot siphon I.S.P. from living beings or places of power.

Limited Psionic Powers: Empathy (4), Healing Touch (6; for use on its artist-slave and fanatic pawns), Mind Block (4), Sixth Sense (2), See the Invisible (4), Telekinesis (varies), and Telepathy (at no I.S.P. cost, triple normal range, and unlimited range when speaking to its artist-slave). Powers are equal to the Devil Muse's level of experience.

Enemies: The Devil Muse despises all humans, especially artists, and takes great delight in tormenting them. A human life, even the life of the artist-slave, has no value: humans are simply fools and playthings. The energy being is also fiercely independent, and thus dislikes greater powers that force it to serve them.

Allies: None per se. The artist-slave, and the fan-pawns of the artist are all viewed as worthless, expendable minions; a means to an end. Obeys Ancient Evil only for fear of punishment and destruction.

Habitat: Can be found anywhere in the world, wherever artists can be found. Generally prefers bleak urban environments and failing Podunk towns as they typically provide an ample supply of artists who feel downtrodden and misunderstood. Such locations also have thriving sub-cultures; self-professed outcasts who can be easily exploited by the Devil Muse or its artist-slave.

Your Guide to the Zombie Apocalypse

By Josh Hilden and Joshua Sanford

Dedicated to the memory of John Gibord

Almost Tomorrow

The footage is shaky and awkward at first, suggesting an untrained cameraman. The view swings clumsily, showing a brief glimpse of afternoon sky smudged with a few columns of black smoke. The cameraman appears to be on a flat rooftop. The camera finally settles on a young woman crouching down and peering over a low wall. Shock and terror are unmistakable in her wide eyes. There's a baseball bat in her hands, and she clings to it with grim tenacity.

"You get that thing working yet?" she asks in a whisper, turning her attention to the camera. The shot tilts up and down as the cameraman nods. The woman looks into the lens, appearing to gather her thoughts. After a moment she speaks into the camera. "My name is Naomi Winslow. I'm a waitress... I was a waitress. My friend Lincoln is working the camera. We... we thought... someone should record this." Naomi pauses, and shudders. "It's the end of the world. Show them, Linc."

The camera peeks over the low wall, showing a typical street that could be any town at all. It's obvious right away that something is very wrong. The four-lane street is littered with stalled cars, many of them mangled and smashed. A couple of cars are burning and smoldering. The tail-end of a small aircraft juts from a smashed, burning storefront down the street. There is a car alarm going off, and the faint sounds of sirens, screams and gunfire can be heard. There are people scattered throughout the street, shambling and limping along. The camera zooms in on one group, displaying a few vacant, slack-jawed faces. Many appear to be wounded, some grievously. Nearly all of their mouths and hands are smeared with blood.

"They aren't people," Naomi says softly, and the camera turns to focus on her again. She's gazing down at the street be-

low, still clutching her bat. "I mean, they were people, but now they're not. They're monsters." Her eyes look into the camera again, with a grim expression. "They're zombies."

Naomi turns and sits with her back to the wall, and runs a hand through her disheveled hair. "There was no warning, nothing. You're just going about your routine when the pain hits you like... like a wave, washing over you. It was like every hang-over, headache, and stomach cramp you've ever had, all at once. It only lasted a few minutes, but it felt like a year in Hell. And it got everyone, all of us. Right at the same time: twelve noon, Wednesday, the 20th of June, 2012. The day the world ended.

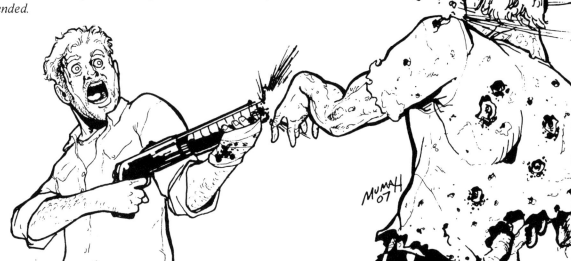

"A lot of people died," Naomi continues. "I'm not just talk-ing about all the cars and planes crashing and all that, either. The pain... the Wave... just killed them. Men, women, old, young, black, white... no pattern at all." She pauses, turning her head away from the camera. After a moment, she resumes. "We did-n't have long to mourn. We didn't even have time to recover from the Wave. The ones who'd died started getting up. Then they started moaning. Then they started attacking."

Naomi looks at the camera with a grim expression. "If the zombies catch you, they kill you. They just bite and tear into you like animals. I've seen it. They kill you, and you become one of them, it's like an infection. They're slow and they're stupid, but they're everywhere. Before the power died, the TV news was showing reports and footage from all over the country and it's the same as here. Maybe the whole world..."

Naomi looks over the wall again, and the camera follows. There appear to be even more zombies shambling down the street. A group of them are gathered around a crashed car. Their fists hammer at the windows, finally shattering the wind-shield. The camera zooms in as the zombies pull a screaming man from the car, and drag him to the ground. The screams stop after a moment.

"The police aren't coming," Naomi says as the cluster of zombies begins to disperse. As she continues, the mangled body of the man they pulled from the car rises and joins their ranks. "The army isn't coming. No one is coming to save you. If you want to live, you run, and you fight them when you have to. They're monsters, but they aren't invincible. Aim for their heads. Crack their skulls, and they stay down."

"There's more coming from over by the mall," says a low, deep voice from off-camera, presumably Linc. "We need to get out of here, out of the city, now."

"Right," Naomi replies, as the camera turns to her again. She looks into the lens, appearing much more composed and re-solved than before. "We'll find more people. We'll band to-gether, and put these monsters in the ground where they belong. It may be the end of the world, but we're not going without a fight."

Introduction

Welcome to Dead Reign, a survival-horror role-playing game based on *Beyond the Supernatural™, 2nd Edition*. The game made its debut (under a different name) at the 2007 Palladium Open House, and seemed to be a hit with the players. Unfortu-nately, that first game met a tragic, abrupt end involving a heli-copter crashing into a shopping mall. Now the game has been revised, revamped, renamed, and presented here for your gam-ing pleasure. We hope you have as much fun playing in this dark corner of the Megaverse as we did creating it.

Although Dead Reign uses *Beyond the Supernatural, 2nd Edition* as its basis, it does not take place in the BTS setting. Dead Reign takes place on an alternate version of Earth, one of many in the Megaverse. This world is much like our own in terms of history, technology, and geopolitics. The world of Dead Reign also had very little supernatural activity prior to the Wave, due to low levels of ambient P.P.E.

(**Note:** Because of this lack of magical energy, many of the O.C.C.s presented in *Beyond the Supernatural* and other Palladium games are inappropriate for use in Dead Reign. Magic and spell casters are all but unheard of before the Wave, as are psionics, cybernetics/bionics, Techno-Wizardry, super abilities, giant robots, demons, monsters, aliens, mutants, and other such staples of the Palladium cornucopia. We recommend players use the Ordinary Person P.C.C. found on page 64 of *BTS 2nd Ed.* Future submissions to **The Rifter®** will present the world of Dead Reign a few years after the Wave, including custom O.C.C.s, new world information, and of course, more zombies.)

The Wave

June 20th, 2012, 12 P.M. Eastern Standard Time: The world as we know it comes to an end with a bizarre global event known as "*the Wave.*" Without warning, every living person on the planet is struck by "waves" of overwhelming pain and nausea. The effect lasts nearly ten minutes, and takes a devastating toll. Millions of seemingly random people die in the Wave, their bodies appearing to simply shut down under all that pain and torment.

The Wave causes incalculable chaos. Cars crash by the thousands, choking most roads with gridlock and mangled steel. Planes fall from the sky. Power grids and communication networks are disrupted worldwide. The sounds of explosions, fires, sirens, and screams fill the air. Then, just as suddenly as it began, the pain stops. The survivors recover, only to find unimaginable death and devastation in the wake of the Wave.

If that were the end of the tragedy, mankind surely would be able to recover and move on. Unfortunately, the Wave is merely the trigger for something much, much worse. A few minutes later, the dead bodies begin to rise, animated by some unseen force. They have been transformed into zombies; mindless, fearless, relentless killing machines.

The zombies' first assault catches many people off guard, and hundreds of thousands (if not millions) more are killed. Those first victims soon rise as zombies themselves, and join the ranks of the walking dead. The remaining survivors have no choice but to fight or flee, but there is nowhere to run, no corner of the Earth that isn't infested. The zombies are everywhere, and they are hungry.

In the hours following the Wave, the foundations of modern civilization continue to crumble. Power stations are abandoned or overrun, shutting down and blacking out vast regions of the world. Satellite links and landlines are lost, crippling local and global communications. Police, military, and other emergency forces are scattered and disorganized, their ranks devastated by desertions and deaths. Vital supplies such as food, potable water, medication, and fuel disappear rapidly as they become the new currency. Dozens of would-be dictators sprout up, often abusing their authority and doing far more harm than good. All the while, the zombies' numbers continue to grow and spread throughout the world.

Luckily, some lines of communication are operational long enough for a few key facts to spread among the survivors:

- The zombies carry an infection called the Z-Virus, which is transmitted via zombie bites or any contamination of the bloodstream. The infection is lethal, killing most victims in an hour or less. The victim will rise as a zombie within a few minutes after death.

- Three types of zombies have been spotted since the Wave: Slouchers, Runners, and Thinkers. Slouchers are slow and dumb, and by far the most common type. Runners are no smarter than Slouchers, but are much faster and far more aggressive. Thinkers are the rarest type, and somehow retain their intellect, memories, and the ability to speak.

- The only way to stop a zombie is to destroy the brain or inflict massive damage to the entire body.

- A small percentage of people are exhibiting strange mental powers (psionics), and there are even reports of people wielding "magic."

Player Characters

Your role as a player in Dead Reign is simple: survive the Zombie Apocalypse by whatever means necessary. This post-apocalyptic setting presents many challenges, and plenty of opportunities for heroic adventure and zombie-stomping action. To make your character, use the character generation rules found in *Beyond the Supernatural 2nd Edition*, following the steps listed below. As noted before, it's recommended that players use the Ordinary Person P.C.C. found on page 64 of *BTS 2nd Ed.*

Step 1: Roll the eight attributes as normal.

Step 2: Determine Hit Points and S.D.C.

Step 3: Roll for education/select skills.

Step 4: Select an alignment.

Step 5: Roll for psionics:

01-05%: Major Psionic: Select eight powers from one of the lesser categories (healing, physical, and sensitive), or six powers from any of the lesser categories. Base I.S.P.: M.E. +1D6 per level.

06-15%: Minor Psionic: Select two powers from any of the lesser categories. Base I.S.P.: M.E. +1D4 per level.

16-00%: No psionics.

Step 6 (optional): Roll for level advancement (add 1D4 to the character's experience level).

Step 7 (optional): Roll for insanity.

Game Master's Section

This section details the mysterious cause of the Zombie Apocalypse, as well as zombie statistics, world information, and hints of things to come. If you're a player who enjoys a little mystery in your survival-horror gaming, you may want to stop reading and leave the following section to your Game Master.

The truth behind
the Zombie Apocalypse

The year is 2012, and mankind is celebrating the most significant discovery of the new millennium. A medical science think-tank called the Benford Group has engineered a vaccine to treat all types of cancer. Dubbed "Unisane" by its creators, the vaccine was still being tested when word of it was leaked to the media. The world reverberated with a joyous chorus of approval as the Benford Group announced that they would be providing this vaccine for free to the World Health Organization (WHO), the

International Red Cross, and dozens of other health organizations. In the developed regions of the planet they would be providing Unisane at cost.

The distribution of Unisane began the next week, with hundreds of thousands of doses of the medication shipped to the poverty stricken regions of the world, where there was little or no need to wait for government approval. By June of 2012, fully 65% of the populations of the Earth's "third world" countries were vaccinated. The story in the rest of the world progressed a bit slower. In Europe, Canada, Australia/New Zealand and Asia it took only 2 months for the use of Unisane to be approved and for governments to begin inoculating their populations. By June of 2012, only 40% of the populations in those areas were inoculated.

In the United States of America things were a bit more complicated. The public clamored for the vaccine as soon as it was announced, but the Food and Drug Administration (FDA), along with the powerful and influential pharmaceuticals industry, attempted to delay the vaccine's introduction. With the FDA the desire for the delay was a practical one. How were they supposed to approve a new drug without first enacting their own clinical trials to make sure that the drug would do what it was supposed to do? With the pharmaceuticals industry the concerns were profit driven. How were they to compete when the drug was going to be given away, allowing the entire world to be inoculated before the patent expired and they could create their own knock-offs of Unisane? Furthermore, what would happen to their revenues when high priced cancer "treatment" drugs were rendered a thing of the past?

The American people got what they wanted in the end. On April 30, 2012 by an act of the combined houses of Congress, Unisane was officially cleared for usage in the United States. If they had waited two more months, things may have unfolded differently across the face of the world, but as it stood on June 20, 2012, over 25% of the population of the USA was inoculated with Unisane.

The die was cast.

The Benford Group was hailed as heroic saviors, when in truth their agenda was far more sinister than anyone could imagine. The organization is actually the modern incarnation of an ancient death-cult, worshippers of a demonic entity known as Brulyx. The Unisane vaccine carried with it an evil enchantment, undetectable by the tools of science. The Wave was the result of the ritual needed to activate the enchantment, which turned the inoculated population into infectious zombies.

Zombie 101

Zombies exist only to hunt, kill and feed upon the living. Instinct drives them to bite and tear at their prey, but they are not fueled by eating flesh. Rather, it is the victim's P.P.E., doubled at the moment of death, which feeds the zombie. Once the victim has expired and his or her P.P.E. has been absorbed, the zombies move on to find fresh living prey. Meanwhile, the Z-Virus begins transforming the dead victim into a zombie. The corpse rises after mere moments (1D4 minutes), joining the ranks of the undead.

All types of zombies share some physical characteristics that become more pronounced as time passes. The skin takes on a dry, ashy tone and texture, and loose flesh shrivels and flakes away. The blood dries and blackens in the veins. The muscles harden, yet retain some degree of flexibility despite the lack of circulation. The eyes take on a sickly, milky-yellow tone, and the pupils emit a faint red glow. Zombies have no need to breathe, yet the lungs still function, in a way. In order to moan (or speak, in the case of the Thinker), the zombie pulls air into the lungs and pushes it out.

As undead creatures, zombies have their own strengths and weaknesses. They are immune to a variety of effects, including Horror Factor, poisons, toxins, drugs, disease, fatigue, mind control/hypnosis, insanity, and many psionic and magic effects. They are utterly fearless, but fire, energy blasts, and magic protection circles will keep them at bay. Extreme cold temperatures will freeze a zombie's body, but also keep it in suspended animation until it thaws. Zombies can also remain underwater indefinitely, allowing them to travel along the bottom of lakes and rivers.

The body of a zombie can endure severe punishment and still keep coming. A zombie's Armor Rating (A.R.) reflects its body's ability to soak up or shrug off most types of damage. An attack roll that exceeds the A.R. inflicts damage to the zombie's main body S.D.C. Reducing this to zero destroys the zombie's spine, paralyzing it from the neck down, or it may even amputate the head (G.M.'s discretion). The zombie's head can still bite, but only if someone gets close enough.

Destroying a zombie's limbs reduces its mobility and attacks. Destroying an arm lowers the zombie's attacks per melee by one, while destroying both arms drops it to one bite attack per melee. Destroying one or more of its legs forces the zombie to drag itself along with its arms, reducing its speed attribute to one (5 yards per round, at best). Destroying/removing the jaw negates the zombie's bite attack.

Zombies are animated by magic, and without a steady supply of P.P.E. they will starve. They must absorb at least 5 P.P.E. per day, or they begin to deteriorate. For each day that passes without consuming enough P.P.E., the zombie's P.E. attribute drops by one point. When it reaches zero, the zombie simply collapses and rots away normally.

Unfortunately, there is a way for zombies to supplement their P.P.E. requirements. Certain locations around the globe (ley line nexus points) act as "zombie recharging stations" where they can simply soak up the ambient P.P.E. These locations are always "hot spots" of zombie activity, as the undead are drawn to them like iron filings to a magnet.

Due to the nature of the enchantment that animates them, zombies are walking P.P.E. batteries. Any excess P.P.E. that they absorb is somehow siphoned away to the secret, central temple of Brulyx, which sits on a powerful nexus point. The magical energy siphoned from the zombies is used to strengthen the demon's powers, and eventually to set Brulyx free upon the Earth.

All zombies carry the Z-Virus, an infection created by Brulyx's dark magic. When a character is bitten by a zombie he must make a saving throw versus magic (requiring a 15 or higher with bonuses). If the save is failed, the character is infected with the Z-Virus. The infected character loses one Hit Point for every minute (4 melees) that passes, and suffers painful cramps and spasms. The character dies when he has zero Hit Points, and will rise as a zombie 1D6 minutes later.

Note: Although zombies will attack and kill animals for their P.P.E., the Z-Virus will NOT reanimate any type of animal.

Zombie Population Density Chart

Roll to see how many zombies are in any given area or building. Game Masters may want to modify the roll based on the location (lower for rural/isolated areas and small buildings, higher for urban/suburban areas).

01-15%: No zombies.

16-30%: Sparse (1D6 zombies).

31-45%: Low (3D6 zombies).

46-60%: Moderate (3D6+10 zombies).

61-75%: High (3D6+25 zombies).

76-90%: Very high (3D6+50 zombies).

91-00%: Swarm (3D6+100 or more zombies).

Zombie Damage Chart

Roll to see if an individual zombie is damaged, and if so, how it affects its stats.

01-20%: No damage.

21-30%: Minor damage: reduce main body S.D.C. by 2D6.

31-40%: Damaged arm: reduce one arm's S.D.C. by 1D6.

41-50%: Damaged leg: reduce one leg's S.D.C. by 1D6, reduce Speed by 1.

51-60%: Missing arm: reduce attacks by 1.

61-70%: Missing leg: reduce Speed to 1, can only drag itself along the ground at a rate of 1D6 yards per melee.

71-80%: Blinded: -4 to strike, reduce Speed to 1.

81-90%: P.P.E. starvation: reduce P.E. by 2D6.

91-00%: Roll twice, ignoring rolls of 01-20 and 91-00.

Types of Zombies

Slouchers

Slouchers are the most common type of zombie, and the least threatening on an individual basis. As the name implies, they are slow, clumsy, and dumb. Their strength lies in numbers, and their utter relentlessness. With their low Speed attribute, Slouchers can only move about 10 yards per melee under the best conditions. Furthermore, they are slow to react (as reflected in their low number of attacks and penalty to initiative rolls). These traits make them easy to evade under most circumstances. Slouchers are at their most dangerous in large groups, and in confined spaces where their prey has little room to maneuver.

Slouchers are susceptible to the influence of Brulyx, his priests, and Talker zombies. They will obey simple commands, but they are far too stupid to perform any sort of manual labor. They will forget long-term commands (such as "stay here" or "guard that") in 2D4 hours.

Alignment: Considered Diabolic.

Attributes: I.Q. 1D4, M.E. 1D6, M.A. 1D4, P.S. 3D6+4, P.P. 1D6, P.E. 3D6, P.B. 1D6, Spd 1D4.

Hit Points: 1

S.D.C. by Location: Main body: 4D6+20, head: 2D6+6, arms: 2D6 each, legs: 2D6+4 each.

Armor Rating: 16

Horror Factor: 12

P.P.E. 1D6 (most of the P.P.E. that zombies absorb from their victims is channeled to the central temple of Brulyx).

Natural Abilities: Sense the P.P.E. of living creatures: 10 foot (3 m) range, cannot pinpoint the source unless within 5 feet (1.5 m).

Immunities: Poison, toxins, drugs, disease, Horror Factor, fear effects, mind control/hypnosis, and many psionic and magic effects. The spell Turn Dead has no effect because zombies are undead.

Skills of Note: Climb 25%.

Attacks: 2 per melee.

Damage: Bite: 2D6 S.D.C. plus infection, punch/slam: 1D6 S.D.C.

Bonuses/Penalties: +1 to strike, -2 to initiative.

Vulnerabilities: Severe cold temperatures will freeze a zombie's body, and hold it in suspended animation. Although Slouchers are fearless, fire will hold them at bay.

P.P.E. Vampire: The zombie must absorb at least five P.P.E. each day. For each day that passes without meeting this requirement, subtract one from the zombie's P.E. When it reaches zero, the zombie dies and rots away normally.

Runners

Runners are zombies who possessed major or master psionics in life. They are no smarter than Slouchers, but they are much faster and far more dangerous. They somehow retain their speed and reflexes, and develop keen predatory instincts. Runners are pack hunters by nature, which will lead to serious trouble as their numbers consolidate. Luckily, Runners are rare compared to Slouchers, accounting for about 5% of the zombie population.

Alignment: Considered Diabolic.

Attributes: I.Q. 1D4, M.E. 1D6, M.A. 1D4, P.S. 3D6+6, P.P. 3D6, P.E. 3D6, P.B. 1D4, Spd 3D6.

Hit Points: 1

S.D.C. by Location: Main body: 4D6+20, head: 2D6+6, arms: 2D6 each, legs: 2D6+4 each.

Armor Rating: 16

Horror Factor: 14 (packs of 6 or more Runners have a Horror Factor of 16).

P.P.E.: 1D6

Natural Abilities: Sense the P.P.E. of living creatures: 20 foot (6.1 m) range, but cannot pinpoint the source unless within 5 feet (1.5 m).

Immunities: Poison, toxins, drugs, disease, Horror Factor, fear effects, mind control/hypnosis, and many psionic and magic effects. The spell Turn Dead has no effect because zombies are undead.

Skills of Note: Climb 40%, Track Humans 36%.

Attacks: 4 per melee round.

Damage: Bite: 1D6 S.D.C. plus infection, punch/slam: 1D6 S.D.C.

Bonuses: +2 to strike, +1 to initiative.

Vulnerabilities: Severe cold temperatures will freeze a zombie's body, and hold it in suspended animation.

P.P.E. Vampire: The zombie must absorb at least five P.P.E. each day. For each day that passes without meeting this requirement, subtract one from the zombie's P.E. When it reaches zero, the zombie dies and rots away normally.

Thinkers

Thinkers are an enigma amongst zombies. While they do retain their intellect and memories, as well as some degree of free will, they are still undead. They must feed on the P.P.E. of living creatures, and only the most disciplined Thinker can resist the urge to kill and double the amount of P.P.E. Thinkers possess the ability to summon and verbally command Slouchers, potentially the most dangerous aspect of their powers. On the other hand, Thinkers themselves are susceptible to the influence of Brulyx and his human priests.

Thinkers are extremely rare, accounting for about .05% of the zombie population. Quite a few were loyal members of the cult of Brulyx/Benford Group before the Wave, and continue to serve as elite zombie generals and priests.

Thinker Zombie R.C.C.

(not recommended as player characters)

Requirements: In life, Thinkers were people with high levels of P.P.E., such as spell casters. Due to the near-total lack of magic lore on this world, many of them had no idea of their untapped, innate ability to wield magic.

Alignment: Any, but tend to be evil.

Attributes: I.Q. 3D6, M.E. 3D6, M.A. 3D6, P.S. 3D6+4, P.P. 2D6, P.E. 3D6, P.B. 1D6, Spd 2D6.

Hit Points: 1

S.D.C. by Location: Main body: 4D6+20, head: 2D6+6, arms: 2D6 each, legs: 2D6+4 each.

Armor Rating: 16

Horror Factor: 14

P.P.E.: 3D6 + M.E. attribute number, +2D6 per level (unlike other zombies, a Thinker's P.P.E. base is very high, and cannot be siphoned away by Brulyx without the Thinker's consent).

Natural Abilities: Sense the P.P.E. of living creatures: 10 foot (3 m) range, cannot pinpoint the source unless within 5 feet(1.5 m).

Immunities: Poisons, toxins, drugs, disease, Horror Factor, fear effects, mind control/hypnosis, and many psionic and magic effects. The spell Turn Dead has no effect because zombies are undead.

Verbally Command Slouchers: Thinkers can control Slouchers to a limited degree by giving them simple commands (stay here, go there, attack, stop, and so forth). Bear in mind that Slouchers are nearly mindless and cannot perform even the most basic manual labor.

Skills of Note: Thinkers retain all skills that they knew in life.

Attacks: 2, or by Hand to Hand Combat skill.

Damage: Bite: 1D6 S.D.C. plus infection, punch/slam: 1D6 S.D.C.

Bonuses: +2 to strike, +1 to initiative.

Psionics: Standard, same chance as any character.

Magic: Thinkers have the innate potential to cast spells, but many have no clue about their power.

Vulnerabilities: Severe cold temperatures will freeze a zombie's body, and hold it in suspended animation.

P.P.E. Vampire: The zombie must absorb a minimum of five P.P.E. every day. For each day that passes without meeting this requirement, subtract one from the zombie's P.E. When it reaches zero, the zombie dies and rots away normally.

Other Threats

Zombies aren't the only challenge that the players must face. In many cases, other survivors can prove to be just as dangerous as the undead. Bandits, for example, become a very serious issue. These are people who take what they want, and bully, hurt, or kill anyone who gets in their way. Some bandits operate alone, but many band together in small groups and gangs. Either way, they can spell trouble for any group of survivors.

Another danger for survivors is madness. Some survivors simply cannot endure the scope and terror of the Zombie Apocalypse, and they just lose it. There's really no telling who might snap, or when. Some become delusional, psychopathic killers, while others degenerate into mindless savages. Their unpredictable nature makes them a serious danger to themselves and others.

Other threats are less obvious, but no less dangerous. Finding proper medical care, for example, is next to impossible. Once-simple illnesses and injuries become life-threatening issues in the wake of the Wave. Unsanitary conditions are no help, as waste and rotting bodies become breeding grounds for bacteria and disease. Food, fuel, and clean drinking water grow scarce as the weeks pass, becoming valuable commodities and prime targets for bandits. Even something as simple as the weather can pose a challenge in the hands of a crafty Game Master.

In the weeks and months following the Wave, another threat will rise. The Cult of Brulyx has agents scattered around the world, poised to speed along the Zombie Apocalypse by any means at their disposal. Some are priests, with an arsenal of spells and an army of Slouchers at their command. Others are ordinary people, fanatical followers of Brulyx who've been placed in positions of power and influence. Their job is to undermine any attempts by the survivors to organize into a resistance. Whether it's done through force and violence or lies and subterfuge, these cultists perform their task with grim efficiency.

The Benford Group – the Past

The origins of the Benford Group stretches back into the depths of time to pre-Roman Europe. In the years after the fall of the Hellenistic civilization that dominated the whole of Southern Europe and Northern Africa, thousands of cults and sects rose among the ruins. To go into the intricacies of these lost religions would be pointless due to the fact that 99% of them were crushed and relegated to the trash heap of history with the consolidation of the Roman Empire.

The original incarnation of the Benford Group was founded by Gregius Bonophat, a former priest of the Greek god Hades. During the burning and destruction of his temple by barbarians, Gregius was driven insane by the apparent abandonment by his god. Escaping to the hills while his followers were raped and murdered by the barbarians, Gregius swore vengeance on his enemies and beseeched the universe for the power to destroy them.

As he screamed and wailed, a voice spoke from the ether, telling him to hold his sniveling tongue and listen. Gregius fell to his knees, struck dumb by the power of the voice. The voice identified itself as Brulyx, a Demon Lord who had been cast from the realm a millennia before. He needed an agent on Earth, and made Gregius an offer. Brulyx would convey tremendous power and long life to Gregius, and in return Gregius would be his high priest. Together, they would breach the dimensional barriers that kept Brulyx from reaching the Earth.

In his hate and madness, Gregius quickly agreed to the pact. The fate of the world pivoted on his choice.

The next evening the barbarians who had sacked Gregius' temple and savaged his followers were encamped among the ruins of the village. Gregius fell upon them like a dark avenging spirit. Empowered by his pact with the demon, Gregius slaughtered them all without mercy. With his vengeance complete, Gregius set to work on fulfilling his master's agenda.

Gregius gathered new followers around him, promising them power and eternal life in the service of Brulyx. These converts and their descendants became the core of the Brotherhood of the Eternal Flame. As the centuries passed, the members of the Brotherhood became influential political and religious leaders throughout the Eurasian continent. The Priests and leaders of the Roman Empire made a valiant attempt at destroying the Brotherhood, but in the end the Brotherhood controlled the empire for all practical purposes.

To this very day, Gregius considers the destruction of the hated Roman Empire to be his crowning achievement.

Over the centuries, Gregius has made several attempts at bringing his master forth. During his orchestrated decline of the Roman Empire, a cholera epidemic killed millions. While the sacrifices gave Brulyx more power, it failed to open a portal. The Black Death, or Black Plague, killed an estimated 75 million people across the world, 20 million of them in Europe alone. Yet dwindling P.P.E. available on Earth rendered the increased number of sacrifices insufficient for Gregius to bring forth his master. The advances in medical science that occurred at the beginning of the Renaissance seemed to crimp Gregius' plans for a juggernaut pandemic to supply the P.P.E. needed to open the portal.

After the last failed attempt to gather the mystic energy needed through natural means (via the Spanish Flu Pandemic of 1918), Gregius decided to rethink his strategy.

Throughout the centuries Gregius had constantly changed his identity and kept himself out of the public eye. That changed in 1919, when Gregius became Louis David Benford the First, and founded the Benford Group as the modern day incarnation of the Brotherhood.

As the Benford Group delved into good works that endeared them to the general public, Gregius bided his time and watched for an opportunity to finally fulfill his pact with Brulyx. In the 1970s Gregius finally found the tool he needed to bring about the apocalypse: genetic engineering. Using decades of genetics research, the keystone of which was the Human Genome Project, the Benford Group created Unisane, an actual cancer vaccine that would pass third party testing. It was the perfect instrument with which to strike at all mankind.

The terrible facet of Unisane was a unique enchantment, provided by Brulyx, which was placed on the vaccine before it was shipped across the world. This enchantment would lie dormant and undetected in the inoculated population. Another spell was required to activate the enchantment, a ritual also provided by Brulyx. The effect of this ritual would come to be known as the Wave.

In order to cast a spell of such magnitude, the cult of Brulyx needed massive amounts of P.P.E. They waited for the summer solstice, when the Earth's levels of ambient P.P.E. were at their highest. Even that was insufficient, but the cult was prepared. Dozens of their priests were sacrificed, and the spell was cast. The Wave swept the planet, and the inoculated population was transformed into zombies.

The nature of the enchantment turned every zombie into a sort of P.P.E. relay. All of the magic energy released by the mass deaths in the Wave was siphoned to the temple of Brulyx. There, the P.P.E. was channeled into a spell to breach the dimensional barriers that kept Brulyx from physically reaching Earth. The massive flow of P.P.E. also served to increase the power of the planet's ley lines to a small degree.

Although the power released by the deaths of almost half of the world's population dwarfed all of the previous attempts to bring Brulyx to Earth, it was a still a failure. But it is important to quantify the failure. While Brulyx was not brought bodily to the Earth, a permanent portal to his home dimension was opened. Brulyx is still barred from entering our dimension, but it is possible for him to send small numbers of his demonic servants to Earth, where they serve as elite shock-troops and advisors to Gregius.

The Benford Group – the Future

The next phase of Gregius' plan is fairly straightforward and direct: use his new legions of the undead as an army (in conjunction with his Dark Priests, demonic servants, and human supporters) to conquer the world. Once the surviving population has been herded like cattle, they will be sacrificed in order to set Brulyx loose upon the Earth.

Gregius is no fool, and several millennia of experience has taught him that patience is a virtue. He has meticulously planned the next phase of the plan, and had all of the components ready months before the Wave. Using the island of Aurora as his central base of operations, Gregius commands a large human mercenary army (all cult members, of course) that he plans on using as his technological hammer. The mercenaries will crush any organized resistance, allowing the hordes of the walking dead to feast on the defenseless survivors.

The first steps that will be taken by Gregius and his dark disciples will be the conquest and pacification of mainland Asia. Although Asia has the highest concentration of survivors, it also has the largest gathering of zombies. Gregius and his Dark Priests will use the millions of zombies as an undead tidal wave to overwhelm the survivors.

Though Gregius is concentrating the bulk of his resources on the Asian continent, he has dispatched teams of priests, cultists and mercenaries to all the corners of the world. They intend to sort the survivors into two distinct groups, the "sheep" who will be used as additional sacrifices to bring forth Brulyx, and those special few who can be recruited to join them.

Also of special importance to Gregius and his minions are the "Points of Power" spread across the globe. Places such as Stonehenge, the Nazca Plains, and the former Mound City near St. Louis must be secured by his forces and used to help channel as much power as possible to Brulyx.

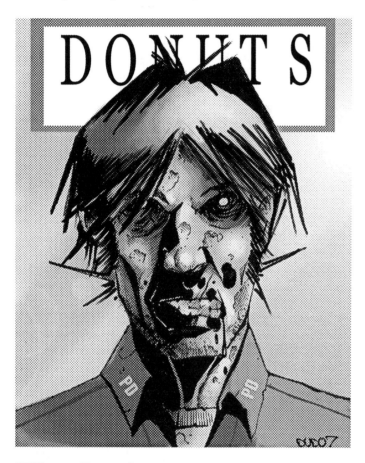

The Setting

The World of Dead Reign

Just about every inhabited corner of the Earth has been affected by the zombie plague. Urban centers were obviously the hardest hit due to their dense populations, but in very little time the rural areas were overrun with the undead. Those who have managed to make it out of the "Death Zones" or have been able to hold a fixed area against the undead now make up the vast majority of the living population of the world.

(Note: What is presented here is not necessarily information that the Player Characters will be aware of. Unless they have access to the "Wireless Web" the player characters will have almost no idea of what is happening more than a few miles from their current position. Most times they will be thankful just to know what is happening in their immediate vicinity.)

North America

Ironically, the United States was almost spared the worst of the disaster. With only 25% of the American population inoculated, there was a real chance that a recovery could have taken place. Unfortunately it was not to be. With the majority of the U.S.A.'s active duty and reserve military forces dispatched across the globe, most of the nation was left virtually defenseless against the undead onslaught. The civilian population, aided by the law enforcement organizations, managed to keep the undead off balance and distracted while millions tried to find a safe place to hide and wait for help to arrive. The government was crippled at the initial outbreak. With most of the members of Congress and the executive branch having received the Unisane inoculation, the American Government fell without a shot being fired.

Most of the American military was spared the horror of joining the ranks of the living dead, as the Department of Defense had not wanted to spend hundreds of millions of dollars on inoculations for their troops if they didn't have to. The military commanders in the field were left with a terrible choice, defend the positions that they already occupied, or go home. Unfortunately, by the time that most of the commanders had decided to return home their routes for escape were blocked and they were surrounded by the living dead.

Some troops did remain in the continental United States, and it was due to the heroic actions of many of theses brave men and women that many of the people who later carried on the fight were alive to do so. The "Wright Patterson Airlift" alone managed to get almost one hundred thousand Americans to eventual safety in the Alaskan Freehold.

Winnipeg was the exception to all of the rules. In the spring of 2012, the residents of the central Canadian city of Winnipeg in the Province of Manitoba were outraged. The shipment of Unisane that had been promised to the city was gone, the casualty of pilot error. The cargo plane carrying the vaccine from the Benford Group's Toronto warehouses crashed seventy miles (112 km) from its destination. Unfortunately, the people of Winnipeg were informed, no more vaccine would be available till fall. When the Wave hit, less than 5% of the population of Winnipeg were affected.

In the weeks that followed the initial outbreak, Winnipeg acted as the information center of North America. Eventually they became the arsenal, the manufacturing powerhouse, and the breadbasket of North America.

Across the rest of the continent, survivors fared much worse. What remained of a shattered United States Air Force began a Herculean effort that culminated in the movement of almost three hundred thousand Americans from the lower forty eight states to the theoretical safe zone that was Alaska. Alaska was the least inoculated state per capita, and with the shells of dozens of active duty and National Guard bases scattered across the continent as a legacy from the Cold War, Alaska seemed the last refuge of the desperate. The organizing of the Alaskan Freehold would take months, thus they had effectively removed themselves as a major player in the opening stages of the game.

The city of Denver, Colorado was as infested as any other across North America in the opening stages of the outbreak, but it didn't stay that way. Deputy Fire Chief Janet Armstrong of the City of Denver Fire Department rallied her people during the initial stages of the outbreak. Gathering the surviving firefighters and police officers from the Mile High City, she congregated them and as many civilians as they could find at the football stadium. The proportions of the sports complex and the number of preexisting internal and external barricades that it contained made it the rival of any medieval European fixed fortification. Chief Armstrong and her people, armed mostly with hand to hand weapons and fire hoses, spent the next three weeks retaking the city and securing its perimeter. But at a terrible cost – less than twenty-five thousand people remained in the Mile High City.

Survivors in the Republic of Mexico were in a worse predicament than their cousins to the north. Mexico City fell within a few hours of the Wave, and 90% of the country's government was wiped out in the initial outbreak. But a ragtag group of farmers and National Guard troops managed to take refuge in the oppressive climates of the Yucatan peninsula. The natives of the Peninsula, mostly descended from the native Mayan populations of pre-Columbian times, were some of the first people on the planet to realize that the old magic had returned. Because they had never truly abandoned their old beliefs, merely blended them with the beliefs brought to them by the Spanish conquistadors, the sudden return of ambient P.P.E. supercharged their already existing mystic abilities. In the months that followed they returned in droves to the old stone cities of their ancestors.

South America

South America as a political and military entity crumbled after three days of chaos. This is in no way to imply that the South American people crumbled. While they have not, as of yet, coalesced into any new organized groups of continental, or even regional, significance, South America is home to some of the most resourceful zombie hunters on the planet. They work in small groups, family or tribal in organization. Lightning quick strikes into the old urban centers, which are the cores of the zombie infestations, are the hallmarks of theses tenacious warriors and survivalists. They have relocated to the highlands and mountains that cut through the continent, or in the case of the Amazon basin, the people have simply begun to live on the rivers and in the trees. Using shallow draft boats on the rivers, and an absolutely ingenious system of pulleys, rope bridges, and platforms in the jungles, they will hold out for years.

Europe

Continental Europe was decimated during the opening days of the outbreak. Unisane was being provided to the population as fast as it could be produced and shipped. Contact was lost with vast tracts of the continent within hours of the Wave. Most of the major urban centers were complete death zones in less than twelve hours. Pockets of survivors have gathered in the more mountainous areas of Western Europe, and quite a few of the old medieval castles and fortifications have been reclaimed by the people who made it through the first days of the outbreak. The rumors that permeate Europe's version of North America's "Wireless Web" speak of a Russian Army group that managed to pull back from the chaos and destruction that was Western Russia and establish a picket line at the Ural Mountains. It has been said that a Russian General of Imperial heritage has proclaimed himself Czar Sergei Lermatov, and that he has established his new center of operations at the northern port city of Arkangel. Many survivors, in their tiny holdouts across the continent, pray that the Russians will return from the east and save them, but that may only be wishful thinking.

The northern regions of Europe are an entirely different story. The dense populations of England, Wales, and southern Scotland almost guaranteed that they would fall to the hordes of the undead eventually, although the people of the United Kingdom lasted far longer than most odds makers would have be-

lieved. In the end, the remnants of the UK pulled into the extremes of the Scottish Highlands. They are said to be led by a distant member of the Royal Family who made it out of the south just ahead of the undead.

If there is a story of hope in this blighted world it is the Republic of Ireland. Ireland has always been a lightly populated nation of few cities and many small communities that were largely self-sufficient. The lasting heritage of the great potato famine of the nineteenth century had taught the Irish people that they could never count on anyone but themselves. This spirit of independence and a tightknit culture allowed them to weather the opening days of the outbreak.

Ireland was the least inoculated region per capita in all of Europe. During the initial stages of the crisis, the Irish government was quick to act. The Irish were extremely lucky in that only a small percentage of the civilian and military command structure had been inoculated with Unisane. The greatest danger facing the republic was the large number of zombies streaming into the country from Northern Ireland. As a nominal part of the United Kingdom, Northern Ireland had been heavily inoculated, and thus once the undead had overwhelmed the region they began to range further south looking for prey.

It would take several months for the Republic of Ireland to purge the island of the undead plague and begin making plans for the future.

Africa

Africa may well end up being the thorn in Gregius' side. With the exception of South Africa, Gregius, and through him the entire Benford Group, considered the continent as a non-issue. What Gregius has failed to consider are two factors. The first is that there are more firearms per capita in sub-Saharan Africa than any other place on the globe. In the times before the Wave, fifty American dollars would have gotten you a fully functional and loaded Kalashnikov rifle in any decent sized city. The second factor that both Brulyx and Gregius have overlooked is the continuing belief in the old ways of magic that still permeates Africa to this very day. The renewal of the Earth's P.P.E. and the return of magic and psionic powers may very well turn the often neglected African population into a potential mystical juggernaut that may be able to stand against Gregius and his minions.

Asia

Asia is where Gregius has decided to stake his position and make his opening gambit against the world. The island fortress of Aurora is located in the Indonesian archipelago, one of hundreds of small islands in that region that have been of very little value since the end of the Second World War.

The island of Aurora measures fifteen miles (24 km) at its widest point and is just shy of thirty miles (48 km) in length. Gregius purchased the island primarily due to the largely unknown ruins found scattered around its surface and beneath the surface of the ocean surrounding the island. The ruins bear a striking resemblance to the underwater ruins discovered off the coast of Japan at Yonaguni, a site suggested to Gregius by Brulyx in a divine vision. When Gregius arrived on the island he was astounded to find six different nexus points and a virtual web of Ley Lines crisscrossing the island.

(G.M. Notes: The island of Aurora and the ruins at Yonaguni are both part of an ancient south Pacific civilization that once helped thwart an attempt by Brulyx to dominate this dimension. Upon his failure to do so, the Old Gods forever sealed this dimension from Brulyx's direct control. Or so they thought. In the aftermath of the botched invasion, many of the costal cities of this forgotten people were swallowed by the sea.)

Within an hour of the Wave, Gregius's mercenary army and his Dark Priests made landfall on the major islands of the Indonesian archipelago. Using the industrial resources and slave labor captured on the islands in the opening months of the outbreak (remember, the modern day nation of Indonesia, and other nations on the islands, has a population of approximately three hundred million), Gregius plans to mount a full scale invasion of continental Asia, starting with the Chinese mainland. The belief is that six to ten months of zombie infestation will be more than enough time to soften up the Asian landmass. He may be disastrously wrong in this assumption.

While almost every government and military organization on the mainland collapsed within a few days of the outbreak, not all hope is lost. The Indian government has not completely vanished from the face of the Earth. A crack division of the Indian Army's mechanized infantry, supported by the fragments of other military units, have established a strong defensive zone in what was the country of Nepal. General Rajah Kumar led his people on a grueling march across the Indian subcontinent in the full hellish heat and humidity of the tropical Indian summer, constantly fending off the swelling legions of the recently deceased. Picking up stragglers and refugees as they marched, they were greeted as saviors by a Nepalese population that was on the brink of extinction.

Slowly, as they harden their positions, and develop a never before needed industrial base on the roof of the world, the "Himalayan Commonwealth" will become the secret arsenal of an Asian continent that is not only being assaulted by the ravenous dead, but also their demonically ruled masters armed with the cutting edge of military hardware.

Australia

Most of the population in Australia was clustered in several urban spurs around the coasts before the Wave. This is still the case, but now the population is almost exclusively made up of the walking dead. The Aussie survivors did the only two things that made any sense to them at the time of the outbreak. They boarded whatever would float and headed to New Zealand and Tasmania, or they headed for the interior.

The people who made it to the central area of the continent were greeted by the hearty frontiersman and aboriginal people who already called this area home. If the influx of refugees to the interior had been much higher, violence probably would have been the result. (That very thing happened on the island of Cuba as refugees from North and South America flooded its shores.) But because so many of the initial survivors failed to make it out of the Australian cities, the locals in the interior were able to integrate with the refugees just as the swarms of living dead began to penetrate the area.

There are weird rumors about the interior, the most prevalent of which is that the dead won't or can't come within 20 miles (32 km) of Ayers Rock. This rumor has lead to many of the survivors in the interior setting out for the rock, but none of them are ever heard from again.

By and large, 80% of the surviving coastal population headed for the islands. Tasmania and the islands of New Zealand were broadcasting in the clear and accepting refugees weeks into the outbreak. Some of the local populations of the islands fear that the refugees will overwhelm them and leave them unable to protect themselves from the dead that they are only now, after massive losses in the opening days, beginning to get the advantage over. Also, the newly reforming governments of Free Oz (Tasmania) and New Zealand are concerned over the tales they have been hearing from the refugees from the north. They speak of an army of the dead controlled by evil priests and protected by living soldiers who are digesting everything in their path.

Antarctica

The fate of the scientists and adventurers living at the bottom of the world is unknown. It is known, however, that none of them had yet been inoculated with Unisane.

There were also rumors within academic circles that a major find had been made in the Antarctic. Some were speaking of finding ancient ruins that dated back more than ten thousand years. But, of course, these are just rumors.

The Oceans

A whole new realm of human habitation has sprouted in the short time since the outbreak. Life on the high seas is now a reality for more than twenty million survivors around the globe, although this number will eventually stabilize at less than ten million.

Seafaring craft and small isolated islands have now become some of the safest places for the surviving human population to seek refuge from the hordes of the living dead. Food and re-sources are some of the biggest problems faced by the people that now call the oceans home. Most ships had only supplies that were adequate for their original reason for being on the sea in the first place, and many of the islands that are safe for the average refugee ship to approach are either already claimed or are very limited in what they have to offer.

This has led to vast fleets of ships drifting across the open sea and pooling their resources for the common good. Also, piracy has now become a huge threat for the people exposed to the almost endless waters. Many believe that the only way to survive is to take what they need and the consequences be damned.

Rumors have begun to fly amongst the oceanic community that an international force of naval vessels is attempting to pull together an alliance of ships to retake the Hawaiian Islands. Many refuse to get their hopes up regarding this rumor, but more and more of the military and industrial vessels that have been plying the open seas have been slipping off, not to be seen again.

Space

At the present time of the game, less than a year since the initial outbreak, 95% of the Earth's satellite network is still functioning and accessible. As the years pass the network will exponentially begin to fail and become no more than orbital debris. Roughly 5% of the satellites in orbit are of the latest design and could conceivably remain useful to the survivors for another ten years.

It is known that all of the crew members on the International Space Station had been inoculated with Unisane. In the months that follow the outbreak, a survivor from the Houston Space Center will relate a story to the survivors in the Denver Safe Zone that they were still communicating with a completely healthy station crew after the initial outbreak. The Houston

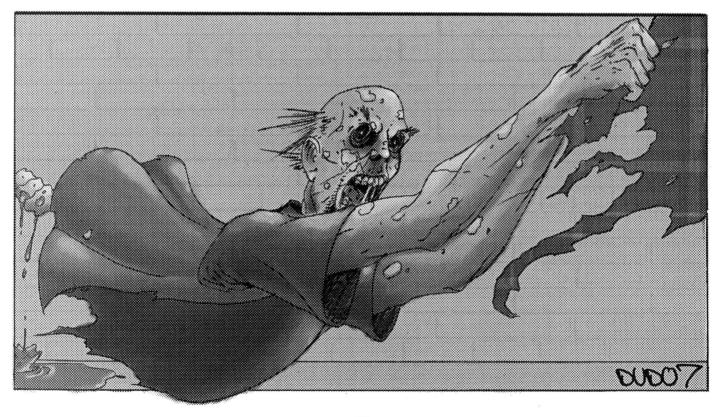

Space Center was overrun, so the fate of the astronauts is unknown.

Communications

The modern reality of instantaneous global communication is effectively a thing of the past. A few of the "safe zones" have managed to retain modern communications to a limited degree. New Zealand and Free Oz have reestablished a limited satellite link using automated communications relays in geosynchronous orbit over Australia, and regional telecommunications are still viable in Ireland, Alaska, and Winnipeg. But the vast majority of communication is done via the "Wireless Web."

The "Wireless Web" is the name given to the system of ham radio and shortwave relay communications being used across the globe. In North America especially, the new Web has been spearheaded by the Free City of Winnipeg and Fortress Denver. Using the few long-range links they still have under their control, they manage to make regular broadcasts that blanket the North American continent and even Western Europe. This has allowed for some direct communications with the Republic of Ireland.

Web broadcasts are used to inform people of potential safe zones, the movement patterns of large swarms of zombies, and general information that might help people make it through one more day. There are also hundreds of other broadcasters besides the cities. Most of the others are isolated people who are trying to keep their sanity by communicating with the outside world, but one broadcaster who claims to be all alone in a tower in downtown New York City says he has all of the answers. He spews on and on about Unisane, and the Benford Group, and the lady who comes to him in his dreams. Most people have dismissed him as a crackpot, but some of the powers that be in the cities are starting to wonder if the man might actually know what he is talking about.

(G.M. Notes: Daniel Gregory worked for the Benford Group and was an initiate in the cult of Brulyx. But when the truth of what was going to happen to the world was revealed to him he ran and didn't stop running until the day of the Wave. Daniel is actually quite safe from the dead, as he possesses the intricate series of cabalistic tattoos that all members of the Brotherhood have. These tattoos allow the members of the Brotherhood to be masked from the zombies' P.P.E. seeking sense, although a Thinker would realize this if confronted with a member. Daniel could provide a lot of useful knowledge, but he is smack in the middle of millions of the living dead.)

Transportation

By and large, people have been reduced to foot power when it comes to transportation. The vast majority of the world's available refined gasoline and diesel was exhausted before the end of the first winter after the Wave. One exception to the fuel crisis is in Winnipeg. In 2008, the government of the Province of Manitoba encouraged the building of several ethanol distilla-tion and bio-diesel refining plants in the Winnipeg area. The availability of fuel is now only 25% of the quantity that existed before the outbreak, but that is still far more than most other places. This resource has allowed the defenders of Winnipeg to fend off the hordes of the undead despite the fact that Winnipeg lacks any true natural features to aid in the defense of the city.

The availability of fuels throughout the remainder of the world is spotty to nonexistent, with the possible exceptions of Alaska, Free Oz, and Ireland. The possibility that a free Russian government is still refining oil behind the Urals exists but is unconfirmed.

Agriculture

The inability for the vast majority of the population to farm and raise food animals has leveled a devastating blow against post Wave society. With the exceptions of rare safe zones such as New Zealand, Ireland, Alaska, and the city state of Winnipeg, agriculture has ceased to exist. Starvation in the first year of the crisis has claimed as many lives in some areas as the living dead.

Education

Education is a thing of the past in most areas of the planet. When people are spending their days working and fighting so that they can be safe for one more night, education tends to take a back seat. There is a movement toward family education, with the older members in a given area passing on the knowledge that the children will need to survive in this world. But in the more secure and advanced areas, a concerted effort is being put forward to make sure that fundamental education is not neglected. The leaders in these areas realize that without education their civilization is doomed to slide into barbarism.

A note about the supernatural

In the wake of the Wave, Earth's ley lines have grown quite a bit stronger. They aren't powerful enough to be seen with the naked eye, but the increased levels of ambient P.P.E. have triggered some supernatural abilities in mankind. As noted in the character generation section, 15% of the living population develops psionic powers. Furthermore, a smaller percentage of people find that they can manipulate and channel the raw powers of magic itself.

Handling magic in your campaign can be tricky. Bear in mind that magic lore is extremely rare in this world (most of it is in the hands of the cult of Brulyx), and there is no one to provide the training necessary to master the art of spell casting. At best, characters with some innate magic ability might learn to cast a handful of low-level spells. Alternately, the Game Master might allow players to use the Mystic O.C.C., who uses magic and psionics by instinct. As time passes, mankind is bound to rediscover some of the secrets of greater magic. Future material will deal with this topic, so stay tuned.

2007 Christmas Surprise Package

Palladium Books' annual **X-Mas Surprise Package/Grab Bag** is a fun tradition and our way of doing a little something special for our loyal and dedicated fans. Our way of saying thank you, delivering a little Christmas cheer, and putting a smile on the faces of some big kids. This year is a celebration of perseverance and community.

The Christmas Surprise Package is only being publicized to readers of **The Rifter®** and on **Palladium's Web Site** – www.palladiumbooks.com – so tell your friends, buy one for everyone you know, and have a very, Merry Christmas.

When you can order

Now till December 21, 2007.

Note: Orders received by Palladium after December 14th can *NOT* be *guaranteed* to arrive *before Christmas.*

The Cost

$32.00 plus $8.00 for shipping and handling (same as last year) in the USA and Canada – that's **$40 total.** The eight dollars goes toward shipping and handling per *each* individual X-Mas Surprise Package/Grab Bag (i.e. one Grab Bag is $40, two are $80, and so on). Those ordering *online* can select their method of shipping, but you will pay for the *additional* shipping costs as well as a $3.00 handling fee.

Overseas Orders require additional postage of $34.00. Sorry, we are only passing along the increased postal rates of Priority International (typically 2-5 weeks delivery; Parcel Post no longer exists). Such orders may take extra time to arrive. If you want faster or special delivery you will need to *call* us or order *online* where you can select different methods of shipping. YOU, the customers, pay ALL special or rush shipping costs.

All North American orders are shipped *U.S.P.S., Media Mail (the "slow" Book Rate), UPS,* or the way *Palladium* decides is best. Those ordering online can select the desired method of shipping but will pay accordingly. We strongly suggest UPS because it is fast, reliable and can be tracked. Media Mail cannot be tracked, and one-of-a-kind items, like art or a gold edition, can NOT be replaced.

Credit card orders are welcomed. Visa and MasterCard are preferred. Order by mail, telephone or online.

No C.O.D. orders, and we must have a *street address* (no P.O. Box) to ship via *UPS.*

What you get

● **$70 or more worth of goodies.** A minimum of *seventy dollars ($70) retail* in Palladium product, probably more. Last year, Kevin Siembieda was so full of Christmas spirit that many Surprise Packages got more than $80 worth of goodies!

● **Autographs** from Kevin Siembieda, and available staff and Palladium freelancers. If you "request" autographs we will sign *every* book in your box! For many, especially those overseas, this is the *only* way they are likely to ever get autographs from Kevin Siembieda and crew. Take advantage of that.

● **Each order handpicked by Kevin Siembieda** from a "wish list" *you* provide!

● Special items may include out of print books, gold editions, original artwork, prints, bumper stickers, books, T-shirts, and posters.

● The Grab Bag makes a wonderful Christmas, birthday, or anniversary gift for the gamers in your life.

● Impress your friends with a gift worth $70 *or more* for a cost of only $40. Or fill holes in your own collection.

As a "grab bag/surprise package" you *never know* exactly what you will receive, but that's the fun "surprise" part of this offer and we always try to send as many of your "special wants" as we can (at least two, usually more). Extra items may include other RPG books, The Rifter®, posters, prints, art books, bumper stickers, back stock items, or a surprise or two.

Multiple orders *will* result in some duplication.

If you ask for signatures *every book* will be signed by *Kevin Siembieda* and available staff members and freelancers.

Note: If you do *NOT* want autographs, please state as much.

Ideas for "Special Wants"

To insure your X-Mas Surprise Package is everything you want it to be, send us a *wish list* of your "wants." The more items listed, the more likely you are to get items you want most, and list them in order of preference (at least 7 items, the more the better). PLEASE do *not* ask for books you *know* are not yet available or out of print like *Tome Grotesque, Dimensional Outbreak, Rifts® China One,* or *Mechanoid Space®.*

Note: Santa Kev and his elves are NOT mind readers. If you do not give us a clear idea of your wants, you *may* be disappointed by what comes in your Surprise Package.

You do NOT make our job easier when you say something like "I own everything, surprise me," or "I don't care, anything special." It makes our job much more *difficult.* We want to make each Grab Bag special, but because we don't know you or what books you own, like or want, we don't have a clue as to what to send you unless you give us a variety of items on your list.

Please say something like this: "I own it all, but would love any duplicate Fantasy books signed by the Palladium crew." Or "I have most of it, surprise me with T-shirts or unique items like signed proofreader copies of books, or artwork if available;" and so on.

Ideas to help you make your selections

● For Rifts®: **Rifts® & the Megaverse®** – the Art of John Zeleznik ("soft cover" art book), the **Zeleznik Coloring Book, Rifts® WB 30: D-Bees of North America™, Rifts® Sourcebook One Expanded** (epic), **Hades, Dyval™** (not available till November 1), **Rifts® Machinations of Doom™** (graphic novel and sourcebook), **WB 11: Coalition War Campaign** (back in print), **Rifts® New West™** (back in print), **Rifts® Spirit West™** (back in print), **Rifts® Dinosaur Swamp™** and/or **Rifts® *Adventures* in Dinosaur Swamp™, Rifts® Mercenaries, MercTown, Rifts® MercOps, Rifts® Merc Adventures, Rifts® WB 28: Arzno, Rifts® WB 29: Madhaven,** etc.

● **Dimension Books** like **Hades** (new; Minion War), **Dyval** (not available till November 1; Minion War), **Wormwood™** (more demonic horror), **Phase World®, Phase World Sourcebook,** and others.

● **Rifts® Ultimate Edition** core rule book.

● **Rifts® Core Books** like **Rifts® G.M. Guide, Rifts® Book of Magic, Rifts® Adventure Guide.**

● **Conversion Books.** All three are great references: **Rifts® Conversion Book One, Rifts® Conversion Book 2: Pantheons of the Megaverse®,** and **Rifts® Dark Conversions™.**

● **Rifts® Ultimate Gold** (limited). We have approximately 30 copies put aside special for the 2007 Grab Bags. That means only those of you who win us over with a short, but compelling pitch on why you should get one will be considered. **Note:** The *Rifts® Ultimate Gold* originally sold for $70 and currently has a value of $100+ as a collector's item – request it, and it *may* be the ONLY item you get in your X-Mas Surprise Package.

● **Gold Machinations of Doom** (limited). Only 400 signed and numbered copies were created and there are only about 180 copies left. We have about 40 printer proofs put aside special for the 2007 Grab Bags. Only about one in 300 people will get a copy. This is a $45 item.

● **Beyond the Supernatural™ "Gold" Hardcover, 2nd Edition RPG.** Limited to 600 signed and numbered copies (half already gone). Only about 1 in 100 will get a copy if it is requested. This is a $50 item.

● Are you a **Phase World®** fan? Do you need a copy of **Rifts® Dimension Book 2: Phase World®** or the **Phase World® Sourcebook?** What about **The Anvil Galaxy™** or **Three Galaxies™,** or **Rifts® Megaverse® Builder** or **Naruni™ Wave Two?**

- **Rifts® Miniatures.** Many are already out of stock, others are running low and we don't have plans to recast them anytime soon. Get 'em while you can. Normally sell for 4-6 dollars per pack, but order 'em for the 2007 Surprise Package and we'll send you a heap of 'em along with your other goodies.
- **"Glitter Boy" Limited Edition Print** signed by the artist, Scott Johnson, and Rifts® creator, Kevin Siembieda. Limited to only 700 signed and numbered copies. 20x28 inch image on silk paper stock – suitable for framing. $20 value.
- **"Heroes of the Megaverse" – Limited Edition Print –** *"Special Williams Grab Bag Edition"* signed by the artist, *Freddie E. Williams II* and *Kevin Siembieda*. Only 200 – suitable for framing. $20 value.
- For Heroes Unlimited™: **Powers Unlimited™ Three, Powers Unlimited™ Two** (back in print), **Villains Unlimited™ Revised, Heroes Unlimited™ G.M.'s Guide, Century Station™, Gramercy Island™,** or the **Aliens Unlimited Galaxy Guide™, Ninjas & Superspies RPG,** and **Mystic China,** among others.
- Palladium Fantasy RPG®: **Western Empire™** (back in print after being absent for several years), the **RPG** itself, **Dragons & Gods™, Eastern Territory™, Mount Nimro™, Northern Wilderness™, Land of the Damned™,** and others.
- For Beyond the Supernatural™: There's only the **BTS-2™ RPG** soft cover RPG or the **Beyond the Supernatural™ "Gold" Hardcover, 2nd Edition RPG.**
- All Nightbane® titles are in stock except the discontinued *Shadows of Light*. Did you know *Nightbane characters* can be used in *Heroes Unlimited™, Ninjas & Superspies™* and/or *BTS-2*?
- **Palladium T-Shirts** ($18 value) available while supplies last; some sizes are already gone. Available only while supplies last; first come, first served. All have a $20+ value.
  Going through Hell (Minion War) – All sizes Medium to 5XL.
  F___in' Brilliant – All sizes Medium to 5XL.
  I Saved the Megaverse® (blue) – XL to 4XL.
  2006 Open House (25th anniversary) – XL and XXL only.
  Lazlo Society T-Shirt – XL and XXL only.
  Rifts® Logo – XL only.
  Rifts® Dog Pack – XL only (only about 200 left).
  Rifts® Grey Summoner (Perez artwork) – XXL only.
  Rifts® Borg (Color) – "Small" size only.

Back Stock Items & Other Considerations:
- **Back stock:** RPGs, sourcebooks, world books and supplements you've been meaning to get, but haven't gotten around to. This is a great way to *fill those holes* in your collection, get hard to find back stock items or try a new game like **Rifts®, Palladium Fantasy®, Nightbane®, Heroes Unlimited™, Ninjas & Superspies™, Mystic China™, After the Bomb®, After the Bomb® Sourcebooks, Beyond the Supernatural™, Chaos Earth™** or **Splicers®.**
- *Rifter®* Back Issues. Palladium has stopped reprinting back issues of The Rifter® and issues *1-13* are no longer available – *except* for the X-Mas Surprise Package and conventions attended by Palladium. We have kept 30-100 copies of most of *The Rifters®* especially for this purpose, but some issues are already *completely gone* (including issues #4, #8, #22-26, #29-30, #34). Other numbers are nearly gone, so they are available only while supplies last. Oh, and don't forget **The Best of The Rifter®** (which includes a listing and index of everything that has ever appeared in Rifters #1-32).
- **Out of print and hard to find items.** Still need that copy of the collected **Magic of Palladium Books®** or **RECON®** (Vietnam era RPG), or the **Compendium of Contemporary Weapons,** or the **After the Bomb® RPG** or AtB sourcebooks?
  Hmm, what about **Ninja Turtle®** sourcebooks? Kevin has pulled out about a dozen file copies of the TMNT sourcebooks we have left for a handful of Surprise Packages that *specifically ask* for them. Available only while supplies last (sorry, no copies of the TMNT RPG nor Trans-dimensional Ninja Turtles). However, we have plenty of the new **After the Bomb® RPG** and *After the Bomb®* sourcebooks like, **Road**

Hogs™, Mutants Down Under™, Mutants in Avalon™, Mutants of the Yucatan™ and **Mutants in Orbit™.**

Have you been wanting to try **Splicers®, Beyond the Supernatural™, Nightbane®, Heroes Unlimited™, Ninjas & Superspies™, After the Bomb®** or **Rifts® Chaos Earth™**? Well this is a great way to do so.
- **The Magic of Palladium Books® Collection,** a reprint of the original tabloids, only available upon request. Almost out of stock.
- **Original artwork! Rare and limited.** We expect to get approximately 50 pieces of artwork – mostly quarter page illustrations (a few larger) – donated by the artists (or from Kevin Siembieda's personal archives).
  *Only people who request artwork will be **considered** for it!* We have a very limited supply so only the luckiest will receive art. You can beg or you can be witty, but only Santa Kev will decide who gets artwork.
- **25th Anniversary Laser Etched Glasses** – Six different glasses (25th Anniversary Logo, Rifts®, HU2, BTS-2, Nightbane®, and Palladium Fantasy®). 17 ounce glasses; dishwasher safe. $45 value. Only 400 sets were made, we are down to about 80 sets and they will NOT be reissued.
- **2007 Palladium Greeting Cards** – Mixed set of six different cards, or six of the same (we have two Christmas Cards ideal for Rifts® players, two birthday cards, one thinking of you and one, um, funny card). Value: $12. They look GREAT.
- **8x10 autographed, color photo of Kevin Siembieda** or of Kevin and the key Palladium staff. We include this only because more and more people seem to ask for them every year! Estimated Value: Priceless. Okay, how about six bucks value?

REMEMBER, this is a "Surprise Package." While Kevin Siembieda and the Palladium staff *personally* try to make each and every Surprise Package something special, we cannot guarantee satisfaction. It is a "Grab Bag." Buyers may *not* always be satisfied (although we seem to succeed with most) and duplication *will* occur with multiple orders. Also note that some items *may* be slightly damaged (so we can send you *more*), and we cannot control damage that may occur in the mail/shipping.

Ordering the 2007 X-Mas Surprise Package

Include *ALL* of the following information . . .
- *Special Wants* – list *several* specific books, new and old, or other items like Hades, T-shirts, Rifts® miniatures, Gold Edition Hardcover, Compendium of Contemporary Weapons, etc. (at least 7-10 items please).
- Indicate "No T-shirt" if you don't want to be considered for one. If you *DO WANT* a T-shirt include *your size* (many shirts are limited to only XL & XXL; see above).
- Favorite Palladium games.
- Palladium games you have not played but always thought looked fun and interesting.
- Would you like autographs?
- Comments and suggestions.
- Accurate mailing address! UPS cannot ship to a P.O. Box; provide a *street* address.

Cost: $40 ($32.00 + $8 for shipping & handling) in USA & Canada for *each* 2007 X-Mas Surprise Package. Multiple orders of the 2007 Surprise Package *will* result in some duplication. $66 overseas due to the high cost of postage ($32.00 + $34 for shipping & handling).

Credit cards are welcomed: Visa and MasterCard preferred (but most major credit cards are accepted). Go to the Palladium website (www.palladiumbooks.com) and fill out the **2007 Christmas Surprise Package Order Form** and pay with a credit card. Or order by telephone (734-946-1156); this is an *order line* only.

Place orders by mail by enclosing a check or money order along with your wish list and address, and send to the address below.

Palladium Books – Dept. X – 12455 Universal Drive – Taylor, MI 48180 – USA

Happy Holidays from all of us at Palladium Books®

Spell Books of the Megaverse®!

Optional Rules for Rifts®, Palladium Fantasy®, and Other Games

By S. E. Gibbons

Images of wizards carrying, using, or surrounded by books and scrolls of magic fill our modern popular culture, fantasy fiction and artwork. While magic scrolls do already exist in the Palladium Megaverse, spell books are a different matter entirely. Though individual books are occasionally described in various reference materials or listed as treasures to be won or lost as part of a grander adventure, there have never been rules set out for including such books in game-play, either as they are being written or used by player characters and NPCs. This article is meant to address that gap. (Please keep in mind that the alternate rules for learning/gaining new spells for leveling up presented here do not prevent the character from purchasing and learning additional magic as is normal for their particular O.C.C. And though this article was written with Rifts in mind, its principles could easily be applied in any of Palladium Books' games that utilize magic in any form.)

What are spell books and what are they used for?

Randall the Red sat in a comfortably overstuffed armchair in his neat, book-lined study, leafing through a thick, well worn tome, the pages crackling just a bit with age. The book was the first spell book he'd ever owned, and it held a wealth of memories. His face occasionally broke into a smile as the passages he read reminded him of good times and old friends, daring quests and great adventures. Those were the days of his first experimentation and innovation, the first steps on a path that had led to a life of beauty and growth. Amazing how much treasure an old book could hold!

A large grandfather clock set in a corner of his study began to chime softly, pulling him from his reverie. Getting up, he carefully set the book with its many companions and closed the doors of the special bookcase that held these, his most prized possessions. Enough of visiting the past for today. It was time to meet his new apprentice and get on with shaping the future!

In game terms, spell books are somewhat of a cross between a personal journal and a lab book for many magic users. Traditional spell casters such as the Ley Line Walker and Shifter primarily utilize spell books as a means toward figuring out new spells, whereas Techno-Wizards use them not only as an instrument to help learn new spells but also as a tool in successfully creating their next TW invention. Spell books are also employed by many magic users to record major events in their lives and/or important information for immediate or future use that they do not want to forget or misplace. Thus a spell book can act as a record of a magic user's life and activities as well as his continued magical research.

Before one can integrate spell books into a new or continuing campaign, there will be a few things that will need to be considered by both the G.M. and the players. To start, a big limiting factor on the use of spell books is that a mage must be able to read and write before he can begin keeping a spell book. Remember, on Rifts Earth, the general level of education for the vast majority of people is very low. Except for a few scattered locations, such as the city of Lazlo or the New German Republic, there are no organized public school systems as we know them today. Most communities just don't have the resources to spend on educating the general populace. Then there are the Coalition States, where knowledge represents power for those who possess it. For this reason, the Emperor has criminalized not only education in general but literacy itself, except for the ruling elite. And even if the community does have the resources to devote toward teaching its people to read, that doesn't mean they will choose to do so. Remember, in many wilderness communities there is great suspicion toward and even outright fear of those who have been formally educated; leftovers from the days of the Second Dark Age and the tales of how unnamed gods destroyed mankind for becoming too powerful. Thus it is no wonder that many magic users start their careers not knowing how to read, especially those who grew up in small wilderness villages or kingdoms.

What all this means is that for any magic user to write or otherwise make use of a spell book, he must first have or gain the required literacy, either in his own native tongue (which is most common) or some foreign language (Dragonese/Elven being the most popular alternative). This skill selection must be made as an O.C.C. Related Skill either during the character's creation or later during an appropriate level up, as a Secondary Skill selection will not give the mage a sufficient mastery of the language to be able to write a really useful spell book.

Prerequisite Skill: Literacy selected as an O.C.C. Related Skill in at least one language.

The next question then becomes, "When should a roll under the Literacy skill be required when writing in one's spell book?" Surprisingly enough, the answer is not when the character is writing in his spell book, but when he is *reading* what he originally wrote. This is because when a person writes something down, the knowledge that has just been recorded is fresh in their mind, and so re-reading the passage just written is done without difficulty. However, coming back to that passage after some amount of time, be it days, weeks, months or even longer, the character may have forgotten some critical piece of the larger puzzle that he had not thought to write down, and thus not be able to decipher his own notes. Most of us have had at least some experience in looking back at notes taken in a class and not being able to decipher our own handwriting or understand what we ourselves wrote. Nothing is more frustrating than knowing that the information you need is right in front of you, but you can't find it!

Ultimately, the question of when to roll under the Literacy skill is really best left up to the individual G.M. and should be done to heighten the role-playing of the individual group. It is not generally necessary for Literacy rolls to be done for spell-related notes, since the mage will either be currently working on

the spell and thus have it fresh in his mind, or he has already learned the spell and will probably not need the specific research again. On the other hand, such a skill roll is very likely to be made when the character is trying to go back in his spell book and find something that he recorded that *isn't* related to his spell research (recall that many mages keep notes in their spell books about things other than spells). Examples of this might include the mage having taken notes about what turns to take to reach a certain destination, the characteristics (and weaknesses) of a race of demons, or what the password is to gain entry to a restricted area. Remember, the Literacy skill gives the character the capability to read and *write* in his own language, but it doesn't necessarily mean that he can write in a clear manner that allows him to easily find the information he is looking for again.

Of course, to find something in the spell book, it must first be written therein. Thus a player should state to the G.M. when his character is taking note of something in the character's spell book. Also, it is the G.M.'s role to make sure that the player doesn't use the spell book as a catch-all container of important knowledge of the world. For example, if the character learns of an important code word to get past the guards he will have to face later in the game but the player didn't specifically state that his character wrote down the information, the G.M. should make a judgment call whether or not the character can go back in his spell book to find it if the player can't remember what the password was.

G.M.s, this is a great chance for role-playing that should not be overlooked. It can be played for laughs ("Did old Bob the trapper say to turn right or left at the river to get to Lazlo?") or in a much more serious manner ("You have only a few moments to find the combination you wrote down and open the safe door before the guard returns on his patrol. Hurry!") At this point, a roll under the Literacy skill could be very appropriate, even if the player remembers the information needed by his character. After all, in the real world only a few minutes might have passed for the players, while it has been hours, days, weeks or even longer for the characters in the game. These rolls should help determine if the needed information is found or not and how long it took to do so. A good roll might mean that the combination was found quickly and the safe door opened and shut again with the patrolling security guard none the wiser, or a poor roll might mean that the character couldn't find the combination in time and had to retreat before the guard caught him. If a really bad roll is made, it might even mean that the character became so frantic in his search for the information that when he realizes the guard is only a few steps around the corner he panics, leaving the spell book behind in the rush to get away. G.M.s need to be careful, though. These rolls should be done when it is logical to do so and should generally be done more to highlight role-playing than to make the character's life more difficult.

Why do magic users write spell books?

Argus, an adolescent Elf, had started his apprenticeship two days ago with Randall the Red, famed sorcerer and retired adventurer, and quickly found that it was not at all what he'd expected. So far, there had been no magical summoning of exotic creatures from alien dimensions, no spectacular shows of power or changing the fate of the world. Instead, his training had consisted of long discussions on philosophy, morality and the belief in magic. Frankly, it had been rather boring. So Argus had been very excited when his new master announced during breakfast that today after he'd finished his chores, his education would take its first big step.

"Here you are, my lad!" Randall exclaimed, coming to the kitchen table where all of their discussions so far had happened. He handed a large bundle wrapped in plain brown paper to his eager student. Ripping off the paper, Argus beheld a new, leather bound book with mystic symbols embossed on the cover. A spell book! His heart beat faster as he quickly began paging through the new book that his master had just given him. A look of confusion slowly replaced the excitement on his face. The pages were all blank!

"Uh, excuse me... sir?" Argus said, looking up, "What is this for?"

"Well, you want to become a great magician, don't you?" boomed Randall, sitting down across the table from him.

"Well, yes, but..."

"Then you have to have a good spell book!" interrupted Randall, thumping his palm on the table. "Can't make a proper mage out of you without a spell book, now can we?" He grinned at the look on his apprentice's face, then continued more softly. "Actually, it will take quite a few spell books over the course of your career, but you need just one to get started; the others will come in time," he said with the air of one talking about a commonly known subject.

"But... but sir! The pages are all blank!" Argus said in exasperation.

"Of course they're blank," Randall retorted good-naturedly. "You only just got it! You expect to fill it all up in one day?"

So what is the main advantage for a spell caster who uses a spell book versus one who does not? Simply put, a mage who makes regular use of a spell book will learn new spells more quickly, gaining two spells per every new level of experience instead of only one. In all other respects, the character follows the regular restrictions on selecting spells normal to the character class. Take Bob and Jim, for example, two first level Ley Line Walkers who have been making their way in the world using their magic (gaining Experience Points) and are now on the brink of a new spiritual awakening (reaching second level). Normally, both Bob and Jim would gain one new spell each upon achieving second level, as they become more proficient in the use of magic, have been exposed to new ideas and ways of thinking, and have devoted some of their time toward figuring out a new spell. Bob, however, has been writing in his spell books, making notes about his ongoing research – what seems to work and what doesn't – and keeping track of new thoughts and ideas that come to him. Jim, on the other hand, doesn't keep a spell book because he can't read, and instead relies on his memory to keep track of his own ongoing research. Upon reaching second level, Jim gains one new spell as is standard, but Bob gains two new spells. Why is this?

Bob knows something that most of us who have gone to school learned a long time ago: that keeping notes is a GOOD THING! Most people rarely learn something perfectly the first time they read or hear about it. Instead, they learn about it in class, then later on go back and read about it in a textbook or their notes that they took (or both). The more complex and difficult the subject, the more times one must review the information to get it committed to memory. The human mind is set up to learn by repetition (ever wonder why your math homework is so boringly repetitive?). The more times we go over something, the deeper it is engraved in our thoughts. That's why taking notes helps us to learn; we can go back and review the information in a format that we already understand. So Bob, who has been diligently keeping and reviewing notes in his spell book, learns more quickly than Jim, who relies solely on his own memory. He also doesn't have to worry about forgetting something important later on if he writes it down in his book.

Alternative Rule: The player character figures out/selects *two* new spells equal to or below his level of achievement when using a spell book. To gain this bonus, the character must have been using the spell book for the *entire* time it takes to go from one level to the next. Should the spell book be lost, stolen or destroyed before achieving the next level up, it is up to the discretion of the G.M. as to whether the character will still get the extra spell and other bonuses detailed below. Note: If the book is lost or stolen but recovered in a short period of time, the character should still receive his extra spell. G.M.s, this is a great avenue for a side adventure or even a full blown campaign since your players should definitely want to help recover the spell book of the magic user in the group. Alternately, if they come into possession or destroy an NPC's spell book, they may have to worry about a vengeful mage trying to track them down, whether they were the ones who stole his spell book or not.

Who writes spell books?

Argus sat cross-legged on his cot in his small personal chamber, chin in his hand, staring at the spell book that his master had given him and idly toying with a pen in his hand. He'd had the book for three days now and hadn't written anything in it. Randal had told him when he received it that writing in the book would help him learn spells more quickly, but he hadn't said how it would help him learn.

Argus thought about his uncle Tim, the only magician that he'd ever known before his family had moved to Lazlo because of Coalition persecution. Uncle Tim had made magic look so easy! No confusing talks about philosophy, no hours spent studying manuals and scrolls. Uncle Tim had known plenty of spells, and he didn't keep a spell book, Argus thought. He didn't even think that Uncle Tim could read. This just didn't make sense!

As if summoned by the doubting thoughts running through his mind, Argus heard his mentor knock on his chamber door. Opening the door and sticking his head in, Randall looked on his glum apprentice. "I noticed that you seemed a bit down during dinner tonight," he said in a kindly voice. "Want to talk about it?"

"Um well, I don't know, I guess..." Argus muttered, dropping his eyes back to the book on his lap. Randall entered his apprentice's chamber and stood looking at him with compassion.

"It's not like you imagined it would be, is it?" Randall asked in a quiet, penetrating voice. Startled, Argus stared up at his master. Randall grinned at the shock on his apprentice's face at hearing his doubts voiced by another. "How did I know?" he

chuckled. "Remember, I was once an apprentice too, my boy. So what's eating at you? All the talking? The reading?"

"No, sir," Argus replied, trying to recover his wits. "I expected to do a lot of listening to lectures and studying when I came here."

"Then what's the matter?" Randall asked again, softening his tone. Reassured by his teacher's kindly manner, Argus felt himself opening up.

"It's this spell book, sir," he said, glancing down at it again, then back at Randall. "I don't understand why you gave it to me, or what I'm supposed to do with it. I've never seen any sorcerer use one before, and I just can't see how it can help me. I haven't even written anything in it yet." It felt good to finally be talking to Randall about this. Argus spoke on, explaining about his uncle and how he hadn't used a spell book yet was a powerful and respected magic user nonetheless. Randall listened, nodding thoughtfully.

"So, let me see if I understand," Randall said, sitting down on the corner of Argus' cot. "You're confused by the spell book because you never saw your uncle use one when he cast a spell, is that it?" Argus nodded in agreement. "If you don't mind my asking, do you know what type of magic user your uncle is?"

The question startled Argus, and he had to think about it for a few moments before he could remember the answer. "I think my father told me once that he's considered a Mystic."

"Well, that explains it then!" Randall beamed at his student. "You see, Argus, not everyone who uses magic can benefit from using a spell book. In fact, there are very many good and respectable magicians out there who would get no use out of a spell book such as yours no matter what they did with it."

"Then who can use spell books, sir, and how do you use them?" Argus asked.

Randall smiled at the eagerness in his pupil's face. This was what he had been waiting for in his new apprentice. The true desire to learn without regard to preconceived notions was finally showing in his apprentice's eyes.

"I think we can kill two birds with one stone here, Argus," Randall said. "Open that book, young man. Your first entry is going to be a listing of those who can and cannot make use of a spell book!"

Argus quickly opened his book to the first page and grabbed up his pen. Now he was going to get somewhere!

Not all practitioners of magic will have the ability or a desire to keep a spell book. Beyond the need for literacy, there are some general restrictions on which magic users can benefit from the use of these special tomes. For example, magic users who primarily gain their mystic knowledge from intuition and gut instinct, such as the Mystic and Shaman, cannot learn new spells except by reaching new, metaphysical plateaus (new experience levels). Others, such as the Conjurer and many supernatural creatures, make use of magic as an extension of their own will and have only limited spell casting abilities. Such magic users would find conventional spell books a waste of time and/or resources, though they very well might keep a conventional journal to write down important information. Additionally, Witches and Warlocks, who largely gain their mystic knowledge from their link to supernatural forces, would have no need or desire to write their own spell books, though a Witch may gather those written by others as symbols of her might or to lure foolish adventurers to their doom.

Who, then, can make use of and get the full benefits from keeping a spell book? In general, any magic O.C.C. that allows the character to learn spells at times other than when leveling up can gain the benefits of spell books. The most obvious for Rifts characters would be the Ley Line Walker, who can learn new spells at any time, given the proper circumstances. There are many others as well, like the Shifter, Necromancer and Temporal Wizard, to name a few. All of these characters can keep spell books and enjoy all of the benefits thereof. There are also some supernatural creatures, such as most types of dragons and some types of demons and Deevils, for which spell books provide an additional avenue toward the magical powers that they so crave. Such creatures will not only write spell books of their own but will very likely covet the spell books of others and often amass huge libraries of such works.

Of especial note in the categories of who can or cannot use spell books are the Techno-Wizards of Rifts Earth (and throughout the Megaverse). These incredible magic users gain bonuses above and beyond those listed for other magic users when they keep spell books. For Techno-Wizards, keeping a spell book will add an additional +10% bonus to construction rolls for any device they are working on or creating, as long as it is not extremely alien in design or construction. The spell book also allows them to construct copies of devices that they have already invented one third faster than usual, since they can confidently move through the steps written down in the book during construction instead of having to concentrate and remember how it was put together. (Take the normal construction time and multiply by two-thirds to get the new construction time.)

Writing your own library

Randall the Red sat eating a dinner of rich cabbage stew and reviewing a letter that he was going to send to the Lazlo City Council of Learning protesting the lack of good plumbing to be found in the outskirts of the city. Suddenly, his thoughts were jarred away from the paragraph he had been mentally revising. "I'm sorry, what was it you said?" he asked Argus, who was seated across the table from him eating his own helping of the stew.

Argus had his spell book propped open in front of himself and was idly flipping through the notes he had taken on the day's lesson as he spoke with Randall. "I was just wondering about something you mentioned the other day when you gave me this," he said, looking up and using his spoon to gesture at the book. "You said that it would 'take quite a few spell books' to make me a wizard. Did you mean that I'm going to have to fill up a bunch of these notebooks before I finish being an apprentice?"

"Well, only if you want to learn quickly," Randall agreed pleasantly, taking another bite of his stew.

"But that will take forever!" protested Argus.

"Oh, not so long as you might think," Randall disagreed with a smile, "though it might take a bit longer if you keep dripping stew on your lessons like that."

So you, the player, decide that your character is going to keep a spell book to help him learn new spells. That's great, but where do you get started? First, there is the question of just what can serve as a spell book for a magic user. A spell book by its very nature is an object of magic and as such, must conform to the rules of magic. It must, for example, be made of natural materials. Just as a spell caster has difficulty casting magic if weighed down by artificially-created armor of steel or ceramic, a spell book will not be able to provide any of its many bonuses if it is made of artificial materials. In other words, no computers, video/audio recorders or any other modern devices can be used as a spell book. The spell book can be a modern notebook made using manufactured paper and binding methods or an old fashioned tome with laced spine, hard leather covers and parchment pages. Furthermore, the spell book must, indeed, be a book, with front and back covers and some type of bound spine. Scrolls, spiral bound notebooks and notepads will not do the job.

The next consideration is, how fast is your character going to fill up his spell book and thus need a second (or a third, fourth, fifth, etc.)? Short of having you, the player, write a book in the real world, try using this handy rule of thumb: each spell book can contain the notes for anywhere from one to six spells, depending on the size of the spell book and the complexity (level) of the spells therein: e.g., up to six first or second level spells per tome versus only one eighth level spell. This means that, starting out, a first level character with a blank spell book will probably not have to worry about getting a new one until he gains level three; whereas, a tenth level mage would probably need two separate spell books, one for each spell he is currently researching! This rule of thumb will mean that the G.M. and the player should work together to determine when each book is filled and a new one needs to be started.

Finally, when initially creating the character, the player and the G.M. should work out beforehand as part of the character's background history if he kept a spell book during his apprenticeship, and how many books were penned. These spell books will need to be added to the list of items the character owns. This might also mean that the character will need to figure out a place to safely store his spell books while he is away adventuring or find a way to carry them with him during his travels. (See the new T.W. inventions at the end of the article for some unique storage items!)

The lifelong value of a spell book

"Master?"

"Hmm..." said Randall, still staring into the small crystal ball he had set on his work table.

"After I finish filling up this spell book, what do I do with it?"

Turning slightly on his stool, Randall looked at his apprentice. The boy had been making good progress over the last few months and was beginning to show some real promise for the near future. Currently, Argus was sitting at another work table in the lab, making some notes in his spell book from a scroll he was studying about the wiles of demons.

"Finished with that one already?" Randall laughed, covering the crystal ball with a black velvet cloth.

Argus turned a little red around the edges of his pointed ears and mumbled, "Well, no, not yet. I was just curious, that's all."

Randall smiled. The curiosity that his apprentice constantly showed was like a breath of fresh air.

"All right then, what do you think you should do with it once you've filled the pages up completely?"

"Well, um..." Argus floundered for a moment, "it doesn't seem right to just throw it away or something like that." He struggled with it, trying to put his thoughts and feelings into some type of order. "I don't know, keep it maybe, sort of store it somewhere safe or something like that..." Argus trailed off lamely, not sure what else to say.

"Exactly!" Randall said with an intensity that surprised Argus. Leaning forward and pointing one long finger at the perplexed young man, he continued, "Keep it. Don't throw it away, don't lose it or trade it or give it to anyone else. Keep it as the starting point for your own library and add each book you write thereafter to your collection. Your spell books will be the milestones of your life, each one a record of who you were, who you are, and who you are becoming. You'll find that, as you get older, all of your learning, all of your power and purpose and sense of life, will become bound up in those books. They will become more precious than gold to you. Who knows," he said, straightening on his stool and turning back toward his table, "they might even save your life one day." With that, he took the velvet cover off of the crystal ball, again peering into its depths and completely ignoring the look of astonishment on his apprentice's face.

The value of a spell book to its author extends well beyond the moment when he has finally learned to cast that new spell he was researching. Besides acting as a record of his past thoughts and explorations, the spell book grants its author a small – but potentially life-saving – bonus for as long as it continues to exist. This is because a magic user invests a tiny sliver of his own life force into each spell book that he writes! This is an unconscious process that takes place as he sweats and toils to make the spell on the pages come to life, and is only invested once the first spell recorded in the book is completed. At the moment of his first successful casting of the spell, the mage permanently infuses one P.P.E. point into the book, which he cannot regenerate nor draw out of the book to use, and which permanently connects him to that book. (Note, only one P.P.E. point is ever invested in each individual book, no matter how many spells are actually learned using that book.) Beyond the loss of the single point of P.P.E., there is no other detrimental effect to the spell caster, but there are some subtle and profound benefits for both the author and the spell book.

First, the investiture of a small amount of his own life force into the spell book helps to boost the spell caster when his life is on the line by acting as a sort of metaphysical anchor to his world. This means that every empowered spell book the magic user pens gives him a cumulative +2% bonus toward rolls to save vs coma/death no matter how far away the books are, but only if the books are in the same dimension as the author. Yes, this does mean that clever players can gain huge bonuses to their characters' saving throws by putting only one spell in each book and penning a large number of books. This advantage is coun-terbalanced by the fact that they will have to safeguard and worry about a large number of books that will be increasingly difficult to carry around. The mages will also have to permanently invest a larger proportion of their P.P.E. into books, thus possibly limiting the amount of available energy they have to cast the spells that they're learning. **A Note to G.M.s:** If, after considering these disadvantages, your players still want to pen large numbers of spell books, let them run with it, but remember that actions have consequences. And keep in mind that, regardless of the number of spells books they are writing in, their characters can learn a maximum of only one *additional* spell per level in this manner.

Second, the author/mage can sense the general direction and the approximate distance of each of his spell books in relation to his current location. Since the books have a small portion of his energy in them they are, in effect, extensions of the mage. Thus, by leaving one or more spell books at a known location, he can always know which direction to go to return to them. He will also know the general direction to go in to find one, should it be stolen. Similarly, he will be able to tell if they are being damaged and will sense the exact moment that one is destroyed.

Third, the link between the author and the spell book is such that the author will always be able to read what he has written in the book, even if the book has been damaged to the point that it is illegible to anyone else! This means that should some or all of the pages be covered in ink, blackened by fire or even completely missing (the spell book must have at least one page left in it with the spine still intact, but front and back covers can be missing), the author will still be able to see a ghostly image of the information recorded therein, though this takes extra concentration, effectively doubling the reading time. This ability applies to anything the author of the book writes in the book at any time before or after investing it with his P.P.E., even non-research related items and journal notes. In fact, some sorcerers have been known to deliberately mutilate their own spell books after they complete them as an additional safeguard against anyone else reading them!

Finally, the bonding physically strengthens the spell book and makes it much more resistant to damage than a normal book. Double the book's S.D.C., and it only takes 1/10th damage from any non-magical attacks directed against the book itself. The book is impervious to normal wear and mild abuse (it will not become dog-eared no matter how many times it is read) and always appears to be in the same condition it was in when first endowed with its author's life force. Neither will the writing fade with time. Only extreme abuse, such as being thrown from a moving vehicle or used as a shield during combat, will damage the book enough to change its appearance. Similarly, the effects of fire are also lessened by the same amount, with the book difficult to light on fire, slow to burn and easy to extinguish. Once damaged, though, the book does not regenerate, but can be restored in the same manner as normal books as long as the damage is not too extreme. This resistance to damage lasts for the entire life of the author, but once the author dies, the imbedded P.P.E. vanishes and the spell book becomes a normal book again. Also, should the book be destroyed while the author lives, he will not regain the invested point of P.P.E.

Learning new spells using someone else's spell book

Argus stared at the half-filled page in his spell book with one crossed out arcane equation after another marching across the sheet. "I'm never going to get this figured out," he muttered to himself, ready to fling the book against the wall with frustration. He had been trying to cast a Globe of Daylight spell for several weeks now but had thus far only been able to conjure a faint shimmer that was shaped more like a dinner plate than an actual globe. Looking across the study to where Randall sat reading an old, pre-Rifts western novel, Argus gathered his courage and asked again if he could use one of Randall's spell books to learn the spell.

"No," the old mage replied without even looking up as he turned a page. Made reckless by his frustration and the callous rejection of his rather reasonable request, Argus blurted out "Why not?" just a trifle more bluntly than he might have intended.

Momentarily glancing up from his book, Randall said, "You need to learn the process of figuring out things on your own, Argus. If I let you use my spell books right from the start, you'd never learn anything more than I have already learned. That, I think, would be a disservice to us both."

Argus thought about this for a while as his master went back to reading his book, until he thought he saw a hole in the argument he could exploit. "Maybe," Argus said, "by studying your spell books I could learn from your mistakes instead of sitting here repeating them myself. Then I could devote the time that I saved toward learning new things."

Looking up from his western again, Argus thought he could see the wheels spinning in his mentor's head. That was one thing that Argus really liked about Randall, that he would always take the time to listen and think about what his apprentice said.

"Maybe you're right," Randall finally said. Carefully laying aside his book so he wouldn't lose his place, he rose and made his way to a nearby bookcase that looked quite a bit worse for wear. Muttering an incantation to release the magical safeguards on the doors of the bookcase, he bent and retrieved a large, weathered-looking, leather-bound book from the bottom shelf. Walking over to the table where Argus sat, Randall said, "Start on page 22," as he slid the book across to him. Argus eagerly opened the book to the page indicated, only to find row after neat row of writing in a language he didn't recognize. With consternation he flipped back and forth through the pages at random. The whole book was written this way!

Looking up in confusion, Argus saw Randall sit down and pick up his western again. Glancing at Argus and reading his confusion on his face, Randall grinned and said, "Oh, did I forget to mention that I write all of my spell books in a secret language of my own design?"

There are many routes that a character might take to gain mystic knowledge; keeping a spell book is just one of them. Another common way to learn magic is to learn from the spell books of others – that is, if you can gain access to them.

Arguably, the easiest way to gain access to a large number of spell books is to join a magical guild or brotherhood. Such organizations often bring together magic users who share a common area of expertise so they can share their accumulated knowledge among themselves and/or to educate rising generations. Guild libraries will often have extensive sections devoted to spell books, most penned by mages long dead. Thus, it can be very useful for a low level mage to join such a guild to expand his mystic abilities. There are downsides to membership, however. The guild will almost certainly require donations of time, talents and funds from the character to maintain his membership with them. Additionally, the character's access to any spell books with truly powerful mystic knowledge will most likely be restricted until he has proven himself worthy of the knowledge, meaning devoting a *lot* of time and effort toward advancing the goals of the guild. One must also be careful of which organization he enlists in, as the guild or brotherhood may have goals that are unsavory or downright evil, goals that are often not immediately evident to the new initiate. (For more information on magical guilds and brotherhoods, read the magic sections of the **Rifts® Ultimate Edition** or the **Palladium Fantasy RPG®** core book.)

Other ways of gaining access to the spell books of others include apprenticeships, partnerships, purchasing or finding the belongings of deceased mages, and outright theft (though this last option is likely to result in a *very* angry wizard coming in pursuit of the character and, most likely, the rest of the group). Any or all of these methods can be used and can be great avenues for new and fun adventures. G.M.s should especially take note of the many chances to weave new plot lines into existing or new campaigns.

Regardless of how one obtains access to these spell books, just getting to them does not instantly grant new spell abilities. Magic has to be learned, remember? Learning new spells from a spell book will take a character many hours of in-game time in a quiet, non-distracting environment. How long? For spells commonly known in the character's homeland, it will generally take only the standard two days per spell level if he devotes eight hours per day to that spell. On the other hand, if the spell is one that is exotic or alien to the character's background (such as learning South American Biomancy spells in North America, or Russian Living Fire spells in Africa), the learning time can be quite a bit longer as the mage struggles to internalize the new concepts and paradigms presented by the spell book. This is especially true if the book contains a Spell of Legend. At the G.M.'s discretion, use the following table for learning spells that are out of the ordinary for the character.

Spells Level 1-4: 2 days per level of the spell plus 2D4 days.

Spells Level 5-8: 2 days per level of the spell plus 2D6+1 days.

Spells Level 9-15: 2 days per level of the spell plus 1D4 weeks.

Spells of Legend: At least 30 days plus an additional 2D4 weeks (possibly longer at the discretion of the G.M.).

In all cases, having the original author present to help teach the character the new spell and answer his questions can halve the time it takes to learn the spell (G.M.'s discretion). Alternatively, the character can halve the time it takes to learn the new spell if he is willing to spend at least fourteen hours a day studying the spell (meaning no going out with his buddies to adventure or have fun, which can impact how quickly the character gains Experience Points). Yes, that does mean that the learning time for a new spell can be cut to one quarter of the norm if the character can find a mage who is willing to spend 14 hour days teaching him (heck, how do you think Tolkeen was able to teach so many of its warrior mages high level spells such as Steel Rain so quickly?). The G.M. should also take into consideration modifying the required learning time if the character has the psionic ability of Total Recall or exceptional I.Q. and M.E. scores.

Additionally, Game Masters should consider possibly rewarding magic-using characters who make special sacrifices in order to learn a particular spell more quickly. An example might be Joe the Ley Line Walker studying eighteen hours a day and skipping going out adventuring with the rest of the gang because he needs to learn that special healing spell to save little Susie's life (or stop the evil horde and save the village, etc.). In this case, the G.M. would be perfectly justified in not only cutting the character a little slack on the time it takes to learn the spell, but also might reward him with extra Experience Points for self sacrifice and possibly playing in character. And don't forget the special delight the character (and his player) will get when little Susie throws her arms around his neck and kisses his cheek and the grateful parents express their heartfelt gratitude to him. Such sacrifices have incredible potential for rich and vivid role-playing that will be remembered for years to come.

On the flip side of the coin, trying to learn a new spell from a spell book in a distracting environment (such as a swaying vehicle, noisy apartment, etc.) or when out adventuring can double the time it takes to learn a new spell; even longer depending on how much free time the character has to devote to studying and how disruptive the surrounding environment is. If the character group is making a leisurely trip with unhurried progress and plenty of down time, then there will be little if any change to the regular time it takes to learn a new spell (maybe a day or two extra, tops). On the other hand, if the group is trying to outrun an opponent or make it somewhere by a certain deadline, the learning time might be doubled or tripled even if the mage is riding in a vehicle piloted by someone else (if it's possible to learn at all, that is). Once again, G.M.s should use their heads about any time penalties and use this as a way to deepen the role-playing experience. A great way to play this could be that the players are escaping from their adversaries but can't flee at maximum speed since their mage must learn the spell that will complete their getaway. Will their pursuers catch up to them before the spell is fully learned? Play it out and have fun with it!

Protecting one's spell book

As part of his apprenticeship, one of Argus' tasks was to clean the rooms of his master's rather large home every morning. Each chamber had to be vacuumed, dusted, and put in order before he could begin his studies for the day. The only exceptions to his cleaning regimen were the laboratory, Randall's personal bedroom, and one particular bookcase crammed full of old books and scrolls that stood against the wall in the study he was now vacuuming. Argus gladly accepted the prohibitions on his entering into his mentor's lab unaccom-

panied, and he certainly understood his master's need for privacy in his own chamber, but he couldn't understand why he'd been told never to clean or even touch the old wooden bookcase in this room.

The bookcase stood alone in one corner of the library and seemed quite out of place among the other furnishings of the room. While the rest of the room was filled with comfortable (and obviously expensive) furniture and ornate bookcases and shelves, the forbidden bookcase was made of plain, unfinished wood that had faded to a gray color with age. It had a set of glass-paneled front doors that quite obviously didn't fit together properly. The bookcase and its contents also had a thick layer of dust on them, contrasting further from the rest of the room's furnishings, which were scrupulously neat. In his six months as an apprentice, Argus had only seen his master open the case once, to retrieve the spell book that Argus had been unable to read. Otherwise, it stood alone and seemingly forgotten, a weed among the roses of the otherwise tastefully adorned study.

As Argus moved beside the old bookcase, pushing the Techno-Wizard vacuum ahead of him, some of the dust that had gathered on the bookcase's door frame was blown into the air by the exhaust from the side vent of the vacuum. Argus stopped and sneezed as the dust tickled his nose, then sneezed again as more dust blew off the top of the case from the force of his first sneeze. Holding his nose to prevent himself from sneezing again, Argus made a sudden decision. He would clean the dust from off the outside of the case, maybe even wipe off the shelves themselves if he could get the doors open (there was no obvious lock, but Argus knew by now that that didn't necessarily mean that he would be able to open the doors). Shutting off the vacuum and pulling a large cleaning rag from his pocket, he took a swipe at the dust on top of the bookcase. As the rag came into contact with the bookcase, an electric spark seemed to jump through it and into his hand.

Instantly, Argus found he couldn't move! All of his muscles were frozen in place except for his suddenly wildly beating heart. Argus' panic hit a new high as he realized that he couldn't even breathe. Struggling against the compulsion holding him in place, the edges of his vision began to dim. His thoughts ran in tighter and tighter circles as he tried to remember something, anything from his studies that could help him in this situation. The blood was pounding so hard in his ears by this point that he never heard the door to the study fly open with a crash. "I'm going to die!" he thought as his world started to go dark.

As suddenly as he had been trapped by the bookcase, the magic released him. Argus collapsed to the floor, shaking and sucking in huge gulps of pure, sweet air through his wide open mouth. Above him, his master stared down at him with a mixture of concern and irritation in his eyes. "Well then, had a bit of a fright, did we?" said Randall the Red.

A spell book is a precious thing, not only to its author but also to other practitioners of the mystic arts, and even to non-magic users with enough savvy to realize just how valuable a spell book can be to the right people. Spell books represent not only hours upon hours of hard work and a tiny portion of the author's soul, but also mystic knowledge for any who may possess them. The old saying that "knowledge is power" is no idle banter when it comes to the mystic realms. With a few muttered words a trained magic user can call down lightning from a cloudless sky, animate the dead or vanish from sight. Many unscrupulous wizards with dreams of becoming great and important or adventurers looking for wealth and glory will take whatever measures they need to in order to achieve their goals, and the spell books of others are often seen as a (relatively) easy way to accomplish their aspirations. In light of this, it only stands to reason then that most magic users are very protective of their spell books. Even the most friendly and open mage will be extremely reluctant to share his spell books with another person except under the most dire of circumstances or for great personal profit. In fact, keeping their libraries safe becomes an obsession with many mages, especially those who are covetous by nature already. And if you thought an adult dragon was protective of his treasure hoard, you should see them in relation to their magic library (most dragons hide them so well that many adventurers don't even realize that they are there). Woe unto the fool who thinks to plunder the arcane library of one of these great beings.

When it comes to protecting spell books, the creativity of magic users knows no bounds. Many a mage will write his spell books using a secret or forgotten language or code of his own design to keep them from being read by others (the author must have the proper Literacy and/or Cryptography skills to do so). Other spell casters will use magic, secret compartments/rooms, and/or physical locks or barriers to keep the contents of their spell books safe. Most sorcerers, even those of a good alignment, will go to just about any lengths to protect their personal library, both the books they themselves authored and those books, both magical and mundane, that have come into their possession from others. It is not uncommon for such collections to have lethal traps and magic security systems surrounding them. Entry into the library might be magically guarded or through a hidden or trapped door. Magic wards and alarms usually will cover the bookcases and often the walls, floor and ceiling of a magician's library. Golems, mummies and monsters might patrol the room, and magical curses often follow those daring enough to try to steal a magic user's most valued treasure. The stories of those who have pilfered the libraries of great wizards and lived to tell the tale can be truly hair-raising! A magician's lair can be a really enjoyable setting for a dungeon-crawl type adventure and should be used for just that reason. G.M.s should use the alignment of the wizard who built/inhabits the lair to decide what protections are in place and just how lethal a particular lair might be. For instance, a mage with a Principled alignment probably won't have hoards of zombie and mummy protectors patrolling the halls of his mansion and guarding the door of his library.

In addition to these conventional means of protection, the growing practice of Techno-Wizardry gives a mage a few other, less well known tricks to use. Combining magic with technology, some truly amazing new security devices have been created to help safeguard magical possessions against anyone trying to steal them. For a few of these quirky, yet effective, new TW inventions, please see the end of this article.

The disadvantages of authoring and owning spell books

"Drink this," Randall told Argus, handing him a steaming cup of tea. The boy was sitting on a high stool in the kitchen, shivering under a plain brown blanket wrapped around his shoulders. He was suffering a mild case of shock, Randall thought, more from the idea of what had almost happened to him than from any real physical damage. Jerkily, Argus raised the cup and noisily drank its contents, never looking his master in the eye. The muscle relaxant that Randall had slipped into the tea while he stirred the cup started to take effect after a few moments, and the boy stopped shaking so much.

Randall admitted to himself that he felt a little guilty for not having warned Argus more rigorously about not touching that particular cabinet in the study. He knew that Argus wouldn't have died, the magic of the cabinet wasn't designed for that, but the experience would have been traumatic nonetheless.

In fact, the cabinet had been constructed to alert its owner to any unauthorized contact while simultaneously paralyzing its victims until they passed out from lack of oxygen, releasing them once they had lost consciousness. Most of his apprentices in the past had been smart enough to obey his warning about the cabinet. There were a few who had touched it, though, either by foolish accident or deliberate design, and each had suffered just as Argus was now. One such warning was usually enough to convince the foolish ones to pay greater heed to his instructions in the future. For the others... well, Randall hoped that Argus had just been foolish.

"Now, what happened?" The question, though Randall asked it softly, carried an undertone of steel with it that declared firmly to Argus that his master would accept only the truth. Argus gave a quick glance up at Randall then dropped his eyes back to the smooth gray stonework of the floor as he explained his thoughts and actions in the study. Throughout the rambling discourse, Randall didn't move, didn't say a word. Argus didn't dare look up at him, sure that when he was finished Randall would command him to gather his things and return in shame to his parents' home, never to return. When he was done, he stared at a spot on the floor and clutched the empty teacup in his hands, waiting for the blow to fall, wishing now that he had died in the study. Surely that was better than the dreadful silence that filled the kitchen.

"So you decided to dust the cabinet, even though I had warned you not to touch it?" Randall finally said, much more gently than Argus had anticipated. Argus nodded his head, still staring at the stones in the floor. He heard Randall sigh and glanced up to see a faint look of relief cross his master's face. "I believe you," Randall said, and the warm tone of his voice filled Argus with hope. Randall laid his hand on Argus' shoulder until the boy looked him in the eye. "You did something foolish," Randall said, "but it could have been worse." Pulling his apprentice off the stool, the old mage turned and walked with him back toward the study.

"Didn't you ever wonder why I keep that ratty old cabinet in the library instead of throwing it away and replacing it with something better? Or why I forbid you to ever touch it, not even to clean it?" Randall asked as they passed down the hall in the middle of his home.

"Well, yes," Argus admitted, "but I never remembered to ask you when you were around," he said, feeling about six inches tall.

The old man sighed and shook his head as they entered the study. It was time that the boy learned about the problems spell books could bring to their authors. Stopping before the worn-out-looking old cabinet, Randall the Red turned to his apprentice. "Argus, that cabinet protects all of my greatest treasures, and chief among those treasures are my spell books. They are worth more than all of the gold in the Megaverse to me and to many others, both friends and enemies." Randall saw Argus glance at him quickly. "Yes," he smiled, "even I have enemies. And were these books to fall into their hands, it would be such a disaster for me that I might never recover from it."

Walking over to a nearby sofa, Randall sat down, motioning for his apprentice to sit in the chair opposite him. When Argus had seated himself, Randall continued. "You see, Argus, a wizard's spell books are one of his greatest strengths because they fortify his spirit physically in his body as well as grant him greater magical knowledge. But like any kind of strength, they can be turned against their author if his enemies were ever to get possession of one of them. A spell book is a great thing for you to have and always keep, young man, but it must be guarded carefully and constantly, lest it be used to your undoing."

For all of the rewards a spell book brings to its author, there are some significant disadvantages that balance out the benefits. The first and probably most obvious problem, as briefly mentioned previously, is the great value of a spell book to people other than the author. The worth of a spell book to other magic casters is readily recognizable, but what about those who cannot use magic? What value does a magic book hold for a non-magic user? First, remember that a spell book may also hold non-magical secrets or knowledge that is of worth to the character or to someone who will buy the book from him. Non-magic using characters can also sell spell books to those who can use them, often for a small fortune. Thus, coming into possession of a spell book can be a real windfall for any character if he has the knowledge and bravery to turn it to his advantage. No matter how an adventurer gets a spell book, honestly or not, there is always a market that is ready to buy it, often with lots of cash to pay and few or no questions asked. Prices for a spell book will fluctuate wildly from one place to another, depending upon the views of the local community toward magic and how affluent its citizens are. Players also shouldn't overlook the possibilities for profit that even the most rabid, anti-magic societies like the New German Republic or Free Quebec present. One can find buyers for magic books even in the fortress cities of the Coalition States, though it will probably be selling it to the authorities so that they can destroy it (just make sure they don't decide to take your group into custody for having it in the first place). Thus the rewards for the intrepid character(s) willing to do what it takes to search out a spell book and get it to market are usually well worth the trouble. Ultimately, what all this means is that a character who is writing or who owns a spell book must constantly be on his guard against both his fellow magic users and mundane thieves.

A second problem with writing and collecting spell books is that as a mage begins to collect a large magical library, it be-comes increasingly difficult (and eventually impossible) to safely carry it all around with him everywhere he goes, especially if he needs to leave an area in a hurry. While the weight of an individual spell book is usually not all that cumbersome, trying to lug around an entire bookcase full of them can become very tiring, very quickly. This is one of the most important reasons why the majority of powerful magic users eventually settle down in one place: they need a place to keep all their books! Also, a big part of the decision to locate their library in a permanent residence is that it is much easier to protect a library of spell books in a single stationary area rather than having to constantly keep recasting protective magic spells and setting up new traps to keep the books safe. Thus, whether it is in an ordinary house, castle, tower or cave, most magicians who use spell books will eventually want to find a permanent place to store their ever-growing library. This does not necessarily mean that a magic user is going to give up wandering and become a homebody, however. Quite the contrary, many magic users will become even more widely traveled after setting up a suitable retreat, secure in the knowledge that their personal library and possessions are safely awaiting their return. As a side benefit, a permanent residence also often provides a safe and quiet place for the characters to study, reflect and recuperate from their journeys.

Another disadvantage of possessing a spell book is that the book itself will have a barely-perceptible magic aura around it once it has been instilled with the life fragment of its author (this happens after the first spell is completed; see above). This aura is not very powerful, but it can be sensed by anyone who has the ability to detect the presence of magic, for as long as the author of the book is still alive. **Range of detection for the book by itself** is a mere five feet (1.5 meters). However, there is an amplification effect whenever the book is being held or carried by *any* magic user. When a mage holds or carries a spell book (his own or another's), the magical aura for the book becomes ten times stronger than normal and makes the mage's natural aura more conspicuous as well. This means that the detection range for the book is increased to 50 feet (15 meters) and is added to the detection range of the mage himself. For example, a mage who is not using magic can normally be detected by a first level Psi-Stalker at a range of only 50 feet, but this would be doubled if he were carrying a spell book (5 feet x10, and added to the initial 50 foot detection range to equal 100 feet/30 m). Thankfully, this is not a cumulative penalty, so multiple spell books will not lead to ever-increasing detection ranges. Because of this greater possibility of detection, many magic users will leave their spell books behind when going on a covert mission if they can find a secure place to keep/hide them.

The last and arguably greatest liability of spell books comes into play when the author of a spell book loses possession of it to enemies who wield magical or psionic powers themselves. With the spell book in hand, the mage's enemy can now use any psionic power or cast any spell upon the author through the book that normally would take either physically touching him or having something he had owned or that had been a part of him (like blood, hair, etc). Furthermore, the victim of the attack has a -2 penalty toward any saving throws against such attacks because the effects are channeled directly into him through the magical connection he has with the spell book. Worst of all, such powers can be invoked against the author no matter how far away he is from his attacker, as long as they are both in the same dimension and the power is directed toward the author through his spell book! Truly, losing one's spell book to an adversary can be a nightmare come to life for the unfortunate victim. At this point, the author is compelled to expend whatever energy he must to recover the book or books taken from him, or flee that dimension and hope that his enemy cannot follow. In such cases, the mage must rely on his friends or cohorts to search out and recover the lost book for him. This inherent vulnerability is a major reason why *all* magicians are extremely reluctant to lend their spell books to anyone, even trusted colleagues. G.M.s, it should be kept in mind, however, that usually most thieves who are stealing the spell book for personal gain will be focused on escaping with the stolen spell book rather than inflicting damage to the owner of the book, especially if he is not aware of the theft. G.M.s should use great care if they are planning on having a major enemy to the character steal the character's spell book, as this can quickly unbalance an otherwise fun campaign.

All of these problems and shortcomings inherent to writing and owning spell books should be carefully considered by the player who wants his character to keep a spell book *before* he has the character do so. G.M.s should not only consider the player's character but also any NPC characters, good or bad, who might also make use of them. G.M.s should ask themselves not only, "Does mage so-and-so write in a spell book?" but also, "Where does he store it?" and "What sort of security does he have around it?" Players should also ask themselves these questions since a spell book might just turn out to be the Achilles' heel to an otherwise formidable foe or stalwart ally. Again, G.M.s should use their heads in applying these disadvantages to create dynamic and memorable role-playing experiences.

Using spell books in your campaign

Argus stood on the top step of Randall the Red's front porch, gazing up the street toward the edge of the city of Lazlo. His heavy backpack sat leaning against the side of the porch next to him, patiently awaiting the coming journey. It had been six years since he had first crossed through his master's front door, six wonderful years of learning and growth that had shaped him in ways he could not have imagined.

Randall emerged from the open front door, carrying what looked like two small, darkly varnished panels of wood in his hand. "Almost forgot to give you this," he said, coming up to where Argus stood. Stepping up onto the porch, Argus took the proffered gifts. Looking at them curiously, he noted the panels were loosely joined together with some type of leather binding woven through small holes that had been drilled down one side of each. Both boards had elaborate carvings etched into their faces and were inlaid with a few small gems connected by a thin gold wire that formed intricate shapes in the wood. The perfectly-matched panels were about an inch thick each and somewhat wider and longer than one of the spell books in his backpack, yet strangely felt very light. Argus swung the two panels apart, but other than the carving on their faces and the elaborately braided joint, they looked perfectly ordinary.

Looking at Randall, Argus saw the slight tightening around his teacher's eyes that always indicated suppressed mirth. "Alright, Master, I give in. What is it?" he asked, enjoying these last few moments with him.

Smiling openly now, Randall reached for the boards, saying, "Fetch out one of your spell books, boy, and I'll show you."

With a few steps, Argus moved to his backpack. Bending over, he opened it, having to dig toward the bottom, where he had stowed his three spell books both to help balance the load he would be carrying and to keep them safe. Walking back over to where Randall had seated himself on the front porch swing, he proffered the book to Randall. "Hold on to it for a moment, please," Randall said, looking down at the boards in his lap. Caressing one of the gems set in the top panel, he called upon his magic. Argus could feel the magic energy build in his master for a few moments, then flow into the strange object.

"There," Randall said, looking up and parting the two panels again. Argus looked and with a small start, saw that the bottom board, though still only an inch thick, now appeared to be the inside of a shallow wooden box. Looking to Randall, he saw his master smile. "Put the book in there," he said. Argus did so, and Randall closed the top panel like a lid for a moment. Argus felt the magic in the wood vanish. "Here," said Randall, tossing the panels gently to the young Elf. Argus caught them easily, and opened the boards to see everything returned to normal, though he could somehow still feel the presence of his spell book within them. The panels felt a little heavier too, though not nearly as much as the book by itself had weighed. True surprise showed on his face as he looked back at Randall.

It was all too much for Randall, and he started laughing with delight. Gesturing for Argus to come sit by him on the porch swing, he took a deep breath to control his mirth. When Argus had sat down, Randall took the boards from him again and showed him how, by touching one of the embedded gems and infusing it with some of his P.P.E., he could open the box to reveal the missing spell book.

"It's a Porter Box," Randall explained. "It's used to carry and keep your spell book collection safe, for a time at least." Touching each of the gems on the box one by one, he demonstrated how Argus could open up separate containers within the two panels. "It'll only hold three books maximum, but it will keep them hidden from most prying eyes," he explained. "It will also make your pack lighter and less bulky so carrying your spell books with you will be less burdensome. And it will make it harder for someone to steal your books from you if you're careful with it." Randall handed the Porter Box over to Argus, who immediately took it over to his backpack. Digging out his two other spell books, he did as Randall had instructed and soon had the other two books safely hidden. In wonder, he held the Box up in his hands. It was heavier than before, but still seemed lighter than any one of the three books by themselves. He quickly tucked the Porter Box into his backpack then walked back toward Randall, who hauled himself up out of the porch swing to meet him.

"This is a truly wonderful gift, Master. I don't know how to repay you."

Taking Argus' hand in a firm grip, Randall shook it and looked the tall, young Elf in the eye. "No need to repay me, my young apprentice. You've more than lived up to the promise I saw in you when I first agreed to take you on as a pupil." Smiling with genuine warmth, he continued, "I have no doubt that you will make a fine addition to whatever community you enter into, Argus. It has been a pleasure to know you."

"It has been an honor, Sir," Argus said.

The two wizards shared a brief, strong hug then stepped apart. With a mixture of elation and apprehension, Argus shouldered his backpack and walked down the porch steps and across the path to the street. Turning to wave one last time to Randall, he straightened to face the road ahead. He wasn't sure what his future might hold, but he knew that it would be an adventure.

No matter how you choose to include spell books in your particular campaign, they make an interesting and worthwhile addition to any game. Whether they are helping a magic using character grow in strength and casting abilities, or appear as a plot hook to get the players' juices flowing and their imaginations burning, these wonderful texts should be a part of any game that has magic in it. Use them; have fun with them. They will make your game that much more detailed and enjoyable.

New Techno-Wizard Items

The Immobilizer Cabinet

At first glance, the Immobilizer Cabinet appears to be a simple piece of furniture. Only when someone other than the owner of the cabinet touches it is its magic activated, with terrifying effect. The cabinet has two functions: **1)** It immobilizes and repels the person who is trying to gain unauthorized access to the contents of the case through a combination of the Hallucination and Fear spells. Upon touching anywhere on the cabinet, the victim must make a saving throw against ritual magic (16 or higher). Those who fail their saving throw will be suddenly paralyzed. The person believes that he is completely paralyzed, unable to even breathe, and that is the crux of this trap. This is, in fact, a magical hallucination brought on by the cabinet, a compulsion so strong that the person will unconsciously hold his breath, eventually passing out from lack of oxygen and collapsing to the ground. Most characters will wake up on their own within 1D4 minutes after collapsing, and this is where the secondary effects of the magic kick in. Upon waking, the victim must make a saving throw versus insanity, with any applicable bonuses, by rolling an 18 or higher. A successful saving throw means the character suffers no further effects from his ordeal. A failed saving throw means that the victim suffers from a phobia of the cabinet, compelling him to flee from where the cabinet is and not return for a minimum of 3D6 days. Even after this time, he will not want to go near the cabinet and must force himself to even enter the same room it is in. This effect will wear off within a few weeks. Those who do successfully save against magic will also suffer from the hallucination of being paralyzed but will be able to wrench themselves free of the cabinet before they pass out and do not need to roll a saving throw versus insanity. It should be noted that anyone touching the afflicted character after he first touches the cabinet but before he collapses will also need to roll a successful saving throw versus magic or become subject to the same effects as the first victim. Only the owner may safely open the cabinet or release a victim from the magical effects it inflicts before they run their full course. **2)** The second function of the cabinet is to alert the owner to any unauthorized contact using the Mystic Alarm spell. Thus, the owner will know if the cabinet has been disturbed, even if he is in another dimension, and will probably rush home to make sure it and its contents are safe.

Device Level: Five.

P.P.E. Construction Cost: 1740.

Spell Chains Needed: Function **1)** Primary Spell: Hallucination (30). Secondary Spells: Paralysis: Lesser (5), Fear (5), Energize Spell (12+), Negate Magic (30). Function **2)** Primary Spell: Mystic Alarm (5), no Secondary Spells needed.

Physical Requirements: A regular sapphire worth 40,000 credits, an amethyst worth 1,000 credits, a red zircon worth 5,000 credits, a yellow zircon worth 750 credits, a lapis lazuli worth 12,500 credits, and a malachite worth 6,250 credits, plus a wooden cabinet/bookcase with doors (doors may or may not have glass windows in them).

Duration of Charge: Indefinite until activated, can be activated twice before needing to be recharged.

To Recharge: 87 P.P.E. or 174 I.S.P.

Construction Time: Approximately 6 months for a plain cabinet, up to a year or more for a really fancy looking cabinet.

Black Market Cost: 152,500 credits plus the cost of the cabinet (minimum 200 credits up to 10,000+ for a really fancy one).

Porter Box

The Porter Box appears to be two wooden panels, usually about 13-15 inches (33-38 cm) long, 10–12 inches (25-30 cm) wide, and one inch (2.5 cm) thick each, laced together along one edge with leather made from the hide of some supernatural monster. Carvings, jewels and gold inlays create strange and beautiful designs on the outer faces of the wood panels. Those unfamiliar with these extremely rare TW items often mistake them for pieces of artwork, not items of magic. When the panels are closed together, the owner can charge them with the appropriate amount of P.P.E., creating a dimensional pocket in the bottom board that appears to be the inside of a wooden box about 4-5 inches (10-13 cm) deep. The owner can then place a spell book or any writing materials in this compartment – loose papers, notebooks, pens and pencils, etc. (**Note:** The orientation of the magic is such that attempting to place anything other than writing materials in the box will immediately cancel the magic.) Once the writing materials are placed in the box and the lid is closed, the compartment vanishes, returning the panels to their normal appearance and effectively hiding the items: if nothing is placed into the compartment before the lid is closed, the magic is cancelled. The Porter Box can maintain a maximum of three separate boxes/compartments at the same time. The items concealed in the compartments are undetectable by almost any means: the box suppresses the magical aura of any items placed within it and does not radiate magic itself unless opened to store or retrieve an item. Even the weight of the stored items is hidden, with the Porter Box weighing only a few ounces more when it is fully loaded than when it is empty. Only those who can see/detect dimensional anomalies will know that there is something strange about the Porter Box, and even they won't be able to access the contents without investing the P.P.E. needed to open it. When the owner wants to retrieve an item, he simply concentrates on the desired compartment, invests one P.P.E. point into the Porter Box, then opens the boards and retrieves the desired object(s). If all of the items from a compartment are removed, that compartment vanishes, requiring a new investment of P.P.E. to create it again when next needed. Note: A psionic Object Read will reveal the true nature and a complete listing of the contents of the Box to the psychic.

Device Level: Ten.

P.P.E. Creation Cost: 5,800.

Spell Chain Needed: Primary Spell: Dimensional Pocket (140). Secondary Spell: Featherlight (10).

Physical Requirements: A rose quartz worth 750 credits, a malachite worth 12,500 credits, and a diamond or emerald worth at least 50,000 credits, plus two hardwood boards (usually elaborately cut/carved on one face of each), a two foot (0.6 m) length of soft leather cord and about 4 feet (1.2 m) of either gold or silver wire.

Duration of Charge: Each compartment will hold its contents indefinitely.

To Recharge: 150 P.P.E. to create a new compartment, 1 P.P.E. to open an already existing compartment; I.S.P. cannot be used with this device.

Construction Time: 3000 hours, or about 4 months.

Black Market Cost: Minimum of 375,000 credits, will often sell for 4-5 times that amount.

Circus! Circus!

A Short Story for Rifts®

By Jason Marker

"Ladies and gentlemen! Step right this way and experience the greatest exhibition of anatomical oddities this side of the Rio Grande! Explore the mysteries of Mother Nature and stand in awe of some of her strangest creations! You've heard of the Bearded Lady? Forget her! Look on in wonder as Zoltana the Snake Woman charms the deadliest of serpents! The Illustrated Man? Blaine is the King of the ancient and mysterious art of body modification! Next to him, the Illustrated Man is drawn at best. Zip the Geek? Merely an abnormality compared to Marn, who will eat a live Ostrosaurus before your very eyes! And let us not forget The Mantis! A creature so strange and frightening that you will have to sign a waiver releasing Doc Monaco's Flying Circus and Traveling Show of Wonders from any and all responsibility for injuries suffered from fainting, seizures or heart attacks!"

Lydia snorted, peeled off a piece of sugar-sprinkled fried dough and popped it into her mouth. She was on the tall side and lithesome. Tomboyish in a way that people attributed to her having been raised by Dwarves. The late July sun shone in her dark red hair pulled up in a ponytail, and glinted at the corners of her cat eye sunglasses. She wore a white tank top with a red and blue nautical star printed on it that exposed the tattoos on her biceps and the light dusting of freckles across her shoulders. Her dark blue jeans were cuffed to mid-calf, and she was sporting black and white saddle shoes. A length of chain looped from her broad leather belt to her back pocket and jingled slightly when she walked.

Lydia was Atchinson's resident Techno-Wizard. Raised in the mountains of Colorado in a town called Iron Springs, Lydia had grown up under the tutelage of a crusty, old, Dwarven Techno-Wizard named Willen Steadfast. He had found the infant human beneath the floorboards of a shack in a nameless, burned out village somewhere in the Baronies. He took her home, gave her a name, and raised her as his daughter. She took to Techno-Wizarding like a duck to water, and learned the craft along with civil engineering at the little school the Dwarves had up there. She had come to Atchinson after she graduated, sent by her adopted father, who was a friend of Widow Tolliver, one of Atchinson's oldest and most revered residents. She fell in with Gideon and his crew and had been there ever since.

"Whaddaya think, babe?" she said to her companion around a mouthful of fried dough, eyes still fixed on the barker. "You want to explore the mysteries of Mother Nature?"

Alexander shrugged and his injection harness creaked as it settled around him. Alexander was a Juicer, and a damn good driver. He was in his mid-twenties and stood over six feet tall, with ropy muscles defining his spare frame. He wore his sandy hair in a sharp flattop and wore a gray, sort-sleeved work shirt to hide the harness that was the mark of his sacrifice. He hadn't been a Juicer long, two years at the outside, and no one in Atchinson knew where he had come from. He just drifted into town one day and collapsed on the doorstep of Widow Tolliver's clinic. He was delirious with sunstroke and almost flat out of his drugs. The Widow nursed him back to health and he volunteered to work off his debt at the Tolliver Ranch as soon as he was able.

For six months now, he'd worked as a cowboy on the ranch. His quiet competence and ability to work long, hard hours with no complaints earned him the grudging respect of the professional cowpunchers at the ranch, who saw anyone who wasn't born in a saddle as a worthless tin-horn, soft as kid leather. He had turned down numerous offers by the Widow to get him on a detox program, and gently rebuffed any and all inquiries into his past. Lydia immediately fell for him, with his rugged handsomeness and his quiet and slightly mysterious demeanor, and she tackled him the way she would any thorny engineering project; with rock-hard, Dwarven stubbornness.

Now here they were on a clear, hot Saturday afternoon in late July, surrounded by the smell of sawdust and popcorn and excited livestock. They watched the barker rant and holler, his handlebar moustache bristling and his Adam's apple bobbing in his throat like a monkey on a stick.

Alexander flashed one of his rare smiles and said, "Sure, let's see what they've got."

Lydia snaked her arm through his and they walked up to the podium. The barker had reached a crescendo of frenzied, red-faced shouting as they approached.

"Ho there! Barker!" called Lydia as they reached the foot of his raised podium.

"What can I do for you young lady?" replied the barker as he leaned over to get a look at them.

"Two of your finest freak show tickets for me and my partner," she replied, hooking a thumb in Alexander's direction.

"Freak show? Young lady, you insult me! These gentle folks are certainly not freaks, but perfect examples of nature's boundless mysteries!" Lydia rolled her eyes behind her shades and smirked.

"Right, well, how much for two tickets?"

"Four bits each."

"You take Empire scrip?" she asked.

"Certainly! All currencies are welcome here!"

"Right" Lydia drawled as she fished two of the thick, steel Empire Dollars from her hip pocket. "Here you are, good man," she said as she slapped the coins into the barker's sweaty palm. He inspected them for a moment, then made them vanish into his waistcoat. He stepped off of his platform and led them to the entrance, pulled back the tent flap with a flourish and bowed to Lydia as she passed. Lydia laughed and dropped him a half curtsey and Alexander just shook his head in bemusement as they passed into the freak show.

The space defined by the tent was a rough oval, with empty space in the center and the "exhibits" arranged around the perimeter. The entrance was in the center of one of the longer walls, and there was a shadowed doorway directly opposite. It was hot inside and lit dimly by strands of naked, low watt bulbs. Each exhibit was on a dais behind a short wall of timbers and lit with colored floods. Hay bales were scattered here and there on the scrubby ground for any patrons who might want to cool their heels. The air was thick and smelled of canvas, dust and unwashed flesh. Lydia pulled off her shades and hung them from the neckline of her shirt.

"Well, this certainly is festive," she said to Alexander as they took it all in. Townspeople from Atchinson, Arlen and Big Sandy milled about and took in the grandeur of Doc Monaco's freaks.

"Oh! Look at this!" Lydia squealed.

She grabbed Alexander by the elbow and dragged him over to where a thin, dark-eyed young girl in a rubber medusa wig and a drafty costume made a half-hearted attempt to charm some elderly snakes.

"Zoltana the Snake Woman," Lydia read aloud.

She watched as the young girl wrestled a big python onto her bare shoulders, where it hung listlessly as she danced to tinny music from a speaker at the foot of her dais. As she moved, not ungracefully, Lydia noticed, a few scales flaked off the big snake. A crowd had gathered when the song started and Lydia leaned close to Alexander and whispered out of the corner of her mouth.

"Is that thing even alive?"

"It may be, just," said Alexander as a few more scales flaked off.

Lydia felt a pang of sympathy for the girl as she went through her motions with this huge, half-dead snake draped over her narrow shoulders.

"She's gonna catch her death of cold dressed like that," Lydia said, and shook her head. "Let's go see what else they've got."

They wandered around the circle a bit until they came to a tall, lanky man in greasy animal hides chasing something around his fenced-in platform.

"Marn," Lydia read. "Watch him eat a live Ostrosaurus!"

Lydia burst into laughter despite herself. The man on the dais stopped to glare down at her and the animal he was chasing turned and lunged at him, burying its sharp beak in his foot. He howled in pain and started after his small quarry, and it sped off in a flurry of squawks and dark green feathers.

"It's a chicken!" she sputtered. "They've gone and painted a chicken green! Now, that's just sad."

Alexander nodded in agreement.

"It's not even a very good costume," he said, as they left the man to his chase and wandered to the next exhibit.

"Well, it's not a very good freak show either, is it?" she said.

"I'm thinking we wasted our money," Alexander mused.

"Nah," Lydia drawled. "Think of it as a learning experience."

"How's that?"

"Two Empire Dollars is a small price to pay for a lesson in snake-oil sales."

Alexander snorted and they came to the next attraction. Lydia whistled and uttered a low, "Wow."

Standing alone on the dais was a tall, powerfully built man. He was bald and olive-skinned. He wore long moustaches and had a chin you could crack nuts on. He had a look of concentration on his broad, solemn features as he stood there under the colored lights and flexed his muscles. His only attire was a short pair of cut-off dungarees.

"Blaine," read Lydia quietly, almost reverently. "The Tattooed Man."

From collar bone to ankles, Blaine was covered in a dense mass of tattoos picked out in vivid color and detail. Serpents, spiders and birds, great, wild cats and creatures out of legend chased one another over a complex lattice of black knot-work. He struck a pose, his muscles rippled and his tattoos seemed to writhe about him as if they were alive. Here a monster with the body of a lion and the wings and head of an eagle stooped to grasp some sort of winged serpent in its powerful talons. There a huge, gray spider spun a web and trapped a brilliant bottle-green dragonfly. Lydia felt the fine hairs on the nape of her neck stand up as Blaine struck another pose and his tattoos seemed to shift into a better position.

"Wow," Lydia said again.

"You said that already," remarked Alexander.

"I know. I just felt it needed repeating."

Blaine smiled just slightly and turned his back to them. He flexed his broad shoulders and the phoenix that was inked across them seemed to leap out at them.

"I wonder if Sam's seen this guy," said Lydia, thinking of one of the owners of Body Armor Tattoos in Atchinson.

"Probably," said Alexander, taking her arm. "Come on, let's go."

Lydia hesitated and Alexander gently tugged her away.

"Come on, you're drooling."

Lydia turned a shocked look on Alexander. He was grinning slightly.

"I am not! It's just... well..." Lydia stammered. Alexander's grin flummoxed her and she blushed.

"He's got the nicest tattoos I've ever seen," she said.

"Right," Alexander said slowly.

"Hey! Let's go see what's in there!" said Lydia, deftly changing the subject.

They walked over to where a shadowed doorway seemed to lead into another chamber. A hand-lettered sign hung above the door. It read, "The Mantis!" in dripping capitals. A very small, bald man in a white linen suit stood guarding the door with a clipboard. As they approached, he held out one small, stubby-fingered hand.

"Hang on there, Red," he said in a high-pitched voice. "You and Too Tall there gotta sign the waiver if you wanna see The Mantis."

"The waiver?" asked Lydia brightly.

"This waiver here says that if you have a heart attack or stroke out or what have you when you see The Mantis, that you can't hold Doc Monaco's Flying Circus and Traveling Carnival of Wonders responsible. It also says you can't send any friends or family after us either."

He held out the clipboard to Lydia and she took it. She unhooked a pen from beneath the clip and read down through the misspelled disclaimer. She signed it and passed it to Alexander.

"So The Mantis is that scary, huh?" asked Alexander as he read the disclaimer. "Get a lotta heart attacks, do you?"

The little man put his hands in his pockets and rocked back on his heels.

"Could be, could be," he said as Alexander scratched his name on the disclaimer.

"This place is all kinds of dangerous, baby," said Lydia. "I near to laughed myself to death a couple of times."

The midget shot Lydia a sideways glance and took the clipboard from Alexander. "Everybody's a critic," he said as he looked at their signatures. Satisfied, he pulled the curtain away from the dark doorway and motioned them through.

"Come on in, the show's about to start."

Lydia and Alexander shuffled into the darkened room and the midget let the curtain fall heavily behind them. The room was about twenty feet on a side and maybe fifteen feet tall. The only light came from a single flood nailed to the central post. It cast a pool of yellow light over something large and square under a dusty, black tarp. There were some rickety metal bleachers erected opposite the tarp and another door that presumably led back out into the carnival. There was a low murmur from the crowd and Lydia could hear the squeals and bells and alarms from the midway. The bleachers were pretty full, but Lydia and Alexander found a spot at the end of the front row to squeeze in. Lydia squeezed Alexander's leg as they settled in on the hard bleachers.

"Ready to be scared *to death*?" she whispered.

Alexander muttered, "Yep," as the midget in the linen suit stepped into the pool of light. He held up his hands, as if in supplication.

"Ladies and gentlemen!" he called in his nasal falsetto. "What you are about to experience cannot be described! It must be seen to be believed! A creature so dreadful, so frightening, that it calls into question the logic of nature itself. If there are children in the audience, please cover their eyes."

Lydia rolled her eyes at this little bit of melodrama, but sat transfixed, eyes wide in anticipation.

"Ladies and gentlemen. I give you, The Mantis!"

With this the midget grabbed two fistfuls of tarp and gave a tremendous tug. The tarp came away with the sound of canvas on steel to reveal something collapsed in a heap at the bottom of a huge, stout looking cage about ten feet on a side and maybe ten feet tall. The bars were unevenly spaced and poorly welded. Lydia could see that it had been cobbled together from pieces of scrap. She craned her neck to make out the thing on the floor, but couldn't tell what it was. A murmur passed through the crowd and the midget hissed, "Come on you, get up!"

He produced a thin steel rod about two feet long from inside his coat. With a flick of his wrist he extended it about six feet and thrust it into the cage against the creature. There was a small spitting sound and a little flash and the thing in the cage jerked. Lydia could smell the bright smell of an electrical discharge.

There was a low moan like the grinding of gears, and The Mantis began to uncoil itself and twitch and stagger to a crouch. It was big, Lydia guessed that if it stood upright it would be at least twelve feet tall. It sat on its haunches there in the cage, swaying slightly. It looked for all the world like a monstrous, humanoid praying mantis. It was obviously mechanical, Lydia could see that from where she sat.

"It's a robot," she whispered to Alexander, "and an ugly one at that."

Someone shushed her and Lydia turned and made a face in the direction of the sound. The Mantis was covered in scarred metal plates, painted a dull grey and light green with yellow highlights. Its bug-like head slouched between its broad shoulders and swayed back and forth, the bulbous eyes throwing back the glare of the floodlight. Two wicked looking, serrated blades were flipped back along the bulging forearms that lay in the dust to either side of the massive, clawed feet. Its talons dug holes in the hard dirt of the cage floor. There was a gasp from the crowd and the emcee held his hands out again.

"Please, Ladies and Gentlemen, don't panic," he said in a hoarse stage whisper. "Do not make any sudden moves. The Mantis is deceptively fast."

At the sound of the midget's voice, The Mantis turned its head, long antennae rattling. The midget continued around to the front of the cage, still talking. The Mantis followed his movements and the crowd held its collective breath. Suddenly, with a bellow like an angry bear down a well, The Mantis lurched to its feet and threw itself against the bars of its cage.

There was a loud clang and the bars rattled as they took the weight of the huge robot. The emcee jumped a foot straight in the air, the crowd gasped and a woman in the crowd screamed. A huge, twitching metal hand lashed out from the cage and wrapped spindly fingers around the midget. He squealed and hollered for help as the grip tightened. Alexander was half out of his seat when Lydia grabbed his back pocket and pulled him back.

"Wait a minute!" she hissed as he sat back down. "You'll ruin the show."

Suddenly, bright daylight poured in and two burly carnies with long poles rushed through the tent flap from outside. They ran to the cage as The Mantis attempted to pull the screaming, thrashing midget through the bars and set upon the thing with their rods. Every time they made contact there was a blue flash and the smell of ozone. Eventually, The Mantis collapsed with a grinding moan, one hand still tightly wrapped around the emcee. The midget struggled to regain his composure as the carnies pried the thin metal fingers from his waist.

"Okay, folks!" shouted the midget in a shaky voice. "Show's over! Thanks for coming to see The Mantis. Please exit to your right." The crowd hesitated as they collected their wits.

"Please, ladies and gentlemen, before he wakes up!" implored the midget. The crowd began to move and was herded out by the scowling carnies. Lydia, who had watched the whole thing with equal parts disbelief and amusement, followed Alexander from the bleachers, and when she was sure no one was looking, sidled up to the cage. Her curiosity was getting the best of her and she wanted to see how it was done. She crouched over the big metal hand lying there in the dust. She examined it for a moment then placed her hand on its cool, metal surface.

There was a spinning sensation and time seemed to slow down. She rocked back on her heels but kept her hand on the robot. In her mind's eye a vision formed. She saw huge, saw-toothed mountains. She saw a great, windswept plain. She saw a dark forest full of lush, green evergreens wreathed in wood smoke. There was a sound in her ears like the howling of the wind and the crashing of icy waves on a rocky seashore. A deep voice, heavy with pain and an accent she couldn't place, whispered in her ear.

"Help me," it said.

"Here, get away from there!" said another voice, and rough hands grabbed Lydia and hauled her to her feet. A wave of vertigo hit her as she snapped out of her reverie. The face of one of the carnies swam into focus inches from hers.

"Come on, lady. Everybody out."

The carnie gave her a shove and she stumbled, squinting and dizzy, out into the midway.

* * *

After stumbling out into the sun after her vision, Lydia shook off the remains of her vertigo and tried to describe to Alexander what she had seen. He listened patiently and silently as she described the landscapes and the voice. He took it all in with a bit of skepticism, but gave her the benefit of the doubt. He had known her long enough to see that she was really upset, and he knew all he could do at this point was listen.

They wandered through the midway and Alexander tried to steer her away from the subject. Lydia was willing, but just couldn't get back into the spirit of the carnival. Not even a stomach-churning spin on the Tilt-a-Whirl could lighten her up. Now totally engrossed in her own thoughts, she decided she needed to go back to the garage to think some things over.

Later, in Lydia's personal bay at Lone Star Customs, Atchinson's hot-rod wrench house, Lydia was going through the motions of rebuilding her carburetor while her mind raced. She always thought better while tinkering, so she spent a lot of time

with tools in her hands. She pulled the intake boots off the carb and began removing the float bowl. Alexander squatted on a low mechanic's stool opposite Lydia with the bike between them, and took a hit from the orange soda-pop he had grabbed from the old refrigerator in the office. The sun was setting and ruddy light was pouring in the big doorway and tinting everything a deep orange.

"I don't care what you think, Alexander," said Lydia as she crouched beside her bike, bits of carburetor spread on the floor of the garage like an expensive puzzle. "I know what I saw."

"I'm not saying you didn't see it. I just don't think you're thinking this through, is all."

"What's there to think through?" asked Lydia.

She pried the float bowl off and swabbed the dregs of gasoline out with a greasy rag. She pulled the bowl gasket out, tossed it aside and with a plop, dropped the carb and the lightly varnished float bowl into the pan of carb cleaner that sat beside her.

"I know that look, Lydia. That's your 'I've got an idea that's gonna get us in trouble' look, isn't it?"

Lydia fished the carb from the caustic cleaner and began blowing compressed air through all the little passages and needles. The compressor clattered to life as the pressure dropped.

"Maybe," she said, eyes fixed on her work.

"You *are* crazy," growled Alexander, tipping the neck of his bottle in her direction.

Lydia made an exasperated sound and leaned over the saddle of her bike toward Alexander. She propped her elbows on the seat and draped her arms over the other side, the carb dripping cleaner on the concrete floor.

"I've got to do something, Alexander. He asked for my help."

Alexander rolled his eyes at her.

"You don't even know who he is. You don't even know *what* he is, for that matter," he argued in an even tone.

"I know what he is," she muttered, and blasted a particularly stubborn clog from one of the carb passages.

"What in the hell are y'all arguing about over there?" came a voice from the other side of the garage.

Maggie O'Shea, "Mayday" to her friends, was the owner-operator of Lone Star Customs. A locally celebrated motorcycle flat-track racer like her daddy before her, Maggie ran the garage to supplement her income in the off-season. Through a combination of mechanical talent, shrewd business sense and an uncanny ability to spot a good employee no matter what they looked like, Maggie had turned Lone Star from a small shop to one of the best little wrench houses in a hundred miles. She walked across the garage, the heels of her motorcycle boots ringing on the concrete. She was about five and a half feet tall, petite and solidly muscled. She had a mass of black, spiky hair and a heart-shaped face that wore a constant smirk. She wore a gray gas station shirt with her name embroidered above one pocket and the Lone Star Customs logo, a white star with a red outline and two crossed wrenches beneath it, above the other.

"Hey, Mag," Lydia greeted her friend and went back to fiddling with the carb.

"Lydia's got it in her head to spring one of the freaks from the carnival." Alexander said, and then took another hit from his soda bottle.

"Ooo, which one?" Maggie asked as she leaned against a pole and stuck her hands in her pockets. "I don't suppose it's that tattooed man, is it? Sammy went down there yesterday and saw him. Said he was my type."

"The breathing type?" asked Lydia from the other side of the bike and got a chuckle from Maggie.

"No," said Alexander. "She's got it in her head to spring The Mantis."

Maggie's eyes widened.

"What, you mean that great big, green robot they keep under the tarp? I heard it attacked some midget today and almost ate him in front of an audience."

"Well, not exactly..." started Alexander.

"He's not a robot, he's a cyborg," interrupted Lydia.

"Here we go again..." muttered Alexander.

"How do you know he's a 'can, Lydia?" asked Maggie.

Lydia stood up from her crouch, took a rag from her back pocket and began to wipe her hands.

"Well, you know how I can sorta talk to machines, right? We were at the show this afternoon where he attacked the midget. I thought it was all a big gag, so as we were being herded out I snuck over so I could see how it was done. You know, was it remote controlled or some kind of neural programming? Well, I grabbed its hand and bang! It hit me!" Maggie's ears perked up. She stood away from the pole and said, "What hit you?"

"A vision," said Lydia. "First it was mountains, then some prairie, then a big old forest like we have back in the Baronies. There was a sound like a strong wind, then waves. Then he said to me, "help me," in this real thick accent. I kinda got the idea he was in a lot of pain, and he was some sort of captive."

"He told you all this?"

"Well, no. It's more a gut feeling."

"What about the visions?" asked Maggie. "What do you think they were all about?"

"I think he was showing me where he was from."

"Hmmm..." mused Maggie. She began to pace. She clicked her teeth with her fingernail as she considered the story. Alexander looked from one woman to another and knew, even before Maggie spoke, that he was out-voted.

"It probably wouldn't do any harm to go and talk to this 'can," she said slowly.

"You're not helping me out here, Maggie," said Alexander.

"That's what I've been trying to tell *him* this whole time," Lydia said, pointing an accusing screwdriver in Alexander's direction.

Alexander sighed and stood up.

"Fine, we'll go. Happy? I'm just sayin' I don't think it's a good idea sticking our noses where they don't belong."

"Duly noted," Lydia said, and flashed Alexander a bright smile.

* * *

By midnight, the carnival had closed for the night. The last of the townsfolk had left, the clatter and wheeze of rickety carnival rides had quieted, the flashing lights and neon had gone dark, and an eerie calm had settled over the compound. The grounds were lit poorly by floodlights scattered here and there, but they only succeeded in making more shadows. The occasional carnie or performer flitted through the shadows on late-night business, and guards patrolled with antique laser rifles slung over their shoulders. In the quiet dark of the shuttered carnival, two figures crept in and out of the shadows between the tents and held a heated, whispered argument.

"We should have gone to the sheriff," hissed Alexander.

"There wasn't time," replied Lydia, as she crept between two tents and crouched in a shadow to peer out across a wide pathway to the freak show tent. Alexander crept up behind her and stopped.

"We should have talked to Gideon about it."

"We don't need Gideon's permission for every little thing we do. Besides, he would have tried to talk me out of it."

"*I* tried to talk you out of it!" Lydia turned to grin at Alexander.

"Yeah, but he might have actually done it." Alexander stared hard at her for a moment and then shook his head and sighed.

"You're lucky I like you so much," Alexander muttered. Lydia nodded, patted his cheek and said, "yep," and turned to scan the courtyard.

Lydia was dressed for the dark in black mechanic's coveralls with flat black ceramic plates at the shoulders, elbows and knees, and heavy black boots. Her fiery hair was pulled back and tucked into a black bandana, and she wore black mechanic's gloves. She still had her cat eye sunglasses on even in the dark. A heavy tool belt was slung around her hips and was remarkable for the fact that all of the assorted tools and apparatus that hung on it made no noise when she moved. Lashed to her right thigh was a holster carrying a stubby pistol with a massive barrel and a star sapphire winking from the butt. It was also one of her assorted toys. She called it the 'scaregun,' and this was the first time she'd worn it out anywhere. The last bit of kit she had brought along was her custom toolbox, which held more and weighed less than it should have. Alexander was dressed for night work as well, in a flat black set of CS riot armor over a black pilot's jumpsuit and a set of multi-optic goggles strapped to his head. He had his big NG-45 drawn and was covering Lydia's back as she scanned the dusty walkway with its shuttered food stalls.

"Anybody home?" whispered Alexander. Lydia reached up and touched one of the rhinestones on the sunglasses and Alexander felt the fine hairs on his arms and neck stand up.

"Nope. Looks clear to me. You ready, Freddie?" Alexander squeezed Lydia's shoulder and they scooted out of their shadow and crossed to another halfway along the side of the freak show tent. With Alexander keeping watch, Lydia pulled a small Vibro-Blade from her boot and drew it through the heavy canvas of the tent like it was rotten silk. She pulled aside a flap of canvas and peered into the dark tent. She adjusted her shades and the inside of the tent swam into sight in grainy green detail. She could see the cage with its dusty tarp thrown over it.

"Okay," she whispered. "Let's do it." Alexander nodded and Lydia slipped into the tent. Alexander scanned the walkway and slipped in behind her.

Lydia crossed the floor of the tent in a crouch and knelt at the cage. She grabbed a handful of tarp and lifted it so she could just make out the Mantis crouched there in the corner. She looked back at Alexander and saw him crouched where they had cut their way in. She flashed him a thumbs up and he returned it. With that she took a deep breath, hoped she was as smart as she thought she was, and slid her toolbox into the cage and followed it. The canvas fell down behind her with a whisper.

This close, in the confines of the cage, the Mantis looked huge, much bigger than she remembered. She crouched there for a moment and studied it. It was covered in dings and scars and marks from energy blasts. The wicked, serrated blades on its forearms looked able to cut an armored man in half with one sweep. She crept closer, then let out a startled "eep!" as the massive head suddenly swung toward her. The antennae rattled to a stop then began to move about as if searching for something, and the slit-like eyes sputtered to life and lit the inside of the tent in a ghastly green. Lydia sat down hard and scooted away until she came to the cage wall. The Mantis uncurled slowly with a sound of servos and hydraulics and reached a scarred and twitching hand toward Lydia. The only thing she could think was how her father had been right about her outsmarting herself one day.

* * *

Alexander let the flap of canvas fall as he ducked back into the little alley defined by the tents, and scanned the shadows around him. He *knew* that this was a bad idea, now he just had to make sure they got out of it alive. As he considered all of the obvious negative outcomes of their little excursion, he heard a sound that stood all of his hairs on end. There was a low, ascending growl, the sound of a body hitting the ground, and a sickening tearing and gurgling. Alexander turned toward the sound in time to see a long, four-legged shape lope past the end of the alley where he hid, followed by a huge man with a rifle. He brought his pistol up and crept down the alley, stepping gingerly over tent poles and support ropes. At the mouth of the alley lay a guard flat on his back in a growing pool of his own blood. He had been horribly mauled and his old rifle was missing. As Alexander crouched to look at the guard's wounds there was a startled shout and another growl away on his left. As he straightened to back into the shadows, something hard poked him between the shoulder blades.

"Hold it right there, mister," whispered a voice. Alexander stiffened and his assailant poked him again and whispered, "Hands up, you. Drop that pistol."

In the blink of an eye Alexander's Bio-Comp kicked in and he went into overdrive. He dropped his pistol, spun, snatched the rifle from his assailant and knocked her down with a backhand to the mouth. He drew the rifle to his shoulder and sighted down the barrel at the young woman lying in the dust at his feet. As he thumbed the safety off and the rifle cycled up to ready, a small and angry crowd of people rounded the far corner of the tent and came right for him.

* * *

"Who are you?" asked Lydia. The Mantis had lurched toward her and carefully, almost tenderly, brushed the tips of its spindly fingers across her cheek. She reached up and grabbed the cold wrist, and dove head first into a waking dream of steel, gears and circuit patterns. In a moment, she knew everything about this massive machine. Every inch of wire, every bolt and washer, every hydraulic line spooled out before her and she knew them intimately like the lines of her palm. She knew what he was then, and she knew that he was in terrible pain. Now they sat in the cold green glow of The Mantis' eyes, her face cupped in his deadly hand and Lydia hanging on to the scarred wrist as if her life depended on it.

"My name... is Yuri Yevgenovich Belanov," said the thick and labored voice in her head. "Please... help me."

Wide eyed, Lydia whispered to him, "I'm Lydia, Yuri. I'm here to help." Yuri nodded, making his antennae clatter together and seemed to sigh in relief. Lydia came back from her vision and let go of Yuri's wrist. He pulled his hand back with a shuddering jerk and Lydia stood.

"I need you to lie flat so I can get under your hood, Yuri." The cyborg complied as well as he could and stretched out prone before Lydia. She clambered onto his back and inspected the neural interface access cover below the armored collar that protected the cyborg's neck. The cover was a foot long and eight inches high, and matched the contours of the metal shoulders. Its edges were bent and mangled as if it had been pried out with a crowbar, and three of the four latches had been wrenched out, replaced with machine screws with stripped heads. Lydia pulled a small drill from her belt, concentrated a bit as she pumped some of her mystical energy into it, and it whirred to life. She drilled the heads of the machine screws out, snapped a screw extractor onto the drill, and backed out the stripped screws. Then she undid the remaining latch and pulled the thick, armored cover from Yuri's back. Lydia moaned and was nearly moved to tears by the mess she discovered under the access cover.

"Oh, Yuri," she said quietly. "What did they *do* to you?"

Beneath the cover was quite possibly the ugliest bit of jury-rigging Lydia had ever seen. Half of the panels were scorched, apparent casualties of a bad short and electrical fire. There were exposed circuit boards spattered with gobs of solder, holding jumpers that were run here and there to crudely bypass the burned out circuits. The whole mess smelled strongly of ozone and melted plastic.

"Look at this snake house," Lydia muttered as she pulled various tools from her belt and began to poke around inside the panels. "It's no wonder you can't talk. Hell, I'm surprised you can even move with all this stuff burned up back here." Lydia set to work getting Yuri's motor skill processors re-wired and reset. She was so deep in concentration that she never heard the crowd enter the tent until the tarp was pulled from the cage.

Lydia nearly jumped out of her skin as the tarp was pulled away and someone shone a bright light into the cage. She dropped her tools and reached for her stubby pistol as she quickly came to her knees on Yuri's broad back.

"Hold it right there, sister!" someone commanded her in a hoarse stage whisper. She stopped with one hand on the butt of her weapon and raised her left arm to shield her eyes from the light. She could see past the light a motley crowd of freaks, midgets and circus performers. A forest of weapon barrels and ax handles was pointed at her through the bars, and she gasped as she caught sight of Alexander in the middle of the strange throng with his hands bound and a perplexed look on his face.

"Nice and slow, sister, ease that weapon out and toss it through the bars." Lydia squinted and saw the emaciated form of Marn the chicken-chaser behind the sights of an old CS surplus rifle.

She started to slide the scaregun from her holster when Yuri heaved up beneath her. She toppled backward and hollered, "Yuri! No!" as Yuri hit the bars with a loud clang. The wicked, hooked blades on his forearms snapped through the bars and slashed at the crowd, scattering them.

Yuri bellowed, "*Ostavte menya v pokoe ooblyoodkee!*" He grabbed two bars and pulled at them. They bent out, welds popping as Yuri attempted to make a hole in the cage big enough to escape. There was a scream and the crackle of an energy rifle as an ion blast took Yuri square in his chest, sending blue lines of energy dancing across his armor. He was undeterred. Lydia drew her scaregun and fired into the crowd, catching the freak who shot Yuri. There was a loud bang and a bright flash and his rifle clattered to the ground. He screamed and began clawing at his face, tearing bright, bloody lines down his cheeks. He collapsed in a twitching ball and clutched at his arms and wept. Alexander took the opportunity to break free and knock the closest carnie out with a punch that sent blood, spittle and teeth flying. There was a brief and violent struggle there in the tent, fought with fists and ax handles and rifle butts.

Yuri was half out of the cage slashing at the melee and bellowing when a stern and calm voice called out, "Stop this. All of you." There was a deep snarl, and Blaine the tattooed man emerged from the shadows. He was spattered in gore and at his heels stalked a huge black panther, its muzzle and fur slick with blood. Behind him he dragged the white-suited midget by his collar. Amazingly, the riot subsided. Alexander dropped the carnie he was currently working over, and Lydia stood wide eyed and panting in the cage with her pistol before her. Even Yuri had collapsed half out of the cage, lacking the energy and strength to go any further. The only sound in the room was labored breathing, sobbing and the padding of clawed feet on the packed dirt floor.

"What is going on here?" asked Blaine, his dark eyes flashing. He dropped the midget, who made a pitiful moaning sound as the panther came to sit beside him, watching him intently. Blaine walked over to Marn, who was sitting on the ground and cradling a broken arm, payment for raising a welt on Alexander's head with the butt of his rifle.

"Marn, what's going on here? Who are these people?"

"Dunno, boss," the skinny man hissed through clenched teeth. "The big one was out behind the tent when we come around behind ya. We found the girl in the cage when we come in here to get the robot." Blaine took Alexander and Lydia in with a long, even stare.

"Is that so? What's your name, son? What are you and your lady doing here?"

"My partner and I," and here he shot Lydia a "told-you-so" look, "came to get a better look at the cyborg."

"Why? Nothing here is any of your business. Why are you here?"

"I came to help Yuri," said Lydia. "He was hurt, and I thought he was a prisoner." Blaine rubbed his great, hard chin. Lydia holstered her pistol and put her hands on her hips. "He's in a lot of pain. Someone did a lot of damage to his main panel. You know anything about that?"

Blaine seemed amused by Lydia's accusation and said softly, "You were right, he is a prisoner. We all are. Or we were, until tonight."

Lydia gaped at Blaine and said, "Come again?"

"We were slaves. This carnival's a front for a human trafficking ring, and that one there was the brains of the outfit." Blaine pointed to the midget who was trying to quietly crawl away. The panther turned and dropped a heavy paw on his back, smearing his suit with blood.

"Please..." the midget whimpered, "please." Blaine waved the panther away from the ringleader and it stood and ambled off into the shadows. Lydia's hair stood up and she watched as a blank spot on Blaine's right arm was slowly colored in with the likeness of a snarling black panther with yellow eyes.

"He's all yours, Marn, do with him what you will." The crowd of carnies and freaks, those who could still walk after the scuffle, surrounded the midget and he began to plead with them. Tears streamed down his face. He got to his knees and he held up his hands in supplication.

"Please... I'll do anything... I, I was just following orders, just doing my job." Someone ended his protestations with a kick across the teeth and the crowd howled and fell on him with their rifles and tools, their feet and fists. Lydia gasped and turned away, Alexander stared with a faraway look in his eyes and Blaine just watched, hard eyed, and nodded.

* * *

"Now tell me," said Gideon, "why you thought this was a good idea." He stood with his back to the bar, leaning on it. His arms were crossed over his chest and he cast a bleary eyed and annoyed glare down at Alexander and Lydia, who sat silent and chastised at one of the bar tables.

It was as the former slaves were finishing their grisly work with their captor that there were shouts and the sound of running feet in the circus grounds. Sheriff King had been called about a disturbance in the circus compound, and he and a few deputies had come to investigate. Upon finding the mauled bodies of the guards, they fanned out and began a thorough search, eventually finding the ragged group of freaks and carnies and Lydia and Alexander in the Mantis tent. Upon finding this scene, he started taking every breathing person there into custody and hauling all of them off to the jail, where he set to figuring out what this was all about.

Statements were taken from Marn and Blaine, and a couple of deputies were sent back around to the circus to corroborate. Lydia made a sheepish call to Gideon, rousing him from his bed. It took a long time to explain to him why she was calling from jail, and an even longer time to talk him into putting up her and Alexander's bail. By the time Gideon showed up to the jailhouse, the deputies had returned from the circus with documents

and computer drives. There they found the evidence detailing a complicated human slavery ring using the circus as bait. Sheriff King released Lydia and Alexander to Gideon, and let the circus folk return to their tents, where they quietly began to pack up. The only two who didn't return were Blaine, who stayed to talk at length with the sheriff, and Yuri, who was currently on Widow Tolliver's operating table.

Now here they sat. It was Sunday morning and Gideon's didn't open until noon, so it was only Gideon at the bar, glaring, Alexander and Lydia staring into their coffee cups, and Bully banging around in the kitchen preparing for the day's business.

"Well?" prodded Gideon.

"It seemed like a good idea at the time?" said Lydia, and managed a wan smile.

"That's not a good start."

"Gideon, I had to! He was hurting. He asked for my help!" Gideon cut her off before she could continue.

"Lydia, I've told you time and again about meddling in other people's business. You have any idea how stupid it was for the two of you to go in there last night? You could have been killed! Worse yet, you could have been captured, and sold into slavery. You know what would have happened then? We'd have had to call your old man, and he would have had half the Dwarves in Colorado down here cracking heads and kicking ass 'til hell wouldn't have it." Gideon paused and the three of them smiled at that thought.

"Anyway," he continued, "it was a dangerous and stupid idea. But, you saved some people's lives and you put an end to a serious crime. So good on you for that."

Lydia smiled up at Gideon. "Thanks."

At that there was a knock at the door, and Gideon called out that it was open. Blaine stepped into the bar wearing a borrowed pair of chinos and a short-sleeved work shirt. Gideon could smell the stench of magic on him from across the room. It rocked him back on his heels a bit, but he recovered and offered the big man a seat and a cup of coffee, both of which he gratefully accepted. He sat at the table with Lydia and Alexander and received a cup from Gideon. He took a drink and nodded approvingly.

"That's good. I haven't had a good cup of coffee in a long time." Gideon nodded in thanks.

"Blaine, I know you've been over this a hundred times with the sheriff, but would you mind telling me what the hell is going on?" Blaine took another hit of coffee and nodded.

"I'll give you the short version. The circus was a front for a human trafficking ring. They traveled from town to town, stealing promising looking specimens and selling them to the Splugorth down on the Gulf Coast." Gideon drew in a hissing breath and Lydia and Alexander exchanged puzzled glances.

"I see you've heard of them."

"I have," said Gideon. "I've tangled with them once or twice."

Lydia raised her hand, "I haven't," she said. "Who are they?"

"They're from out of town. They live on this big, old island out in the ocean called Atlantis. Slavers and all around copperheads."

Blaine nodded. "That's as good a description as any," he said.

"So wait," said Alexander. "Are you from this Atlantis place?"

"I am. Born and raised into slavery. I was given my gift there." He held out his arms and displayed the thick mat of tattoos on them.

Gideon seemed unimpressed. "So, back to the circus."

"Yes, back to the circus. I was traded to the circus a couple of years ago as muscle. It was the midget's idea to put me on display in the sideshow. The circus had a pretty powerful psychic to keep us in line. He kept us stepping and fetching for Tiny until a few weeks ago, when we were hit by bandits. He got hit by a rail cannon round. There wasn't even enough left to bury, not that Tiny would have buried him. It took a few days for his influence over us to wear off, then we started planning our way out."

"Why'd you choose here?" asked Lydia.

"It was as good a place as any. It was supposed to be quiet, a family affair if you will. We never expected you two to be there." Blaine nodded at Gideon. "I'm sorry I involved your people in all of this." Gideon snorted and waved his apology away.

"Don't mention it. It's not your fault they're too nosy for their own good." Blaine smiled at Lydia and she mustered up a little smile in return.

"Nosy or not, they did us a favor. Your Lydia here got Yuri up and moving, and that's more activity than I've ever seen from him. I don't think any four of us could have moved him on our own."

"Yeah, about Yuri," Lydia said. "What happened to him? Who did all that damage to him?"

Blaine considered the question as he finished his coffee. He sighed contentedly and Gideon asked, "Another?" Blaine said, "Please," and Gideon topped off his mug from the coffee pot sitting on the bar next to him.

"I don't know much about him. We found him a few months ago in a gully after a nasty storm. He was unconscious, and Tiny had the guy who fixed the carnival rides go to work on him with a soldering iron before he woke up."

Lydia made a sympathetic noise, "Poor thing."

"Indeed. As soon as they had him awake and mostly controllable, they slapped him in that cage and he's been there ever since. He didn't start attacking Tiny until after we lost our psychic. That's when Tiny had the stunners made to keep him, and us, in line."

"That's terrible," said Lydia. Blaine nodded and finished his coffee. Gideon waved the pot at him but he declined.

"It was terrible, but that's the past."

"Which leads me to my next question," said Gideon. "What now?"

"Well, the carnival is already packed up and gone. Marn's a good man. He and his people, that carnival's all they know. He'll find a way to keep it running and put food on the table. I can't speak for Yuri, but I know I haven't figured out what I'll do now." He smiled and added, "I think I could get used to the novelty of freedom."

"Well, I think I speak for the sheriff and mayor when I say you're both more than welcome to stay here in Atchinson until you get back on your feet."

Blaine smiled in thanks but said, "I won't take charity, Gideon. Any help you and yours give me, I'll work for."

"Hmm. Well," said Gideon. "I know the Widow has a job opening right now. You any good with animals?"

* * *

A week later, Lydia and Yuri stood in front of Gideon's, saying their goodbyes. Yuri had spent the preceding week convalescing at the Tolliver Ranch. The widow, while not really a cybernetic doctor, did a fine job patching him up with Lydia's help. He spent his days sitting on the porch telling a rapt Lydia and Molly stories of his homeland, a far off place called Russia. He also spent a couple of late nights talking with Duncan, Widow Tolliver's hulking cybernetic housekeeper, about the nature of being a cyborg. He joined Lydia for breakfast that morning, she at a stool at the bar and he standing next to her, while the patrons gave them both a wide berth. Now it was nearly ten in the morning, and Lydia was trying one last time to talk Yuri into staying.

"I am sorry, *dushenka*," he said as he hoisted his travel bag to his shoulder. It was a gift from Gideon and Lydia, and was full of maps, directions, assorted traveling gear and a notebook full of names and contact information of people who might be able to help him find a way home. "I must go. I miss Russia, and my warlord needs me." His translator lent a tinny overtone to his deep voice.

"Well, just be careful, okay? And if you can't find your way home, you know you're always welcome here." He nodded in thanks and his antennae clattered together. She placed her hand on his cold forearm as it rested on the rail. He brushed her cheek with his deadly fingers again, as he had in the cage.

"*Dasvedanya*, Lydia." With that he turned and made his way down the stairs and into the street, humming a song somewhere deep in his chest. Lydia waved him down the street, but couldn't see him through her tears.

The Spoils of War!

A Rifts® Aftermath Adventure, 109 P.A.

By Ed Emmer

Part One

This is an adventure for the **Rifts®** setting shortly after the defeat of the Kingdom of Tolkeen (within the first days and weeks that reports came in of the fall of the cities of Freehold and Tolkeen). It is designed for a party of 6 to 8 mid-level (4th through 6th level) characters, at least some of whom should possess magical abilities, one of whom should be a Techno-Wizard. If none of the player characters are Techno-Wizards, NPC stats for William Sansburn, a New Lazlo Techno-Wizard, are provided in Chapter One.

In the original play-test, the characters were members of a small mercenary/adventure-for-hire company with connections to New Lazlo and were hired to retrieve a powerful Techno-Wizard device left behind, hidden in the ruins of the Kingdom of Tolkeen.

The following books were used in the writing of this adventure: *Rifts® Aftermath, Rifts® Book of Magic, Rifts® Sourcebook One, Rifts® World Book 2: Atlantis, Rifts® World Book 3: England, Rifts® World Book 16: Federation of Magic, Rifts® World Book 23: Xiticix Invasion, Rifts® Dark Conversions,* and the *Coalition Wars®: Siege on Tolkeen* Books 1-6. Most of the Quick Stats for the vehicles, equipment, and generic Coalition NPCs were adapted from the *Rifts® Game Master Guide* and *Coalition Wars®: Siege on Tolkeen Two: Coalition Overkill.* While it is not necessary to have these books to conduct this adventure, using them would allow a Game Master to take full advantage of the creatures, magic, technology, and settings described herein.

Game Master's Note: Only the major plot points of the adventure are outlined here. It is up to the Game Master whether to follow the story as is, skipping from chapter to chapter directly, or to add encounters, challenges, and side adventures along the way.

(The author would like to thank Isaac, Will, Jake, Jeremy, Joe, Anton, Jordan, Soorya, Alan, A.J., and Christian for their imagination in the play-test of this adventure and for re-kindling the author's love for Rifts.)

Prologue: War Criminals and Public Opinions

Just two days ago, news came from the west: The Kingdom of Tolkeen has fallen to the Army of the Coalition States! The following is the leading news story on the New Lazlo Holo-Web Network:

"Good evening, New Lazlo. This is Algen Horwind giving you the latest on the tragic events that have just recently played out in the Kingdom of Tolkeen. As many have already learned from friends and loved ones, the Coalition Army has completely overwhelmed the last remaining cities of the kingdom, Freehold and Tolkeen. The Dragon Kings, seen here in this smuggled out image, have fled and with them, the last hope that somehow the valiant defenders of one of the greatest bastions of free-thinkers in the world would somehow prevail and drive back the diabolic forces of ignorance and persecution: the Coalition Army.

"With the flight of the Dragon Kings and their Princes and Minions, the CS Air Force was left virtually uncontested in the skies over the Tri-City area. Although precipitated by a sneak attack and air raid from the north, it has been only recently that the full scale bombardment of Freehold and Tolkeen began, allowing legions of CS soldiers and robots to move in to engage any remaining ground defenders. And though for weeks the world has watched the slow but inexorable advance of the Coalition Invasion from the south, it was not until the surprise attack somehow crippled the seemingly impenetrable ley line defense network that the citizens of Tolkeen truly considered for the first time that they might fall. Despite days of stubborn, valiant fighting, the bulk of the Tolkeen Defense Force has been routed. No longer concerned with holding back the tide of black armor, most Tolkeen warriors are now trying to save as many civilians as possible. Although there are still reports of scattered resistance in sections of the city, most notably in the vicinity of the King's Tower, the Coalition has clearly won the day.

In a gruesome, though not surprising turn of events, when refugees began to flee the area roughly 48 hours before the final assault, they were met with a nearly unbreakable line of Coalition soldiers who refused to listen to their pleas for mercy and who shot any attempting to escape the carnage. As you can see from this footage, in addition to the well known markings of the Coalition military machine, a new standard now flies with the advancing CS army. This graffiti, clearly a reference to the ill-fated 'Sorcerers' Revenge' campaign, is accompanied by cries of 'No Prisoners!' 'No Mercy!' and 'Death to all!'

"In a surprising move, Tolkeen's ruler, King Robert Creed, who for years has been an outspoken opponent of the Coalition, addressed his people in the midst of the battle, seemingly repentant for his self destructive actions that brought the kingdom to ruin and cost so many lives. All but apologizing to the Coalition for his actions and those of his warlords, he implored his people to flee before it was too late. He begged the advancing troops to allow the innocent to flee.

"So far, there are no confirmed reports of survivors despite King Creed's pleas. Furthermore, unconfirmed rumors from the region, sent via magic and psychic contact, have suggested that the Coalition butchers are slaughtering not only the last remaining military units under the Tolkeen banner, but also anyone they can get their sites on, including the elderly, women and children, whether human or not.

"Our thoughts and prayers go out to those courageous defenders of freedom who still battle to hold back the tide of Coalition oppression as they lay down their lives to give the innocent refugees a chance to find freedom beyond the war-torn lands of Tolkeen."

This was just the first of many such reports aired on New Lazlo's magic Holo-Web, a Techno-Wizardry communications network not unlike modern live television. For the next few days, little new information is heard, though the news web continues to report on the losses, with additional news items summarizing the overview of the Coalition's campaign against the Kingdom of Tolkeen and numerous editorials from prominent citizens of New Lazlo decrying the Coalition States and Emperor Karl Prosek for their murderous invasion of Minnesota, calling it "genocide." News of the fall of Tolkeen also sparked a new debate amongst many in New Lazlo: What should be done about it?

One growing opinion is that with the Coalition weary from four years of war, not only with the Kingdom of Tolkeen, but also their ill-conceived attack against one of their own - Free Quebec - now would be the time to strike. Though in the minority, this growing camp calls for a strengthening of ties with the Federation of Magic, as well as sending envoys to Lazlo to attempt to persuade them to join in and attack the war-weary Chi-Town even as the CS still struggles to quell the last vestiges of resistance in Tolkeen.

The majority opinion amongst the "man-on-the-street" in New Lazlo is that while tragic, the fall of Tolkeen was just as much a result of the magic kingdom's own arrogance as the brutality of the Coalition Army. They point to the ill-fated "Sorcerers' Revenge," in which the Kingdom of Tolkeen unleashed an army of demonic creatures against not only Coalition military units, but also civilians and support personnel not directly involved with the conflict in Minnesota. While this did hinder the CS advance, it also led to the reunification of Chi-Town and Free Quebec and galvanized public opinion in the CS against not only the forces of Tolkeen, but also all non-humans and magic users everywhere. While this faction casts the blame ultimately at the feet of Emperor Prosek, they are not as forgiving of the leaders of Tolkeen who would allow such an atrocity to take place. They claim that to directly engage the Coalition now would simply strengthen Prosek's propaganda that all magic users are evil, hate-mongering demons who strike at the innocent without cause or mercy. They say that while the events of Tolkeen are tragic, they should serve as a reminder that some prices are too steep to pay. This side of the debate maintains that New Lazlo, being remote and relatively small, should manage to remain under the radar of the Coalition's generals and strategists and that if they continue to preach peace and understanding without conflict, the Coalition will come to see that they are no threat.

A third, but very small faction in this debate is a group of seasoned veterans who feel that it is only a matter of time before Emperor Prosek and the Coalition turn their attention towards New Lazlo. While they agree that part of the blame for the fall of Tolkeen should rest with the warlords of the magic kingdom that unleashed the "Sorcerers' Revenge," they do not agree that the Coalition will ever be willing to accept a community of D-Bees, free-thinkers and magic users so close to Chi-Town. They caution that New Lazlo should secretly form a defensive alliance with their parent kingdom of Lazlo (but not the Federation of Magic) and begin to covertly amass the means to protect themselves when the CS Army ultimately comes their way.

During the first few days since the fall of Tolkeen, these debates in the philosophical and peace-loving city have been, for the most part, academic, with only a few resulting in public brawls and outright fights. However, within another two days, the first wave of refugees begin to filter in and with them, a growing of support for the more belligerent camp. The New Lazlo Holo-Web begins reporting around the clock interviews with survivors about the horrors they have witnessed, both during the war and throughout their flight from Minnesota. It is in the midst of these reports, four days after the first reports of the fall of Tolkeen (six days after Coalition General Jericho Holmes launched his crippling sneak attack that all but destroyed Tolkeen's lines of defense), that a breaking story interrupts the latest reports and refugee interviews.

"Algen Horwind reporting with this late-breaking news: Police in New Lazlo have just arrested Galidor Marik on the charge of War Crimes. One of the warlords of the Kingdom of Tolkeen, Marik is believed to be one of the chief architects of the infamous 'Sorcerers' Revenge' campaign that galvanized the Coalition citizenry against the innocent civilians of the Kingdom of Tolkeen and allowed for a peace deal between Chi-Town and Free Quebec. As many know, in a surprise move just over six months ago, the forces of Tolkeen and Freehold launched a surprise offensive against the entrenched CS invasion forces. Going from what was primarily a defensive war to a sudden Blitzkrieg, the warlords of Tolkeen unleashed all manner of demonic and magical hordes against not only the CS frontline military units but support divisions well behind the battle lines. Then, emboldened by their sudden victory, the Shifters and Summoners of the magic kingdom allowed their minions to revel in an orgy of destruction and slaughter that engulfed not only CS military units but also support personnel and even civilians caught in the crossfire.

In addition to routing their enemy, no doubt King Creed and the leaders of Tolkeen had hoped their actions would show the world the superiority of magic over technology as well as unite all of the Coalition's enemies against their common weakened foe. Instead, most watched in horrified amazement at the wanton destruction the Warlords of Tolkeen had unleashed. Condemned by many, including Lord Coake of the Cyber-Knights and Plato of the Council of Learning in Lazlo, Tolkeen's actions only served to convince the world that Emperor Prosek and the Coalition propaganda machine were right about magic, D-Bees, and the supernatural: that they are all cruel, inhuman and wholly evil. As many of our watchers know, the High Council of New Lazlo not only joined the rulers of our sister kingdom of Lazlo in condemning the violent actions of Tolkeen's warlords, but went one step further in declaring the most notorious warlords, those who are known to have not only sanctioned the 'Sorcerer's Revenge' but also commanded and encouraged the indiscriminate slaughter of innocent CS and neutral civilians, as war criminals. Chief amongst these war criminals are Warlord Scard, Warlord Stygian, the Metal Mage Salkind, the Warlock Maxim Current, Warlord Galidor Marik, the Shifter Lojin Y'siril, and the Techno-Wizard Anderson Uleck, also known as the TW Torturer. So far, of all of these, none have been confirmed to have survived the final siege of Tolkeen except Galidor Marik.

Singled out by witnesses as the latest batch of refugees was being admitted into New Lazlo, Warlord Marik offered no resistance as he was taken into custody by NL Police. In a statement to the media at his arrest, the Techno-Wizard claimed to have information about the final days of the siege of the city of Tolkeen that would prove vital in any future conflict with the Coalition Army.

"So far, no date has been set for the warlord's trial, but already, the arrest of one who many regard as a hero in the war against the CS has added fuel to the growing debate in New Lazlo about what course of action should be taken now with regards to the Coalition."

With the arrest of Galidor Marik, debate in New Lazlo reaches a fevered state, with a growing number crying foul at the arrest of a war hero while the majority continue to see the warlord as just as evil and corrupt as Emperor Prosek. Added to this are the rumors flying about whatever this piece of information might be that Marik claims will be vital to the future of New Lazlo.

Into this mix, the player characters, who for whatever reason happen to be in New Lazlo at the time, will find themselves being approached by Cyrus Trebbor, an official claiming to be a representative of New Lazlo's ruling council.

Background on the New Lazlo Holo-Web (NLHW) Network

Established several years after the founding of New Lazlo, the Holo-Web is a network of interconnected Techno-Wizard devices that receive magical transmissions from a central broadcasting station located in the heart of New Lazlo on a ley line nexus. The central transmission station is a Techno-Wizardry marvel combining the effects of a number of spells, including Multiple Image, Ley Line Transmission, Calling, Energize Spell, and Magic Pigeon, amongst others, to simultaneously transmit a holographic (illusionary) image to the thousands of Holo-Vid viewers connected to the network in much the same way that a conventional television signal works. However, unlike a normal radio-wave based signal which can be picked up by anyone within the transmission range, this one can only be received by a special TW device designed to receive Holo-Web transmissions. The exception to this would be anyone with a similar TW receiver patterned after the Holo-Vid, but only as long as they were located on a ley line connected to the nexus upon which the transmission station is located. This invention has provided the citizens of New Lazlo, as well as many in Lazlo who have purchased TW Holo-Vids (see below), with the prime magic-based information network in the world. And because the transmission tower is located on a ley line nexus and utilizes a number of communication spells designed to reach their recipients anywhere in the world (e.g. Magic Pigeon), there is no limit to the transmission range and anyone with a Holo-Vid can receive New Lazlo's magic video signal anywhere on Rifts Earth. The signal can only be jammed by Ley Line Storms, an extremely powerful electromagnetic pulse, or spells designed to hide locations or block psychic and magic probes (e.g. Sanctum, Time Hole, etc.). So far, only a small portion of the NLHW Network's schedule is dedicated to entertainment programming. The majority of the shows deal mainly with education and news information. Game Masters: this can provide you with an excellent tool for sending bits of information and clues to adventurers in the field. This could also be the chance to introduce Rifts Media-type characters, such as the Rifts Performer O.C.C. (an entertainer or news personality such as Algen Horwind) or Field Reporter O.C.C. as originally described in *The Rifter® #24*.

At the Game Master's discretion, one Field Holo-Vid may be given to the players in order to allow them to continue to have up-to-date information.

TW Holo-Vid: This device takes a conventional television and augments its abilities with the addition of several crystals in the place of circuits within the device itself. The only outward difference between the Holo-Vid and a conventional television set is that the device always has a copper antenna capped with a large zircon crystal. Though the Holo-Vid does rely primarily on the Apparition spell, it is not used to create a horrific illusion but rather to generate the image seen through the device. The Tongues spell ensures that any viewer will be able to understand the transmission and the Lantern Light spell provides the basic source of light. The Energy Field spell acts as the power source, giving the device hours of use before needing to be recharged at a ley line or by a Techno-Wizard. The use of the Locate spell links each Holo-Vid to the central transmission station in New Lazlo. As such, while another Techno-Wizard may be able to duplicate the device, it would not be able to receive transmission from the NLHW Network (unless the device were being used on one of the ley lines connected to the nexus where NLHW's transmission tower is located), as such a "knock-off" would never have been directly linked to the network. Device Level: Five. P.P.E. Construction Cost: 365. Spell Chain Needed: Primary Spell: Apparition (20), Secondary Spells: Lantern Light (1), Energy Field (10), Tongues (12), and Locate (30). Physical Requirements: A ten carat Zircon (gold) worth 3000 credits, Quartz (clear) worth 60 credits, Quartz (ruby) worth 300 credits, Agate (fire) worth 80 credits, and Pearl (white) worth 5000 credits, plus a television set and copper wiring worth an additional 1500 credits (for the field version, a Video Communicator is used, raising the cost to 10,000 credits). Duration of Charge: Five hours of continuous use (unlimited while on a ley line or nexus). To Recharge: 18 P.P.E. or 36 I.S.P. will recharge the Holo-Vid for another five hours. Construction Time: 8 days. Black Market Cost: 28,500 credits for a moderately sized home unit, 30,000 for a large, wide-screened home unit, and 35,000 for a durable field unit. Manufacturer: City-state of New Lazlo.

The TW Holo-Vid was created using the rules for creating Techno-Wizard items presented in **Rifts® Ultimate Edition**, pages 129-135.

New Skills

The following two skills are possessed by several of the NPCs throughout the adventure and represent limited knowledge skills available only to characters in a certain region or with a certain degree of experience. At the Game Master's discretion, they may be selected by a player character as they advance beyond their current level as a result of their experiences in the adventure.

Coalition Tactics (Military Skill)

This skill represents a firsthand knowledge of Coalition military tactics based on experiences during the Siege of Tolkeen and the short-lived war with Free Quebec. It includes recognizing the significance of troop movements and maneuvers, the general capabilities of known CS military hardware, the most likely strategy that a Coalition commander might employ in a given situation, and a general knowledge of how the CS army operates in the field. It also includes an understanding of how CS commanders will respond to different magical and technological threats. It must be noted, however, that this knowledge and understanding is based on observations made during the two aforementioned military engagements. As the CS analyzes its own successes and failures from these campaigns, it may ultimately change some of their more obvious tactics and maneuvers. Still, with the CS military machine being what it is, it is likely that the overconfident commanders and generals will employ their proven tactics at least until they suffer a massive defeat and are forced, once again, to reevaluate how their military functions. **Base Skill:** 25%/15% +5% per level of experience. The first percentage deals with the ability to recognize combat tactics and anticipate the strategic goals of a CS lead mission. The second percentage pertains to the recognition of known Coalition military hardware. **Prerequisite:** This skill is only available to non-Coalition O.C.C.s who have directly battled or observed firsthand the Coalition army in the field (not just single battles with Coalition soldiers but full scale military operations). As such, it can *never* be learned as a first level skill and must be selected when the character reaches a level of experience at which they can learn a new O.C.C. Related Skill (not available as a Secondary Skill selection). It may be acquired by *any* O.C.C. regardless of skill restrictions as long as they meet the criteria described above.

Lore: Xiticix (Technical Skill)

This skill represents a firsthand knowledge of the Xiticix insectoid aliens that have invaded the south central Canadian and northern Midwest American wilderness. Unlike the generic *Lore: D-Bee* skill which provides general knowledge of all of the D-Bees common to a region, this skill pertains *only* to the Xiticix aliens. While the skill does not provide any medical knowledge (such as the *Entomological Medicine* skill), it does give the character a detailed understanding of the behaviors and habits of the insect race. This includes recognizing the different (known) members of the Xiticix race, their strategies and tactics, how to recognize where a hive's territory begins, how to act and behave so as not to attract attention when in Xiticix territory, and a very general (limited) knowledge of hive layout. **Base Skill:** 25% +5% per level of experience. **Prerequisite:** This skill is only available to characters who have either grown up in or extensively explored the regions known to be inhabited by the Xiticix. Members of the various Psi-Stalker tribes that inhabit Lower Manitoba, Lower Ontario, and Upper Minnesota automatically gain this skill. It may also be selected by Cyber-Knights and Tundra Rangers at first level. It is also now known by all of CS General Jericho Holmes' men as a result of their ordeal in the Hivelands during the Siege of Tolkeen. All other O.C.C.s may only select this skill if they have had experience in the Xiticix Hivelands or grew up in the region.

Chapter One: Politics and Back Room Deals

And what would your peace-loving constituents say about this little arrangement?"

- Galidor Marik

Prior to being approached by Cyrus Trebbor, the players should have spent some time in New Lazlo, hearing the rumors and perhaps even getting caught up in the debate about what to do now that Tolkeen has fallen and refugees are flooding in. As moderately well known adventurers, they might even have been asked by one or two who know them by reputation to go in search of loved ones (or perhaps they may be questioned as to why they did not take part in the fight against the Coalition). This could lead to some interesting scenarios and give the players a general feel for the tension brewing in New Lazlo as more and more refugees arrive, bringing their stories of hardship and the horrors of war with them.

Cyrus Trebbor will ask for the players to meet with him in a small building adjacent to the ruling council's grounds. Anyone taking the time to investigate Cyrus Trebbor (successful Research or Streetwise skill roll) will learn that he is a minor official connected to the New Lazlo government. Cyrus, a retired Cyber-Knight, will explain to the players that he represents several members of the council who feel that New Lazlo needs to take discreet action to prepare for an inevitable conflict with the Coalition Army. Being in the minority, these representatives are not in a position to effect any major change in current policy and, as such, are looking for a less direct means of acquiring anything they can to help protect their beloved city from ruin. This is where the players come in. Cyrus will ask them if they have heard anything about the recent arrest of Galidor Marik as well as where they stand on the issue of his actions as a potential war criminal, even though those actions were against the Coalition Military. Depending upon their answer, the ex-Cyber-Knight will guide the rest of the negotiation accordingly.

Once in a windowless chamber that looks like a drab conference room with two doors (long table, many chairs, a large Holo-Vid against the wall, currently off-line), Cyrus will explain that Galidor Marik has recently revealed to the ruling council that just prior to the fall of Tolkeen, he had completed construction of a prototype Iron Juggernaut called a Dragon Juggernaut, far more powerful than anything so far seen in the war.

Perhaps the most famous of the magic kingdom's war machines were the Iron Juggernauts, golem-like Techno-Wizardry constructs that were basically magical robots of immense power. Though ultimately Tolkeen did lose the war, these war machines were responsible for the slaughter of thousands of Coalition soldiers and the destruction of vast numbers of robots and armor. Marik, Cyrus will go on to explain, had created a new type of Juggernaut that functioned in many ways like a piloted robot as well as an automaton. This would make the construct similar in many respects to the Automatons created by the city of Dweomer in the Federation of Magic. As New Lazlo lacks the knowledge to create either type of war machine, much less a supremely powerful one that combines the characteristics of both, those council members who believe that war is inevitable, and that they should begin secretly building up New Lazlo's defenses, desperately want this prototype.

At this point, Cyrus will speak quietly into a communicator, saying, "Bring him in."

The door opposite the one the players entered will open and four armored guards will enter the room escorting Galidor Marik. Marik is dressed in rather plan looking black robes and looks to be a human or D-Bee in his mid-forties (in reality, he is a D-Bee similar to an Elf and is over 350 years old). Marik's skin looks slightly tanned, and his black hair is cut short and showing only the first hints of gray. He has a trimmed black goatee (in the classic villain style) and a perpetual smirk. His eyes are dark blue and his ears are only slightly pointed. For a full description of Galidor Marik, see Chapter Eleven.

Cyrus will explain that there is enough support in the council to pardon Marik for his crimes, though not without the swing vote of the representatives on whose behalf he is speaking. Therefore, they have cut him a deal. Marik is to provide the players with directions on how to find his laboratory in the ruins of the city of Tolkeen, assuming it hasn't been discovered by the Coalition yet, and aid in ultimately constructing a working prototype for New Lazlo. In exchange, the representatives will vote to pardon Marik and exonerate him of the charge of war crimes.

Before the players can begin to question him, the door they entered from will burst open and a mage will stride in, followed by two warriors: one who undoubtedly looks like a knight of some fashion and the other who looks like an exotic variety of Cyborg. A brief altercation will ensue in which Cyrus tells the newcomer that he has no place here and that his "offer" has already been declined.

The newcomer is Thorm Ar'tal, a representative of the City of Brass and the True Federation of Magic, and the two guards with him are mercenaries in the employ of the Federation (one is a Mystic Knight and the other is one of Marik's own inventions - a Techno-Wizardry Full Conversion Cyborg; for details see Chapters 11 and 12). He will explain, as he sits down, that he feels that this mission into CS occupied Minnesota should be undertaken by or at least with the aid of the Federation of Magic. He will go on to explain that Marik is being extended diplomatic status as a friend of the Federation and Lord Dunscon personally and, as such, is immune to any prosecution undertaken by New Lazlo (this is pure nonsense as there are no formal diplomatic relations between the City of Brass and New Lazlo). This posturing is all mainly for show as there is nothing honorable about Thorm Ar'tal or those who he represents, namely Lord Dunscon, ruler of the Federation of Magic. He simply wants to get his hands on Marik and his design. Ar'tal will further add that the citizens of New Lazlo might find it interesting to know that this particular meeting is taking place behind closed doors. Throughout the entire exchange, Galidor Marik will sit quietly, his smirk widening as he enjoys the battle. Game Masters should feel free to have this argument play out in front of the players and allow the players to participate if they wish. Ultimately, Thorm and his guards will leave, but not before promising "dire consequences for all of those who stand in the way of the will of the True Federation."

With Thorm Ar'tal gone, Cyrus will return to the matter at hand - basically, he wants the players to sneak into CS occupied Minnesota and acquire the plans for the Dragon Juggernaut and, if possible, the working prototype from Marik's lab. If the players revealed earlier that they believe that Marik is a war criminal and should be tried, Cyrus will attempt to persuade them that by delivering the prototype and plans, they will be preventing others from using it to commit additional crimes. If the players indicated that they thought of Marik as a hero, then he will try to convince them that this will be a chance for Galidor Marik to show to the rest of the world that his actions are good and noble by aiding New Lazlo.

If the players accept, they will be given the chance to ask Marik any question about the layout of his lab, where to find it, and how to reach it. Marik will answer some questions directly but will be evasive about the specifics, especially when it comes to describing any defenses his lab might have in place to prevent theft.

The following include answers to some possible questions the players might ask Marik:

Where is the lab? In a secret chamber within the maze of sewers accessible from the western part of the City of Tolkeen.

Has it been discovered yet? He doubts that in such a short time the Coalition would have found it... yet.

Is there anything guarding the lab? Marik will pause before answering this. Yes, he will explain. He has put in place a number of TW traps designed to prevent Coalition troops from finding his lair.

Exactly what traps? "Oh... this and that." He will explain no more.

How can they be avoided? Any Techno-Wizard worthy of the name should be able to find them and disarm them. They were designed to stop non-magic forces like the Coalition.

Why won't you tell us how to disarm them or what they are yourself? "Professional pride and trade secrets," he replies with a smirk.

Why don't you just build a new prototype here in New Lazlo? It took him years to perfect the design and, quite frankly, while he could ultimately replicate it on his own, it would take a very long time, and there's no telling how soon the Coalition will come to call.

Were you really responsible for the "Sorcerers' Revenge"? "We all do what we must in times of war."

How did you escape the Coalition occupation? He had plans in place long before the final siege... just in case.

What plans, and can he get them back in without notice? "No, one-way trip... sorry."

What is the Dragon Juggernaut? With a sense of genuine pride, Marik will explain that it is a massive construct modeled after the powers of a dragon and designed for frontline combat as well as stealth. It can accommodate a pilot (must be a Techno-Wizard or someone trained to pilot the juggernaut by one) or can function on its own as an automaton.

Why was it not used in the war? It was only just completed before the fall of Tolkeen was imminent and though it would have slaughtered thousands, with only the one prototype, it would have done little to turn the tide of the war. With many more... who knows? Isn't that what these negotiations are all about?

Do you know how to construct the other Iron Juggernauts? No. King Creed spread knowledge of the creation process between three different groups of Techno-Wizards to prevent any one person from knowing too much. He was part of one of these groups but, he feels, he could replicate the process in time in addition to providing New Lazlo with the Dragon Juggernaut of his own design.

Throughout the entire interrogation, Galidor Marik will seem deliberately cocky and very sure of himself, not at all like a criminal bargaining for his freedom. Attempts to use psionic Telepathy or Empathy or the spell Words of Truth will reveal nothing. Marik is very good at being evasive and hiding facts while still telling the truth. Therefore, such probes will indicate that he is telling the truth, but is clearly not telling the whole story.

When the players are done, Marik will be escorted out by the four soldiers, and Cyrus will then turn and offer each player 75,000 credits up front as well as an additional 350,000 if they return with the plans for the Dragon Juggernaut. If pressed, he will go as high as 125,000 credits up front and 500,000 credits upon their successful return. If they can deliver the working Dragon Juggernaut prototype, Cyrus explains, they can expect their reward to be in the millions.

Owing to the need for urgency lest Marik's lab is discovered by Coalition forces or someone else, the players will be given 48 hours to equip themselves before heading out. As this is not an officially sanctioned mission, the city of New Lazlo will not give the players anything they want for free. However, Cyrus has connections and can recommend a few places where his name will earn them a discount on items. Conventional equipment can be purchased for 20-30% off the book cost. "Common" Techno-Wizardry items can also be purchased from Cyrus' friends for 15-20% off while rare and powerful TW items will only be reduced by 5-10%. Conventional (non-magic) weapons and armor can be found, but only for 5-10% off (New Lazlo is fiercely proud of their magical abilities and, as such, there are just not that many merchants dealing in non-magic weapons and armor). Availability of TW items and weapons as well conventional equipment is left to the Game Master. Players will also be given whatever intelligence is to be had about the area between New Lazlo and the Kingdom of Tolkeen (which is admittedly little). Unfortunately, this is little more than one can learn by reading pages of one of Erin Tarn's books (pages 29-31 of **Rifts® Ultimate Edition** cover this area). Specifically, the players will be warned that to travel south of Lake Michigan takes them into the heart of the Coalition State of Chi-Town and to travel north of that Great Lake takes them dangerously close to the Coalition State of Iron Heart as well as into the lands of the Manistique Imperium and Ishpeming, both allies of the CS. If they ask why they can't simply Rift or teleport into Tolkeen (a Shifter, especially one who has been to the Tri-City region, should be able to do that with ease), Cyrus will explain that what few reports they have been able to put together from the refugees all suggest that in the surprise attack, the ley line power network went down in a catastrophic systems failure that caused the Tri-City ley lines to erupt with chaotic power, making any dimensional incursion suicide (true, the ley line instability will calm down after a week or so, but the players will have no way of knowing that). Furthermore, if they use up too much of their P.P.E. teleporting or Rifting in (most invocations of that nature

are quite costly), they will have little strength to combat the waiting Coalition troops who are no doubt poised at every ley line nexus waiting for just such an attempt to be made.

Should the players lack a Techno-Wizard, the following non-player character (NPC) is provided.

William Sansburn IV: 4th level Techno-Wizard O.C.C. with connections to Cyrus Trebbor.

Alignment: Scrupulous.

Age: 26

Attributes: I.Q. 12, M.E. 12, M.A. 11, P.S. 15, P.P. 13, P.E. 21, P.B. 13, Spd 30.

Size: 5 feet, 10 inches (1.78 m) tall; 150 pounds (67.5 kg).

Hit Points: 40

S.D.C.: 32

P.P.E.: 135

I.S.P.: 36 (minor psychic)

Attacks per Melee: 5

Bonuses: +2 to parry, +2 to dodge, +2 to pull punch, +3 to roll with impact, +2 to save versus Horror Factor, +2 to save versus possession and mind control, +4 to save versus magic, +3 to save versus poison, +1 to spell strength, kick attack (1D8 S.D.C. damage).

Weapons: TW Converted Energy Pistol: 2D6 M.D. single shot, 6D6 M.D. triple burst, 20 shots per 10 P.P.E. TW Converted Energy Rifle: 3D6 M.D. single shot, 1D4x10 M.D. triple burst, 30 shots per 15 P.P.E. TW Flame Sword: 4D6 M.D., ten minutes per 14 P.P.E. Conventional S.D.C. Automatic Pistol: with silver bullets - 4D6 S.D.C., 15 rounds per clip.

Armor: TW Converted Light M.D.C. Armor (35 M.D.C.) with the following spells: Armor of Ithan (10), Deflect (10), and Invisibility: Simple (6).

Skills of Note: Ley Line Piloting (80%), Languages: English (98%), Dragonese (74%), French (74%), Literacy: English (65%), Dragonese (55%), Computer Operation (60%), Computer Programming (50%), Computer Repair (55%), Mechanical Engineering (60%), Techno-Wizardry Construction (86%), Sensory Equipment (55%), Land Navigation (53%), Pilot Hovercycle (84%), Pilot Automobile (71%), W.P. Sword (+2 to strike and parry), W.P. Energy Rifle (+2 to strike), W.P. Energy Pistol (+2 to strike), Hand to Hand: Basic, Electrical Engineer (60%), Locksmith (45%), Robot Mechanics (45%), Lore: Magic (25%), Robot Electronics (55%), Cryptography (45%), Computer Hacking (40%).

Magic Knowledge: Armor of Ithan (10), Blinding Flash (1), Breathe without Air (5), Call Lightning (15), Chameleon (6), Cloak of Darkness (6), Deflect (10), Electric Arc (8), Energy Blast (5), Energy Field (10), Fire Ball (10), Fire Blossom (20), Fire Bolt (7), Frequency Jamming (15), Fuel Flame (5), Fly (15), Force Bonds (25), Globe of Daylight (2), Ignite Fire (6), Impervious to Energy (20), Impervious to Fire (5), Implosion Neutralizer (12), Invisibility: Simple (6), Magic Net (7), Magic Shield (6), Power Bolt (20), See the Invisible (8), Sense Magic (4), Shadow Meld (10), Superhuman Strength (10), and Telekinesis (8). Like all Techno-Wizards, William cannot cast any of these spells directly but must focus his magic through an appropriate technological device.

Psionic Abilities: Machine Ghost (12), Mind Block (4), Object Read (6), Speed Reading (2), Telemechanics (10), and Total Recall (2).

Cybernetics: None.

Equipment: In addition to the aforementioned weapons and armor, William has the typical gear common to a Techno-Wizard (see **Rifts® Ultimate Edition,** page 129). Also has a TW Converted Off-Road Truck (130 M.D.C.) with the following spells: Sense Magic (4), Impervious to Energy (20), and Chameleon (6). He also has 150,000 credits worth of various gemstones used in the creation of TW devices as well as 35,000 in credits (plus whatever amount was agreed upon in the negotiations with Cyrus Trebbor).

Appearance and Disposition: William Sansburn is an easy going, friendly person, somewhat optimistic and prone to fits of giggles when amused. He has also been to Tolkeeen once before (just prior to the war) and is eager to see with his own eyes what happened as well as find something that might help defend his home against the inevitable Coalition invasion. He has short dark hair, blue eyes, and a perpetual grin. Dressed in the clothing common to Techno-Wizards and owns a leather bomber jacket (empowered with Impervious to Fire).

Game Master's Note: This NPC entry includes more detail than the average entry on the chance that William Sansburn is employed as an essential member of the party in their attempt to recover the Dragon Juggernaut.

Chapter Two:
Demons and Dragons

"Where are my mommy and daddy?"

- Garimond the Deceiver

Once the players have outfitted themselves, they will need to set off. The most obvious route that will avoid any direct contact with the Coalition forces at Chi-Town or Iron Heart is to make northwest across Lower Michigan and head for the shore of Lake Michigan across from pre-Rifts Green Bay, Wisconsin. This region is predominately wilderness broken up by the occasional small, human or D-Bee village. The level of technology is low, with most small communities just struggling to survive with one or two more powerful protectors to help defend against both the natural elements and supernatural menaces that dominate the wilderness.

Though there is little substantial information known about Lower Michigan, it is well documented that a large number of dragons seem to herald from the area. Rumors about this range from the theory that this relatively unclaimed wilderness appeals to the elemental and predatory nature of these beasts, to the notion that there is a full-fledged dragon colony or even nesting site somewhere within the dense wilderness forests of Lower Michigan. Even the scholars in New Lazlo are at a loss to explain the high number of dragon sightings within their neighboring region.

Lower Michigan is also a region dominated by a large network of ley lines. During the Great Cataclysm, the entire area was overwhelmed with demonic hordes from the Rifts. To this day, the region still radiates strong magical energies. Ley Line Storms are common and frequent Rift activity further unleashes new supernatural menaces to plague the land.

Given the density of the wilderness, it should take the players several days to cross from New Lazlo to the west coast of Lower Michigan. Game Masters should feel free to populate the region with as many or as few encounters as they like, or they may skip directly to the key events of this chapter.

Suggested encounters for the wilderness region of Lower Michigan include:

- Random Ley Line Storm (see pages 191-192 in **Rifts® Ultimate Edition**).

- Random Rift (roll on the Rift attributes tables in **Rifts® Ultimate Edition,** pages 194-197, to determine the nature of the Rift).

- Random ley line. Players may encounter (01-25%) 1D4+3 Entities (Poltergeists or Haunting Entities), (26-50%) a high level Ley Line Walker coasting along, friendly but distant and distracted when approached, (51-75%) a Ley Line Storm, or (76-00%) it is unoccupied.

- Small D-Bee village: Medieval tech level. Will be terrified of the players. (01-25% will have a mid-level magical defender - perhaps a Shaman, Mystic, or Elemental Fusionist.)

- Small human village: Low tech level with some traces of advanced technology. Will have one or two more powerful, experienced veterans who speak for the town and/or defend it against threats. Will regard the players with suspicion.

- A small clearing atop a hill is ringed by standing stones. Though not a ley line nexus, the site registers magic. If the players remain in the area, they will be approached by a friendly Mystic or Psi-Druid who will invite them to join him and his brother and sisters for the night. A small enclave of "nature lovers" has been adopted by a clan of Faerie Folk and live in a thick copse of wood about 30 minutes from the clearing. If the players make the mistake of damaging the standing stones, they will be attacked (though not with lethal force) by the druids and their Faerie Folk allies.

- Smoldering ruins of a small village. (01-50% D-Bee, 51-95% Human, 96-00% Supernatural dwelling.) No sign of survivors. Tracks suggest the assault came from the north and was predominately magic (01-50%) or high-tech (51-00%) in nature.

- Single dragon (actually a Hatchling) circles high overhead and (01-25%) plays cat and mouse with the players, (26-50%) demands payment for trespassing in its domain, (51-75%) ghosts the party for the next hour then flies off, or (76-00%) seems to take no notice of the players and leaves within 1D4 minutes.

- A patrol of Lazlo wizards and warriors scouting the region. They will be aloof and regard the characters with suspicion. They will not remain long and will not reveal what they are doing in Lower Michigan.

- A small village (mixture of D-Bees and humans) under the protection of a benevolent, mid-level Air/Earth Warlock and

his summoned Lesser Elemental (01-50% Air, 51-00% Earth).

- A party of three Cyber-Knights searching for Tolkeen refugees to aid in escaping the carnage of the CS occupation.

- A patrol of Xiticix Warriors led by a Hunter appear out of nowhere and attack the party. Players with a high amount of P.P.E. might be "marked" for capture to be taken back to the Duluth Hive to be turned into "sludge" (see Chapters 6 and 7 for details on this).

- A Greater Demon and its small throng of 2D4 Lesser Demons attack.

- A small horde of Lesser Demons (1D4+3) jump out and ambush the players. Will fight until their leader is slain (the one with the highest stats) or more than half their group is killed.

- While on a large stretch of rolling hills cleared of forest, a distant rumble warns the players of a herd of wild Fury Beetles charging in their direction. Move or be trampled.

- The party spies a Shifter on a small ley line nexus deep in communication with some extra-dimensional entity. If they are quiet, the Shifter will leave within 30 minutes. If they draw attention to themselves, the Shifter will attack, along with the three Lesser Demons bound to his service.

- A seemingly crazy, wild man running amok in the wilderness. He is really a high level Fire/Water Elemental Fusionist and should be treated with care. He is about as stable as a box of nitroglycerin on a roller coaster.

- The players are met by a D-Bee or Human trapper hunting wild animals in the region. If friendly, the players may learn a great deal about the region.

- A tribe of wild Psi-Stalkers challenges the players to a battle of skills (non-lethal unless the players push their luck) before they will let them pass.

- A band of refugees coming from Tolkeen. If the players are tactful and compassionate, they might learn some useful information about current state of the Coalition occupation.

- A pack of "Feral" Dog Boys who have recently defected from their Coalition unit after their Psi-Stalker was killed and their human commander treated them like garbage. If the party plays their cards right, they might learn about a larger Coalition patrol in the area looking for Tolkeen refugees.

- A Coalition Sky Cycle patrol (1D4+1 Wind Jammers or AFC-111 Scouts) attack the party from above before heading off to the southwest. These fly-boys are just buzzing the players for some fun and to show them who's boss. However, if the players prove especially tough or display a great deal of magic, the Sky Cycles may radio for reinforcements before retreating southwest. Support units include 8 Dead Boy Grunts, 2 SAMAS Power Armor units, an IAR-4 Hellraiser Robot, and a Scout Spider-Skull Walker and will arrive in 2D6+10 minutes if the players do not move on quickly and cover their tracks.

- A truly magnificent site to behold: A flock of 2D4+5 dragons suddenly rises from the trees about 100 yards ahead and takes flight (Horror Factor/Awe Factor 18). If the players are wise, they will simply watch and be amazed at such a rare sight. All of these dragons are adults. Why they are all together when most adult dragons are loners and fiercely territorial is anyone's guess.

Game Masters: If you do not have the necessary source books for the aforementioned encounters, feel free to adjust them accordingly.

In addition to these suggested events, two specific encounters are described below in detail.

The first encounter takes place a day or two from New Lazlo along a ley line just as a Ley Line Storm erupts. Those players with the psionic power Sixth Sense may receive a warning just before the storm breaks. For the first several minutes of the storm, nothing too unusual (at least for a Ley Line Storm) will occur, just the ordinary effects described in **Rifts® Ultimate Edition** on pages 191 and 192. However, after the first twenty minutes of the storm, players with exceptional hearing (cybernetic amplified hearing or a Dog Boy's or D-Bee's naturally acute hearing) will hear what sounds like a child's screams. If the players are able to track it to its source some 100 yards (91.4 m) in the direction of the ley line, they will find a trio of Gurgoyles along with their Gargoyle master seemingly surrounding something on the ground. Before the players can advance further, one of them notices their approach and turns to attack.

Three (3) Gurgoyles:
3rd level Sub-Demons from the Rifts.

Alignment: Miscreant.

Attributes: I.Q. 8, M.E. 8, M.A. 7, P.S. 32, P.P. 25, P.E. 24, P.B. 5, Spd 38.

Size: 10 feet (3.1 m) tall; 945 pounds (425.3 kg).

M.D.C.: 200

P.P.E.: 4

I.S.P.: 30

Horror Factor: 14

Attacks per Melee: 5

Bonuses: +2 on initiative, +6 to strike, +7 to parry, +7 to dodge, +1 to save versus psionics, +5 to save versus magic, +5 to save versus poison, +10 to save versus Horror Factor.

Damage: Claws do 4D6+17 S.D.C. on a restrained punch, 4D6 M.D. full strength punch or kick, and 6D6 power punch or kick but counts as two attacks. Tail strike does 2D6 M.D. Bite does 2D6 M.D.

Weapons: L-20 Pulse Rifle: 2D6 M.D. single shot, 6D6 M.D. triple burst, 40 shots per clip.

Giant Vibro-Sword: 3D6 M.D. Each Gurgoyle has 3 E-Clips.

Natural Abilities/Skills of Note: Superior night vision (can see in one tenth the amount of light that a human needs) and superior, hawk-like day vision - able to see a one foot (0.3 m) object up to 2 miles away (3.2 km), Leap 40 feet (12 m), Bio-regenerate 4D6 M.D. every hour. Detect Ambush (50%), Escape Artist (50%), W.P. Energy Rifle (+1 to strike), W.P. Sword (+2 to strike, +1 to parry).

Magic: None.

Psionics: Considered major psionics with the following powers: Meditation (0), Mind Block (4), Presence Sense (4), Sense Magic (3), Telepathy (4), Resist Hunger (2), Resist Fatigue (4), and Resist Thirst (6). Equivalent to 6th level experience.

Appearance: Giant, gray-skinned demons with muscular tails but lacking the wings of a true Gargoyle.

Gargoyle: 5th level Sub-Demon from the Rifts.

Alignment: Miscreant.

Attributes: I.Q. 12, M.E. 17, M.A. 11, P.S. 23, P.P. 25, P.E. 26, P.B. 10, Spd 23 running, 70 flying.

Size: 15 feet (4.6 m) tall; 1400 pounds (630 kg).

M.D.C.: 300

P.P.E.: 3

I.S.P.: 20

Horror Factor: 16

Attacks per Melee: 5

Bonuses: +2 on initiative, +6 to strike, +7 to parry, +7 to dodge, +9 to dodge in flight, +2 to save versus psionics, +6 to save versus magic, +6 to save versus poison, +10 to save versus Horror Factor.

Damage: Claws do 4D6+8 S.D.C. on a restrained punch, 3D6 M.D. full strength punch or kick, and 6D6 power punch or kick but counts as two attacks. Kick does 5D6 M.D. Tail strike does 2D6 M.D. Bite does 2D6 M.D.

Weapons: L-20 Pulse Rifle: 2D6 M.D. single shot, 6D6 M.D. triple burst, 40 shots per clip.

NG-202 Rail Gun: 1D4x10 for a 40 round burst, 300 round ammo belt.

Giant Vibro-Sword: 3D6 M.D. The Gargoyle has 4 E-Clips for the L-20 and 2 extra belts of ammo for the rail gun.

Natural Abilities: Flight, superior night vision (can see in one tenth the amount of light that a human needs) and superior, hawk-like day vision - able to see a one foot (0.3 m) object up to 2 miles away (3.2 km), Leap 40 feet (12 m), Bio-regenerate 4D6 M.D. every hour. Detect Ambush (60%), W.P. Energy Rifle (+2 to strike), W.P. Heavy Energy (+2 to strike), W.P. Sword (+2 to strike, +2 to parry).

Magic: None.

Psionics: Considered a major psionic with the following powers: Meditation (0), Mind Block (4), Presence Sense (4), Sense Magic (3), Telepathy (4), Resist Hunger (2), Resist Fatigue (4), and Resist Thirst (6). Equivalent to 6th level experience.

Appearance: Giant, gray-skinned, winged demon with a muscular tail.

These Sub-Demons attacked a straggler vehicle from a convoy of humans traveling through the region not far ahead of the players, and were in the process of chasing down the only fleeing survivor when the Ley Line Storm struck.

In the midst of the battle, there will be a sudden flash of blinding white light. When their vision clears, the players will find themselves floating in a yellow sky with fast blowing, white and pink clouds. Players familiar with the Astral Plane will realize that the storm has just plane shifted them to that dimension. If the Gargoyle and his Gurgoyle minions have not been slain, they will be there as well and the battle will continue. Game Masters should feel free to have some fun at the players' expense as they try to get their bearings in the Astral Plane and figure out how they are going to get home. (In the original play test, a massive dark cloud that radiated evil began to move swiftly towards the disoriented players with tendrils of mist stretching towards them like tentacles right before they returned to Rifts Earth.)

After several minutes in the Astral Plane, the players are enveloped in another blinding flash of light and find themselves back in Lower Michigan right where they were before the storm began, only the storm is gone and although it seems as if they were in the Astral Plane for only 1D4 minutes, in actuality, 2D6 hours have passed. If the players search for whatever it was that the party of Sub-Demons was attacking, they will find a small girl, approximately 7 to 8 years of age, curled up on the ground in a seemingly catatonic state.

If the players try to revive her, she will act terrified and attempt to flee. If subdued and attempts are made to communicate with her, she will only ask where her parents are. It will be clear to the players that to abandon this child in the wilderness would be tantamount to murder and only the most diabolic player would be willing to leave her behind. About half a mile (0.8 km) further west, the players will find the remains of an off-road truck that seems to have been torn to shreds. Upon seeing this, the little girl will burst into tears and cry for her "mommy and daddy." If asked what happened, she will only talk about the monsters that attacked her mommy and daddy. If the players examine the interior of the vehicle, they will find that it has been totally trashed and is stained with a great amount of blood. Only a few personal effects can be found amongst the carnage, suggesting a husband and wife and a little girl.

In actuality, this little girl is a metamorphosed minor Demon Lord known as Garimond the Deceiver, a being who delights in deception and murder by disguising himself as a loved one and

sowing the seeds of chaos and betrayal amongst those around him. In this case, the demon killed a little girl when she had snuck away from her parents, and assumed the form of the girl with the hope of spreading chaos within the convoy that the family was a part of. As fate would have it, the convoy happened to be traveling close to a ley line and when the storm struck, the Demon Lord could not maintain his disguise and was forced to kill the girl's parents. The rest of the convoy fled and, before the demon could pursue, the Gargoyles happened to come across the vehicle and attack, thinking that it would be easy pickings. As the disoriented Demon Lord fled, the Sub-Demons followed, still thinking they were following a frightened little girl. That was when the players arrived.

Garimond will continue to maintain the form of the little girl and try to play on the sympathies of the players so that they will take "her" with them. If they do, he will begin to subtly use his psychic powers to cause trouble and turn the players against one another or turn strangers against the players. If discovered, the Demon Lord will fight until he thinks he is losing, at which point he will feign his own death before attempting to teleport away. If the players proved particularly tough, Garimond will move on to find easier prey. If their defeat of the Demon Lord was more chance than skill, Garimond will follow the party until nightfall, at which time he will attempt to possess one of the players (or perhaps William Sansburn) when no one is around or watching, in order to exact revenge (see Garimond's special abilities below for his unique form of possession).

Garimond the Deceiver: Minor Demon Lord.

Alignment: Diabolic.

Attributes: I.Q. 17, M.E. 22, M.A. 20, P.S. 24 (Supernatural), P.P. 19, P.E. 18, P.B. 3, Spd 34.

M.D.C.: 418

P.P.E.: 258

I.S.P.: 102 (considered a Master Psionic).

Horror Factor: 16 in natural form (see description below).

Height: 24 feet (7.3 m).

Weight: 1450 lbs (652.5 kg).

Attacks per Melee: 7

Bonuses: +2 on initiative, +4 to strike, +5 to parry, +3 to dodge, +5 to roll with punch, +4 to save versus psionics, +4 to save versus insanity, +3 to save versus magic, +4 to save versus poison, +8 to save versus Horror Factor, +6 to save versus mind control, +5 to save versus illusion, +2 on Spell Strength, impervious to possession, half damage from fire and electricity attacks, double damage from cold and light-based magic and attacks. Full vulnerability to psionics, +60% to invoke trust or intimidate others.

Damage: Punch (2D6 M.D.), Power Punch (4D6 M.D., x2 attacks), Kick (3D6 M.D.), Bite (1D6 M.D.), Tentacle Crush (6D6 M.D. per melee).

Natural Abilities/Skills: Nightvision 1000 feet (305 m), see in total darkness, See the Invisible, Bio-regenerate (2D6 M.D. per melee), Teleport up to 5 miles (8 km) (25%), Dimensional Teleport (45%), Natural Shape Shifter (can assume the shape of any person or animal with 95% accuracy), Natural Disguise Artist (85%), Imitate Voices (87%), Seduction (45%), Prowl (55%), Lore: Demons and Monsters (85%), Lore: Magic (45%).

Discorporation Possession: Unlike the ordinary possession, Garimond can completely discorporate his body in order to inhabit the body of a mortal. Like classic possession, the Demon Lord knows the memories and skills of the person he inhabits (though at only half the normal percentage). However, the demon does not gain any of the special abilities, powers, psionics, or magical knowledge of the person. The person's personality is completely suppressed and has no memory of the experience (though if they survive, the character will suffer a random insanity from the experience). While inhabiting a person, Garimond still retains all of his ordinary abilities and skills. Furthermore, his Supernatural Strength, M.D.C. and physical attributes are assumed by the host body, making his host far more powerful and resilient than he or she would ordinarily be. Because Garimond's body discorporates in the act of possession, there is no vacant body left behind. If Garimond is killed while inhabiting a host body, the body lapses into a coma and must be revived or it will die shortly after the Demon Lord is slain. A successful Exorcism will expel the Demon Lord.

Magical Knowledge: Garimond knows the following spells at 8th level experience: Cloud of Smoke (2), See Aura (6), Sense Magic (4), Aura of Power (4), Befuddle (6), Chameleon (6), Cloak of Darkness (6), Concealment (6), Fear (5), Invisibility: Simple (6), Charismatic Aura (10), Fire Bolt (7; 4D6 M.D.), Fool's Gold (10), Multiple Image (7), Armor Bizarre (15; 120 M.D.C.), Aura of Death (12), Charm (12), Es-

cape (8), Horrific Illusion (10), House of Glass (12), Sleep (10), Apparition (20), Call Lightning (15; 8D6 M.D.), Compulsion (20), Illusory Wall (15 or 30), Mask of Deceit (15), Hallucination (30), Wisps of Confusion (40), World Bizarre (40). As a powerful creature of magic, Garimond can also instinctively operate Techno-Wizardry items.

Psionics: Induce Sleep (4), Suppress Fear (8), Alter Aura (2), Death Trance (1), Ectoplasmic Disguise (12), Empathy (4), Mask I.S.P. and Psionics (7), Mask P.P.E. (4), See Aura (2), See the Invisible (4), Sense Magic (3), Sense Evil (2), Sixth Sense (2), Telepathy (4), Empathic Transmission (6), Hypnotic Suggestion (6), Mind Block Auto-Defense (0), Mind Bond (10), Psi-Sword (30; 8D6 M.D.), Psionic Invisibility (10), Psychic Omni-Sight (15), Radiate Horror Factor (8). All considered 8th level strength.

Appearance: In his natural form, Garimond is a vaguely humanoid mass of dark green and black, writhing tentacles that appear to be intertwined. In fact, it appears as if his entire body is one sinewy mass of thick ropes with a demonic head, a permanently leering mouth and solid red eyes. Garimond lives to cause confusion, chaos and betrayal through deception. He usually assumes the role of a member of a community or group and begins to cause trouble in small, subtle ways that grow increasingly greater until all of those around him are at each others' throats. He then sits back and savors first the anger and hatred that he has engendered and then the pain and sorrow at what his pawns have done to their former friends, allies, and loved ones. If discovered before his manipulations have come to fruition, he fights until he fears for his life, at which point he will usually feign death in order to escape. If those who thwarted him are particularly strong, he may decide to move on to greener pastures but if they defeated him through luck, especially if they do not really understand what they are up against, he will follow them, looking for another opportunity to manipulate them once again.

After another few days travel through the wildness but still about two days shy of the lakeshore city of Lake Side, the players may notice that they are being followed by what appears to be a mountain lion (Perception Roll 14+). If the players use Presence Sense, Sense Magic or any other magic or psychic power used to detect the supernatural, they will learn that this seemingly ordinary predator is something more than it seems. The wildcat is, in fact, a metamorphosed Dragon Hatchling named Tanis Lightwing.

Tanis has been following the players for the past 24 hours and has decided that they might be fun to join. He has spent the majority of his brief life in the wilderness of Lower Michigan and is ready to move on. He is full of enthusiasm and overconfident and wants to prove to the players that they need someone like him with them.

If the players take no notice of the "mountain lion," Tanis will continue to follow the players until he has the chance to prove himself in battle (at some point prior to arriving at Lake Side). If the players figure out that they are being followed and turn to confront the dragon, he will explain that they need him in such a dangerous area as this. If the players accept Tanis' offer, he will assure them that they will not regret their choice (of course, they may end up regretting it anyway). If they flat out refuse his overtures (and he will be very insistent), Tanis will sulk off, but continue to follow from a discreet distance until he can jump into the midst of a battle to prove his worth.

Tanis Lightwing:
3rd level Cat's Eye Dragon Hatchling.

Alignment: Unprincipled.

Age: 5 months old.

Attributes: I.Q. 20, M.E. 15, M.A. 19, P.S. 28 (Supernatural), P.P. 17, P.E. 22, P.B. 22, Spd 24 running, 105 flying.

Size: 30 feet (9.1 m) long; 4 tons.

M.D.C.: 370

P.P.E.: 94

I.S.P.: 69

Horror Factor: 12

Attacks per Melee: 4

Bonuses: +3 on initiative, +2 on Perception Rolls, +3 to strike, +4 to parry, +4 to dodge, +3 to pull punch, +3 to roll with punch, +4 to save versus Horror Factor, +2 to save versus psionics, mind control, and possession, +5 to save versus magic, +5 to save versus poison, +1 on all other saving throws, +55% to invoke trust or intimidate, +55% to charm and impress.

Damage: Punch (3D6+2 M.D.), Power Punch (6D6+2 M.D., counts as two attacks), Claw Strike (5D6+2 M.D.), Kick (3D6+2 M.D.), Bite (2D6+2 M.D.), Prehensile Tail Whip (4D6+2 M.D.), Tail Slap Power Strike (6D6+2, counts as two attacks), Wing Attack: Basic (3D6+2 M.D.), Crush (3D6+2), Flame Breath (3D6 M.D., can be used three times per melee round).

Weapons: None, yet.

Natural Abilities/Skills of Note: Nightvision 6000 feet (1829 m), see the invisible, turn invisible at will, resistant to cold and fire (half damage, including Mega-Damage and magic attacks), prehensile tail, bio-regenerate 1D10 per melee round, metamorphosis (6 hour duration, takes seven seconds to change form), teleport (32%), dimensional teleport at ley line nexus only (16%), Lore: Demons and Monsters (56%), Lore: Magic (46%), Languages: Dragonese (98%) and American (62%), Literacy: Dragonese (98%), W.P. Energy Pistol (+2 to strike), Pilot Hovercycle (82%).

Cat's Eye Gaze: Can compel a person to follow any command as long as it is not extremely contrary to their alignment, victim must be looking into the dragon's eyes, save versus Mind Control 14+, range of initial contact is 50 feet (15.2 m), range of influence is 1000 feet (305 m).

Magic: Tanis knows the following invocations: Armor of Ithan (10), Aura of Power (4), Befuddle (6), Blinding Flash (2), Cloud of Smoke (2), Fingers of the Wind (5), Paralysis: Lesser (5), Orb of Cold (6), See Aura (6).

Psionics: Considered a Minor Psionic with the following powers: Alter Aura (2), Death Trance (1), Ectoplasm (6 or 12), Meditation (0), Mind Block (4), Telekinesis (varies).

Cybernetics: None.

Appearance: In his natural form, Tanis is a dragon with feline features, large, golden, almond-shaped eyes, tan scales flecked with red, tufts of dark fur on the tip of his tail and around his head and neck, massive wings, and long, retractable claws. Tanis prefers to take the form of an attractive young male (late teens to early twenties) with strawberry blonde hair, golden eyes, and tan skin. Tanis is a gung-ho, ready to prove himself adolescent who will shoot his mouth off at the wrong time, goad others into fights, challenge strangers if he feels slighted, and in all ways, be a pain in the rear. He also wears his heart on his. . . wing and is prone to exaggerated emotional outbursts (imagine the maturity level and emotions of a six-year old in a supernatural body). Basically, he doesn't know when to keep his mouth shut. However, Tanis will be extremely loyal to his adopted allies, whether they like it or not, and will sacrifice himself for the welfare of his new friends. If treated with kindness and understanding, the players will have found themselves a powerful, loyal, friend and companion for life.

Chapter Three: Adventures on the Not-So-High-Seas

"We're off for a three-hour tour of the lake."

- Cap'n Harry Jamison

After about five or six days in the wilderness, the players will find themselves on the shore of Lake Michigan. At the point where they emerge from the wilderness, they will see the tell-tale signs of civilization only a few miles to the north along the shore (smoke rising over the trees, a haze of smog in the distance, etc.), situated on a peninsula between a pair of small lakes that empty into Lake Michigan. Once a small lakeside community, like most other towns and cities in Lower Michigan, it was overwhelmed by natural disasters and demonic hordes with the coming of the Great Cataclysm. A pair of artificial lakes once used for recreational boating and fishing overflowed and flooded much of the surrounding area, leaving only a narrow spit of land. Finding it an easily defendable location, wilderness folk eventually built a small settlement there. Now, some 300 years later, that small settlement has grown into the wilderness town of Lake Side.

Originally, Lake Side was little more than a community of trappers and wilderness scouts. As time passed, this community steadily grew as more and more people from the surrounding region clustered together for protection from not only the elements but the demons and supernatural fiends that still haunt Lower Michigan. At its heart, Lake Side is still a wilderness community to which trappers and hunters come to buy and sell their wares. In recent years, however, as tensions increased between the Kingdom of Tolkeen and the Coalition States, the community grew exponentially as mercenaries came to and from the region. As a result, a few weapon and armor shops have established themselves, catering not only to the growing mercenary business in the region, but also the locals, who gladly jumped at the opportunity to improve their chances against the monsters in the wilderness. Even with the fall of Tolkeen, Lake Side will continue to prosper, at least for the immediate future, as the future war against the Xiticix looms on the horizon. Though Lake Side originally resembled an 18th century boom town except for the smatterings of high-tech equipment and occasional D-Bee, it now looks more like a large, walled military compound with sentries walking the walls and several guarded entrances where visitors are checked upon entering.

Fearful of drawing the attention of the Coalition military for aiding mercenaries coming to the region, the rulers of Lake Side, a clan of retired woodsmen and trappers who invested in the growing settlement, decided to crack down on the presence of magic and D-Bees in the city. Though not outlawed, transient D-Bees in Lake Side are finding it more and more difficult to find services willing to deal with them, while magic users are being told that any display of powers will result in their expulsion from the city. Overt supernatural beings, including dragons, are not allowed under any circumstances and will be attacked with lethal force if they attempt to gain entry.

Further restrictions upon entering Lake Side include:

- Entry Fee. There is a 25 credit charge levied on all non-residents every time they enter Lake Side. This money is used to help maintain the town's militia and other public services.

- No heavy weapons. Upon entering Lake Side, visitors are asked to check in any heavy energy weapons and explosives they might have on their person. While they will not be searched, if such weapons are used in an altercation in the city, the person(s) will be kicked out of town.

- Smaller energy weapons (pistols and rifles) are allowed. Visitors are warned that if they cause trouble in the city, even if they did not start it, they will be expelled from Lake Side.

- Energy pistols and rifles are sold in Lake Side, but the sale of heavy weapons, explosives, and missiles is strictly prohibited, with offenders being expelled from Lake Side after their illegal goods are confiscated and a heavy fine is levied.

- No robots, large military vehicles, aircraft, or power armor. A recent addition to keep the peace has been to add a series of garage and storage containers on the outskirts of town. Fees for storage are 100 credits a day for a small storage container big enough for most power armor and 500 credits for a full-sized bay large enough to accommodate all but the largest robots or military vehicles. This restriction does not include hovercraft, but does apply to rocket bikes (e.g. the Coalition Sky Cycle or the Northern Gun Sky King). Despite the obvious opportunity this would be for theft, the administrators of Lake Side have invested in fairly high-tech security and 24 hour monitoring (both video and guards on station) in order to ensure that the city maintains a fair reputation.

- Visible heavy cybernetic and bionic weapons must be deactivated prior to entering the city. At each entrance to the walled compound there is an Operator with enough skill in Cybernetics to safely deactivate most common cybernetic and bionic weapons. A small charge of 75 credits is levied for this service, and the weapon will be reactivated when leaving. (The weapon system can be easily reactivated by a successful skill roll in Bioware Mechanics or Cybernetic Medicine.)

All of these rules are posted at each entrance to Lake Side for all visitors to see.

A recent development in Lake Side has been an influx of refugees from Tolkeen. Just in the past week, there has been a steady flow of people fleeing the CS occupation of Minnesota.

As a result, a number of individuals have created a business providing ferry services to smuggle people across Lake Michigan. This is more dangerous than it sounds for a number of reasons. Not only is Lake Michigan the home to the world's only freshwater Power Triangle (like a mini-Bermuda Triangle) and thus populated by all manner of sea monsters, the Coalition Navy still actively patrols the lake (though their numbers are greatly diminished, having suffered in their war with Free Quebec), looking for fleeing Tolkeenites. Furthermore, pirates have always been a problem on the Great Lakes and have only grown bolder since the weakening of the CS Navy.

Provided the players do not make a nuisance of themselves (and that they hold Tanis' tongue in check and keep his nature well hidden), they should have little trouble finding a ship willing to ferry them across Lake Michigan. At present, there is one vessel large enough to carry a well armed party, complete with vehicles, across the lake. The *Angelina* is a converted super-sized yacht salvaged from a pre-Rifts cache of vehicles discovered several years ago. Retro-fitted with modern armor and weapons with most of the luxury accommodations gutted for cargo space, the *Angelina is* captained by a pirate named Harry Jamison, who has recently jumped on the refugee smuggling bandwagon. Though far from an altruistic person, "Cap'n Harry" has no love for the Coalition and sees this as his small part in the war effort (even if the war has been lost). Still, this does not stop him from charging extravagant fees for his services.

When approached, he will ask the players, more out of curiosity than anything else, where they are heading once they cross Lake Michigan and why they are going. He will not care where they say they are going, even if they are honest about heading to the occupied territories. He will charge them 20,000 credits each for a berth on his boat and will make arrangements to set sail the following morning. Players whose gear and/or vehicles are located in the storage facilities outside of town will be able to receive a permit to move them to a dock on the northern edge of the city where they can board the ship.

Cap'n Harry Jamison: 7th level Pirate O.C.C.

Alignment: Anarchist.

Age: 47

Attributes: I.Q. 11, M.E. 14, M.A. 19, P.S. 13, P.P. 12, P.E. 15, P.B. 15, Spd 10.

Size: 5 feet, 8 inches (1.7 m) tall; 220 pounds (99 kg).

Hit Points: 39

S.D.C.: 38

P.P.E.: 7

I.S.P.: 0

Attacks per Melee: 5

Bonuses: +3 on initiative, +2 to strike, +4 to parry, +5 to dodge, +2 to roll with punch, +3 to pull punch, +2 to disarm, Critical Strike on a Natural 18-20, +55% to invoke trust and intimidate.

Weapons: Conventional Dagger: 1D6 S.D.C.

CP-30 Laser Pulse Pistol: 2D4 M.D. single shot, 4D6 M.D. triple burst, 30 shot long clip (Harry has 8 spare clips).

Wilk's 457 Laser Pulse Rifle: 3D6+2 M.D. single shot, 1D6x10 M.D. triple burst, 30 shots per clip (Harry has 10 spare clips).

Vibro-Sword: 2D6 M.D.

Armor: Gladiator EBA (70 M.D.C.).

Skills of Note: Boats: Motor, Race & Hydrofoil (98%), Boats: Ships (90%/85%), Water Scooters (90%), Sensory Equipment (70%), Ship Mechanics (60%), Gambling (72%), Salvage (65%), Jury-Rig (55%), Weapon Systems (80%), Escape Artist (75%), Swimming (98%), W.P. Sword (+3 to strike and parry), W.P. Knife (+3 to strike, parry, and throw), W.P. Energy Pistol (+4 to strike), W.P. Energy Rifle (+3 to strike).

Magic Knowledge: None.

Psionic Abilities: None.

Equipment: Standard for a fairly successful Great Lakes pirate, including salvage gear, S.C.U.B.A. gear and light armor, underwater weapons, etc.

Cybernetics: Amplified Hearing, Oxygen Storage Cell (30 minute supply), Sound Filtration System, Depth Gauge and Alarm. Cybernetic bonuses have already been factored in.

Appearance: Cap'n Harry is a friendly enough person, though perceptive players will notice that this is part of his guise to put people at ease. While he is by no means an honest person, he has a strict personal policy about taking advantage of clients: he will not harm or help them in any way unless they deserve it. He just wants to get paid and keep his business going. He is bald with a graying beard, blue eyes, a weathered face, and a slight bulge in his midsection.

The *Angelina* (Quick Stats)

Class: Private Armored Yacht.

Crew: 30 total: three officers (Cap'n Harry, First Mate Marley, and Sergeant Jamax), navigator/sensor tech, pilot/communications tech, three gunners, engineer, medic (also a low level Ley Line Walker), 8 crewmen, 12 warriors (four Power Armor Pilots, two Merc Soldiers, one Head Hunter, one Juicer, one Psi-Stalker, one "Feral" Dog Boy, one Ley Line Walker, and one Water Warlock. Sergeant Jamax himself is a Head Hunter Partial Conversion Cyborg).

Main Body M.D.C.: 1250

Maximum Speed: 45 mph (72 km).

Maximum Range: 750 miles (1200 km).

Cargo: 100 tons in addition to the basic ship supplies.

Bonuses: +2 to strike with on-board weapon systems.

Rail Guns (2; mounted port and starboard): Mega-Damage: 1D6x10 per 60 round burst. Range: 4,000 feet (1219 m). Payload: 6000 rounds per ammo drum (2 drums per rail gun; additional ammo in storage below deck).

Anti-Ship/Anti-Aircraft Missile Launcher: Mega-Damage: 2D6x10 (Armor Piercing or Plasma). Rate of Fire: Single shot or volleys of two or four. Range: 5 miles/8 km (Armor Piercing), or 3 miles/4.8 km (Plasma). Payload: 64; another 256 are stored in the ship's hold.

Power Armor: Four of Sergeant Jamax's warriors are Power Armor Pilot O.C.C.s. One QPA-101 Pale Death SAMAS (stolen from Free Quebec), two Northern Gun NG-X9 Samsons, and one FT-005 Flying Titan.

Other Weapons: Smoke grenade dispensers (2), Chaff Launcher, Torpedo Countermeasures.

Black Market Cost: 250 million credits if Cap'n Harry were ever to sell her.

Lake Side is broken up into four main quarters (not including the vehicle storage area). The Middle-Class Neighborhood was once the core of the original wilderness settlement. In addition to a number of private residences, there are a number of shops that still cater to the needs of the transient trapper and huntsman population. The Upper-Class Neighborhood developed as Lake Side began to change from a predominately wilderness settlement to a mercenary stronghold. As more and more services were offered for the growing mercenary business, those becoming wealthy settled on the north shore of the peninsula. Although the occasional shop can be found here, this quarter is mainly residential and patrolled by well paid members of the militia. Almost at the same time, the Slums came into being as those who were not so lucky in their efforts were forced to settle around the old ruins. While mainly low income housing and shacks, there are a few shops in this area. As Lake Side has recently changed its outlook towards D-Bees, this is where most of them are forced to live. The militia seldom patrols these places unless some disturbance threatens to spill out into the other areas of town. As such, one is more likely to find illegal services in this neighborhood, but doing so will require some searching and smooth talking (Streetwise skill roll, etc.). The Tech Sector came into being as the Upper Class did not want their new neighborhood overcrowded with shops, garages, and weapons dealers. This neighborhood mainly consists of shops, bars, and inns and is the part of town where most travelers remain, as there is little to see or do in Lake Side apart from buy, sell, or trade weapons.

Lake Side

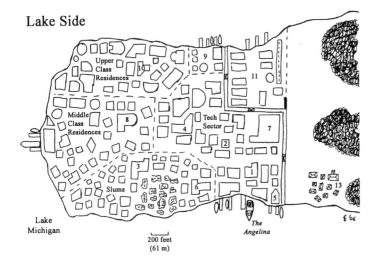

Lake Michigan

200 feet
(61 m)

The Angelina

Additional highlights for the city of Lake Side:

1. There is a Northern Gun shop in the city. Sells most basic gear, weapons, and armor. No power armor, heavy weapons, or vehicles. Costs are about 15-20% above normal.

2. A Wilk's Laser Distributor has recently set up shop. Pretty much all of the Wilk's brand laser weapons and tools are available at only about 5% above book rate.

3. There is a junk shop in town run by a half-crazy, old Ogre woodsman-turned-junk dealer. While most of what lines the walls (floors, counters, and ceiling) of his shop is useless junk, there is the odd chance that a person taking the time to do a thorough search through the collection of junk will find some ancient pre-Rifts item worth something more than the few dozen credits the old man charges (sorry, no magic). Just be nice to him or he will throw you out of his shop. He is one of the few D-Bees in Lake Side who has been a part of the community for so long that his inhuman nature is overlooked by the community authorities.

4. Joe's Secondhand Outfitters is run by a "detoxed" Juicer who now buys, sells, and trades all manner of used gear and equipment. This will be the best place to find a good deal on salvage and repaired equipment, including weapons and armor. It is also about the only place to sell salvaged items. If the items are basically in good to excellent condition, Joe will pay 20% of the book value (or give up to 50% in trade). For damaged or malfunctioning equipment, he will pay only 10% of the cost (or give up to 25% in trade). Joe will not buy scrap unless it is something he can cannibalize for parts and armor, and then he won't give more than 1% of the cost for the junk. Though Joe is not as skilled at repairs as Anderson (see below), he does have a few mechanics of his own on staff that do a good enough job of patching up most of the gear that is sold to him. Armor bought from Joe will still have up to 75% of the original M.D.C. Weapons will work fine but will look banged up and ragged (Joe is an expert on weapons of all designs). Explosives, power armor, and robots are not available from Joe's Secondhand Outfitters.

5. Along the lake shore, there is a dealer who sells water craft. Though most of his wares include small private vessels for river use and for sailing along the shore close to land (fishing, river travel, etc.), he has a few less-than-legal vehicles he has managed to acquire from Black Market sources. These include several varieties of the smaller armored and armed water craft, including generic versions of several military-style sea-sleds and hydrobikes. Prices are 100-150% above normal for his "special" items.

6. The Devil's Den is a rough and rowdy drinking establishment that caters to the transient D-Bees who have recently found most other services now unavailable to them. Though there is no official rule concerning humans, it is generally understood that humans (and other "pretty" D-Bees like Elves, etc.) are not welcome at the Devil's Den. Entertainment at the Den includes a number of noxious intoxicating beverages, several crude games of chance (basic card games and dice games), a reinforced "dartboard" at which players throw Vibro-Knives (not many people sit near this game), physical competitions that include arm-wrestling with shards of glass on the table, and skull bashing. Lake Side authorities tend to turn a blind eye to what goes on at the Devil's Den as long as it does not spill over into the streets.

7. There is a fairly modern garage that boasts the equipment and expertise to repair just about anything. Run by an ex-Ishpeming Operator O.C.C. (9th level) named Anderson, he and his crew will fix anything from a jammed rifle to a robot. His prices are steep, however, and since he is the only really qualified Operator in the region, there is a long waiting list for major jobs (vehicle, robot, and power armor repair) and it may be weeks before he can get to them. Anderson will do a rush job (within 48-72 hours) but the cost will double or triple depending upon how he feels about the person asking. Anderson (never goes by his first name) also has connections to the Black Market and can get illegal items, including heavy weapons, missiles, and explosives, but such special orders take a long time to ship and are 200-500% above book price.

8. Wilderness Furs and Skins is perhaps the oldest establishment in Lake Side. It is still the place to buy, sell, and trade animal skins. Run by a retired trapper (a "semi-civilized" Psi-Stalker) who once hunted everything from bear and deer to supernatural monsters and Xiticix, this shop is usually only frequented by fellow huntsmen who spend weeks in the wilderness before coming back to sell their skins, hides and meats. It is also the best place to find a guide willing to take a party into the wilderness as long as it is not during the peak hunting seasons (which vary from hunter to hunter depending upon the particular prey they are after). The average level of woodsmen is 4th to 6th level Wilderness Scout O.C.C.

9. The Lake Side Militia is headquartered in a small compound and is made up of residents who are paid to take shifts acting as both police force and city defenders. Such an arrangement means that police are more likely to take the side of a local over a transient, even if the local is one of the few accepted resident D-Bees. The average level of the militia members is 3rd to 5th and the O.C.C. is the equivalent of a Vagabond, Wilderness Scout, or Head Hunter (with few or no cybernetics or bionics) O.C.C. The Lake Side Militia is run by a 10th level, Ex-Headhunter Partial Conversion Cyborg of Unprincipled alignment (loyal to his men and the leaders of Lake Side only).

10. Though magic has, in recent years, been outlawed in Lake Side, there is a small underground coalition (how ironic) of magic users (mainly Druids and Warlocks with a small number of Techno-Wizards) who do business in the city. Established by a Rogue Scholar named Phinneus Amstan, these magic users never deal directly with one another but go through him. As one of the city leaders, Phinneus is considered untouchable by the Lake Side Militia and can move about visiting different people without causing too much suspicion. If a transient magic user runs afoul of the law for something innocent, or through an act of self defense is forced to reveal his powers and risk expulsion, members of this secret organization will attempt to hide the individual until the commotion quiets down. Though there are no official services provided, once a magic user knows about this group, he or she can trade magic items, spells, or knowledge, though being such a small group, there is just not that much to offer.

11. As described above, all large robots, power armor and military vehicles must be stored in the armored garage sheds just outside the town's walls. Directly adjacent to the section of Lake Side where the militia has its headquarters, this compound is well guarded and monitored. While theft of vehicle contents does occasionally occur, seldom does an entire vehicle get taken. The mercenaries who guard the storage facilities are surprisingly loyal to the authorities of Lake Side.

12. In the center of the slums is a small collection of pre-Rifts ruins, the few crumbling structures still standing centuries after the Great Cataclysm. Rumor has it that they are haunted by a number of Entities, and occasionally a blood drained body will turn up, giving credence to the rumors that a vampire or some other supernatural menace has taken up residence in the ruins.

13. Refugee tents have begun to spring up just outside the town. At present, the town leaders are not sure what they should do about this. Though they have no love of the Coalition and hold nothing against the Tolkeen refugees, they do not want a Coalition patrol boat to sail by (as they do from time to time, though less frequently of late as a result of their losses to the formidable Free Quebec navy), see the refugee camp and order their town razed as an example to others who would harbor enemies of the CS.

Though it will only take a few hours to cross the width of Lake Michigan, there will be two encounters that could slow their progress considerably. After the *Angelina* has been out of sight of the shore for about an hour (Cap'n Harry has been sailing southwest at a fairly slow rate so as not to tax his engines or arouse suspicion), the players on deck will notice smoke rising in the distance off to port. Through skillful role-playing, the players should be able to convince Cap'n Harry to change course to investigate. If the players themselves seem unwilling to investigate, Game Masters may want to have the *Angelina* receive a distress call.

"Mayday! To any ships in the area this is the... <signal lost> ...under heavy fire from... <signal lost> ...women and children... <signal lost> ... Help us, please!"

When they are within sight of the battle, the players will see what looks like a small cargo barge listing to port and smoking from three fires on deck. The sounds of rail gun fire and energy weapons can be heard even from a distance. However, whoever or whatever the ship is doing battle with is on the far side and impossible to see from the players' position. Cap'n Harry will quickly size up the situation and decide that it is not worth the trouble and make ready to sail off when a small speedboat will be seen coming around from the far side of the damaged vessel. Any player using binoculars or enhanced vision will see that it looks like a group of people trying to flee. Within seconds, a second vessel will round the bow of the barge and open fire, destroying the fleeing boat. Even from a distance, the pursuing vessel is clearly a Splugorth Minion Slaver and Slave Barge.

At this point, the players will clearly be faced with a dilemma. Any character of good alignment will feel compelled to assist, even if only to help hold the Splugorth at bay to allow the rest of the survivors to escape. Cap'n Harry, however, will not in any way want to tangle with the Splugorth. It will take even more clever role-playing to convince the pirate that it is worth taking on the Splugorth (perhaps by proving that they are powerful enough to help tip the balance in the battle, or by tempting him with the prospect of salvaging weapons and magic from Atlantis).

As luck would have it, though the players do not know this at first, the Kittani Slave Raider that is attacking the barge has only a small complement of soldiers as it has just dropped off most of its warriors on the shores of Wisconsin to loot the CS occupied Kingdom of Tolkeen. As such, there is actually a fairly good chance that the players, along with Cap'n Harry's men, will be able to drive off the Raider if not destroy it entirely.

KY-HSS Slaver Raider (Quick Stats)

Class: Hydrofoil/Hovercraft Assault Ship.

Crew: 22 total: captain, two pilots, navigator, two communications officers, two sensor officers, three petty officers, four weapons officers, and seven sailors. The normal compliment of soldiers is reduced as a result of most of them being deployed to loot the Kingdom of Tolkeen. At present, there are only two Minion Slaver Barges, eight Blind Altara Warrior Women, and Four Kittani Flying Fox Power Armor units.

Main Body M.D.C.: 1,768 remain of the original 2,500.

Maximum Speed: Hydrofoil: 100 mph (160 km). Hovercraft (over water): 400 mph (640 km). Hovercraft (on land): 40 mph (64 km).

Maximum Range: Unlimited.

Bonuses: None.

Pulse Cannon Turret: Mega-Damage: 1D4x10 (single pulse); 2D4x10 (double burst); 3D4x10 (triple pulse). Range: 6,000 feet (1829 m). Payload: Unlimited.

Long Range Missile Launchers (2): Mega-Damage: Varies with missile type (typically Armor Piercing). Rate of Fire: Single shot or volleys of two, four, six, eight, twelve, or fourteen. Range: 500 to 1800 miles (800 to 2880 km). Payload: 128; 64 per launcher.

Other Weapons: Depth Charges.

Splugorth Minion Slaver and Barge (2)

Alignment: Miscreant.

Attributes: I.Q. 10, M.E. 25, M.A. 6, P.S. 28, P.P. 19, P.E. 23, P.B. 4, Spd 77 (hover).

Size: 10 feet (3 m) from belly to head in the barge, tentacles reach 16 feet (5.6 m).

Hit Points: 70

S.D.C.: N/A

M.D.C.: 120 (from Armor of Ithan force field; regenerates at full strength 15 seconds after it is depleted).

P.P.E.: 120

I.S.P.: 40

Horror Factor: 16

Attacks per Melee: 10

Bonuses: Cannot be surprised or attacked from behind, +6 on initiative, +4 to strike, +10 to parry, +4 to dodge, +4 to save versus magic and poison, +5 to save versus Horror Factor, +5 to save versus psionics.

Damage: Tentacle Strike (6D6 +13 S.D.C.), Power Strike (2D6 M.D. but counts as two attacks), Claws (3D6 M.D.), and Bite (2D6 M.D.).

Weapons: Staff of Eylor: 3D6 M.D. as a blunt weapon plus the following spells that can be cast at 8th level strength (14+ to save versus magic) twice per day: Extinguish Fire, Repel Animals, Fear, Chameleon, Befuddle, Call Lightning, Energy Disruption, Dispel Magic Barriers, Negate Magic, Tongues, Oracle.

Forearm Plasma Blaster: 5D6 M.D. per blast, 20 shot payload (can be recharged by a Techno-Wizard for 70 P.P.E.).

Head Laser: 2D6 M.D. per blast, 20 shot payload (can be recharged by a Techno-Wizard for 60 P.P.E.).

Vehicle: Eylor Slave Barge: Main Body M.D.C. 500, silent hover (prowl 60%) 53 mph (85 km), two (2) barge blasters (4D6 S.D.C.), can perform the following spells at 8th level strength twice per day: Blinding Flash, Globe of Daylight, and Chameleon. Five (5) Eylor Floating Eyes accompany the barge wherever it goes and the Minion sees whatever they see: Nightvision 600 feet (183 m), telescopic vision 6000 feet (1829 m), magnification to the 300th power, polarized vision, see aura, see the invisible, sense magic, see P.P.E. energy, prowl (70%), mini-jolt gun (2D6 or 4D6 S.D.C. or 1D4 M.D.), same spell abilities as the barge.

Natural Abilities: Swim (98%), hold breath for 6D6 minutes, smell blood up to 4000 feet (1219 m), track by blood scent (66%).

Magic: Limited to the powers of the barge, the Staff of Eylor, and Eyes of Eylor.

Psionics: Considered a Minor Psionic with the following powers: Mind Block (4) and Telepathy (6).

Appearance: A massive reptilian monster with a gaping maw, eight tentacles, and powerful arms whose lower body is bonded to the large, floating Eylor Barge.

Altara Blind Warrior Women (8)

Alignment: Anarchist.

Attributes: I.Q. 14, M.E. 18, M.A. 17, P.S. 24, P.P. 24, P.E. 23, P.B. 22, Spd 34.

Size: 6 feet (1.8 m) tall and 160 lbs (72 kg).

Hit Points: 50   **P.P.E.:** 8

S.D.C.: 110   **I.S.P.:** 90

Attacks per Melee: 6

Bonuses: +2 on initiative, +6 to strike, +7 to parry, +7 to dodge, +4 to roll with punch, +2 to pull punch, +4 to save versus psionics, +2 to save versus insanity, +5 to save versus magic, +4 to save versus poison, +4 to save versus Horror Factor.

Weapons: Conventional Dagger: 1D6+11 S.D.C.

Vibro-Blade: 1D6 M.D.

Net Gun: Fires up to two *Magic Net* spells per melee, duration of net is 20 minutes, 20 shot payload.

Laser Wrist Blaster: 2D6 M.D., 60 blasts, backpack recharges in 24 hours.

Mental Incapacitator: Fires up to 2 *Wisps of Confusion* spells per melee, duration of spell is 50 minutes, 10 blast payload.

Armor: Lightweight Body Suit (30 M.D.C.) and an amulet that provides Armor of Ithan (100 M.D.C.) three times a day for a ten minute duration each time.

Vehicle: Four warrior women can ride on the Minion Slaver's Barge behind decorative shields which provide 100 M.D.C. of protection.

Natural Abilities/Skills of Note: Gymnastics (6th level experience), Swimming (85%), Prowl (50%), W.P. Knife (+2 to strike, +3 to parry), W.P. Energy Pistol (+3 to strike), W.P. Energy Rifle (+3 to strike), heightened sense of hearing, heightened sense of smell, heightened sense of touch, radar sense 1200 feet (366 m), cannot be surprised from behind. Reduce all combat bonuses and special sense in half in stormy conditions (fouls natural radar sense).

Magic: None, other than her Bio-Wizardry Splugorth items.

Psionics: Considered Major Psychics with the following powers: Sixth Sense (2), Presence Sense (4), Empathy (4), Sense Magic (3), Sense Evil (2), Object Read (6), Clairvoyance (4), and Mind Block (4).

Appearance: Beautiful women in skin-tight body suits, wearing helmets with visors over their eyes.

Kittani Flying Fox Power Armor (4): (Quick Stats)

Pilot: One (1) 3rd level Kittani Warrior R.C.C.

Main Body M.D.C.: 350

Physical Strength: Equivalent to Augmented P.S. of 40.

Speed: Running: 50 mph (80 km). Leaping: 15 feet (4.6 m); jet assist to 200 feet (61 m) high or 300 feet (31 m) across. Flying: Hover up to 300 feet (91 m) or fly up to 600 mph (960 km). Maximum altitude is 20,000 feet (6096 m).

Maximum Range: 12 hours of top speed flight or 36 hours at half speed before overheating.

Attacks per Melee: 8 (the pilot has 6 attacks per melee round outside of his armor).

Bonuses (including pilot's Hand to Hand skills, W.P., and attribute bonuses): +3 to initiative, +7 to strike hand to hand, +3 to strike with energy weapons, +9 to parry, +8 to dodge, +13 to dodge in flight, +6 to pull punch, +7 to roll with punch, +2 to save versus Horror Factor, +2 to save versus psionics and insanity.

Double Bladed Plasma Axe: Mega-Damage: 1D4x10 (energized strike or short-range blast). Range: Close combat or 200 feet (61 m). Payload: Unlimited.

Class One Shield and Mini-Missile Launcher: Mega-Damage: 3D4 as a blunt weapon or 1D4x10 from the mini-missile. Rate of Fire: Single shot or volleys of two, three, or four. Range: Close combat or one mile (1.6 km). Payload: Four mini-missiles.

Other Weapons: Wing Mini-Missiles (4), Wing Lasers (2), Wing Vibro-Blades (2).

The Kittani Slaver Raider will use its cannon to engage the *Angelina,* as its long-range missiles are too heavy to use at such close range. After the players and Cap'n Harry's forces engage the Slaver, the Splugorth will battle until the Raider is reduced to less than 1000 M.D.C. or half of its remaining troops are slain before it attempts to flee (it is still a long way from Little Atlantis on the island of Newfoundland). If the players seem particularly effective at driving off the Splugorth, the remaining laser cannon mounted on the damaged barge will open fire, adding to the assault against the slaver.

Game Masters, it would be best if you only role-play the part of the battle involving the player characters and assume that Cap'n Harry's seasoned warriors can hold their own. In the play test, the players faced off against one of the Slaver Barges, four of the Blind Warrior Women and two of the Flying Foxes.

When the Splugorth are either driven off or sunk, the players will discover that the barge is actually conveying a large number of refugees (350; mainly women, children and the elderly) from Tolkeen across to Lake Side. Though they have little to offer as reward for their rescue, the players (and Cap'n Harry) may be able to salvage a few Splugorth items which will fetch a high price on the Black Market. The barge will take about 16 hours to repair (this could be reduced with help from any skilled players or William Sansburn), during which time Cap'n Harry will begin to get nervous about remaining still for so long. Still, he cannot help but enjoy the boost to his reputation that he has just earned for taking on the Splugorth and surviving.

Halfway through the next day, after the refugee barge has continued on its way east and when the players are only a few hours from the Wisconsin shore, the *Angelina* will encounter a Coalition patrol boat. Cap'n Harry will recognize it as the *CSS Viper*, a regular patrol destroyer on Lake Michigan commanded by Lieutenant Commander Edward Trenham. At first, he will act worried and fret about being discovered with mercenaries on board, especially if they are D-Bees or practitioners of magic. He will then wait until the players begin coming up with plans to deal with the rapidly approaching CS destroyer before he suggests hailing them on the radio. As he nervously licks his lips and lifts the radio to his mouth, he will give the *Angelina's* registry. When Commander Trenham responds, Cap'n Harry will let out a laugh and ask the Commander over for a drink. This will be followed by raucous laughter from both him and his crew when they see the look on the faces of the player characters (Cap'n Harry and Commander Trenham have a quiet "arrangement" whereby the captain makes regular "contributions" to the commander's unofficial retirement pension and the commander looks the other way).

When the laughter dies down, however, another voice will cut in from the CS destroyer, identifying himself as *Captain Jacobi* of the Coalition Navy. He will decline the offer for a drink and order the *Angelina* to come broadside and prepare to

be boarded and inspected. Cap'n Harry will curse and cut the line, saying that he has heard of Captain Jacobi and that this is not good. He will order the players below deck, where some of his crewmen will hide them away in a secret compartment in the cargo hold.

Commander Trenham is, on the surface, a model officer in the Coalition Navy. He is well loved by his crew and was responsible for some of the few naval victories in the war against Free Quebec. However, in reality, Trenham realizes that he would not make the best CS Navy career officer, where the higher up the chain of command one gets, the more watched over you become by your superiors lest you show signs of disloyalty. He had planned to spend another year or two building up his "retirement" before taking his ship and heading out to sea for good. His crew, all ultra-loyal to their commander, both because they see him as the reason they survived the war with Free Quebec when most of the CS Navy was sunk and because they are fortunate enough to share in his profits, are all planning on following Trenham wherever he takes them.

These plans have recently hit a snag, however. With his successes in the war, his superiors have decided to place him on a fast track for promotion and, as such, have already placed him under closer scrutiny to confirm his loyalty. Unlike Trenham, Captain Jacobi is a pure blood, by-the-book career naval officer and is not happy about what he feels is a babysitting duty for what, in his opinion, is an under-qualified officer. He has been looking for a chance to show the commander for the misfit he really is and now it may have just arrived.

Within five minutes, the two vessels will be side-by-side and the *Angelina* will be swarming with Coalition sailors searching her for refugees, D-Bees, magic users, contraband or just about anything that they can use as an excuse to impound the boat and arrest her captain and crew. This encounter should be played for tension even though the players will spend most of it in hiding. The glimpse they saw of the *Viper* as she approached should have been enough to convince the players that they are in no shape to take on a fully armed and crewed destroyer, even on their best day, and especially not after tangling with the Splugorth the day before. Game Masters, feel free to heighten the suspense with the players hearing sounds of arguing above deck, the noise of circling helicopters, the whine of SAMAS jets, the scraping of cargo boxes as the search progresses into the cargo hold, and the uncertain feeling that one of the CS sailors might have glimpsed their hiding place. Fortunately for Cap'n Harry (and the players), while Jacobi is out for Trenham's blood, he does not suspect his crew, and they are being careful not to find anything that will endanger their lucrative arrangement with the crew of the *Angelina*. So as long as the players remain in hiding, quiet and nervous, there is nothing to worry about. The *Viper* will depart 30 minutes later and Cap'n Harry will come for the players. If the players are foolish and draw attention to themselves (or worse, actually attack the search party), then a battle with the destroyer will ensue. Commander Trenham may like Harry and his crew, but he will not directly oppose the CS Navy if his men are attacked.

CSS Viper (Quick Stats)

Class: James Bay Class Guided Missile Destroyer.

Crew: 120 total: 8 officers, 13 chief petty officers, 99 enlisted crew. Also carries a complement of 20 Naval Infantry RPAs in

Super SAMAS power armor and 10 in Sea SAMAS power armor.

Main Body M.D.C.: 1450

Maximum Speed: 42 mph (67 km).

Maximum Range: Unlimited.

Bonuses: None.

Heavy Torpedo Tubes (2): Mega-Damage: 4D6x10. Rate of Fire: Single shot or volleys of two. Can fire four volleys per melee round. Range: 20 miles (32 km). Payload: 80 torpedoes.

Medium Missile Launchers (2): Mega-Damage: 3D4x10 to an area of 30 feet (9.1 m). Rate of Fire: Up to three shots per melee round. Range: 10 miles (16 km). Payload: 50 missiles.

Other Weapons: Five-Inch Cannon Turret, Rail Gun Turret, Depth Charge Launchers (2), Landing Pad with two Sea Storm Helicopters.

After another hour on the lake, the *Angelina* will make port at a small wilderness outpost on the ruins of what was once the pre-Rifts town of Kewaunee, Wisconsin.

Chapter Four: Refugees

"Watching from a distance as our loved ones fought and died... We thought the horror of the war would be the worst. That was before we tried to flee."

- Arianna Konaras

Unlike the city of Lake Side, with its growing population and sustained trapper and mercenary industry in Lower Michigan, the tiny landing where the *Angelina* makes port is little more than a collection of wooden shacks and earthen buildings, well camouflaged to look like piles of wood and stone if seen from above or from the shore of Lake Michigan. Originally a native tribal community blasted away by an overzealous Coalition Sky Cycle patrol at the onset of the war with Tolkeen four years ago, now a small collection of Wilderness scouts, Psi-Stalkers, and similar folk call this place home. They hide from the CS patrols and supernatural predators, both of which frequent southern Wisconsin, and make a living in the wildness much the way trappers once did in the 1800s. Now, with the war in Tolkeen recently ended and a slow but steady trickle of refugees making their way east hoping to find some way to escape CS patrolled areas, smugglers have been using the site as a convenient landing place. The CS suspects refugee activity in the region but, so far, no patrols have discovered the semi-permanent encampment, and the smugglers and pirates have been wary enough to avoid the area when a patrol is nearby. This is accomplished by the pirates and smugglers dropping off part of their crew and then retreating from the area to return at a pre-set time. This is what the *Angelina* does under cover of darkness as the players, Cap'n Harry, and a few of his crew head for shore and the tiny village nearby.

The general population of the Landing (as it is unofficially called by the pirates) varies from season to season, as huntsmen go out for months at a time during the warmer seasons and return to hold up for the winter. During the summer, there will be less than two dozen permanent residents, a mix of human and D-Bee woodsmen and natives who fish and hunt small game in the area. During the winter, when the snow and ice blankets the area, the camp becomes a small village of about 100. There are no formal services for hire or goods to purchase in the Landing, as the few locals have no real need for credits. Trade for goods or services is about the only currency in the area. The heart of the village is a large lodge-type structure half sunk in the ground and covered with rocks and wood to look like a natural hill. This large, open chamber is not unlike the great hall of a Hearth and Home with tables, benches, and a fire against one wall. It is to this building that Cap'n Harry will lead the players.

While the seasonal population hovers around 20 residents, this does not include the number of refugees who will be present at any given time of late. They come in groups, as few as two or three or as many as a few dozen at a time. Few groups larger than that survive the crossing from Tolkeen to the shores of Lake Michigan, especially with the stranglehold the Coalition has put in place to prevent the Tolkeenites from escaping. Most larger groups attract too much attention and are easy pickings for the CS patrols whose orders are to shoot to kill ALL unauthorized personnel in the region.

At present, most of the population is hunting, leaving only the two dozen locals as well as a few transients and about a dozen refugees waiting for word of a ship willing to take them across the lake. Cap'n Harry's arrival will bring a small amount of relief to this lot, as they have been waiting for three days now and are paranoid that the longer they sit still, the more likely the Coalition will find them. As Harry begins negotiations with the refugees for passage (the cost will be steep and the refugees will seem hard-pressed to pay it at first - any player who offers to chip in or pay for it should receive bonus experience!), he will give them some parting advice: Find a guide. With that, he will leave them to finish making arrangements with the leader of the refugees.

At the present, with most of the experienced woodsmen in the wilderness, there are few experienced guides present at the Landing. The only one willing to take the players west into the ley line dominated, CS patrolled wilderness is a Simvan Monster Rider named Zanchavex.

Exactly where Zanchavex came from, none of the locals at the Landing can rightly say. One day, three years ago, the Monster Rider appeared at the village one winter, nearly frozen to death. Though the few Psi-Stalkers present at the time were against it (Psi-Stalkers and Simvan see one another as rivals), the overwhelming majority of the population refused to turn anyone out into the blizzards, as many of them had themselves benefited from the kindness of strangers who may have otherwise cast them out instead. Since that time, Zanchavex has spent the better part of the intervening years becoming familiar with his new home, learning the patterns of the CS patrols in the region, and defending the Landing on several occasions. Even the Psi-Stalkers who winter over at the Landing were forced to grudgingly accept the newcomer as a valuable member of their rural community. Of his past, the Simvan will not speak, though one refugee recently commented that his accent seemed to suggest the southwest, perhaps from the region of the Pecos Empire. While visitors speculate at what such an unusual D-Bee is doing in a peaceful wilderness encampment, the locals have all accepted him as one of their own. Exactly how this cannibalistic D-Bee eats is anyone's guess. From time to time, he heads out

into the wilderness and comes back with spare weapons, armor, and equipment to trade. No one asks about it since most of the gear is Coalition hardware.

Zanchavex is willing to guide the players across the wilderness, though he will only do so if they are willing to tell him the truth about where they want to go (he will use Empathy to judge the validity of their responses). He will warn them that the Wisconsin wilderness is dominated by three hostile influences. First, even before the war with Tolkeen, the CS sent patrols into the monster laden land. Now, with the war over and so many refugees fleeing in all directions, the patrols have only increased. Second, the number of ley lines and nexus points in the area have resulted in the region being a supernatural playground of sorts where Rifts open periodically, unleashing an ever growing number of monsters into the wilderness. Third, as if the random monsters emerging from the Rifts were not enough, the Xiticix menace is strong in the region, with the oldest established hive located to the northwest. While the bulk of the Xiticix territory is in northern Minnesota, Zanchavex has seen the occasional flying patrol of insects as far south as mid-Wisconsin.

After all this, if the players are still willing to cross into such a dangerous territory, he will take them. However, he makes it clear that they absolutely must listen to his directions in the wilderness and that if they disobey him, he will leave them on their own. He will also only take them as far as the edge of the Kingdom of Tolkeen's border, not deeper into the occupied territory and certainly not into the city itself. For payment, the Monster Rider will accept a trade of either equipment or weapons (preferably, the latter) and will not accept credits as they are of no use to him in the wilderness. The value of the trade should be a good quality weapon between 25,000 and 75,000 credits along with ammunition. He is not interested in magic or TW items.

Zanchavex: 8th level Simvan Monster Rider R.C.C.

Alignment: Aberrant.

Age: 55

Attributes: I.Q. 12, M.E. 19, M.A. 9, P.S. 21, P.P. 17, P.E. 20, P.B. 8, Spd 24.

Size: 6 feet (1.8 m) tall; 200 pounds (90 kg).

Hit Points: 60

S.D.C.: 95

P.P.E.: 11

I.S.P.: 59

Attacks per Melee: 9

Bonuses: +3 on initiative, +3 to strike, +4 to parry, +4 to dodge, +3 to roll with punch, +3 to pull punch, +2 to entangle, +3 to save versus magic, +3 to save versus poison.

Weapons: Conventional Dagger: 1D6+10 S.D.C.

Compound Hunting Bow: +1 to strike (well balanced). Zanchavex has the following arrows on his person at any time: 24 Conventional Arrows: 2D6 S.D.C., 10 Light Explosive Arrows: 1D6x10 S.D.C., 10 High Explosive Arrows: 3D6 M.D., 4 Smoke Arrows: 20 foot (6.1 m) radius, 4 Signal Flare Arrows: burns for 60 seconds.

Bandit IP-10 Ion Pistol: 3D6 M.D. single shot, 20 shot long clip, +1 to strike (Zanchavex has 6 spare clips).

NG-IP7 Ion Pulse Rifle: 3D6 M.D. single shot, 1D4x10 M.D. triple burst, 30 shots per clip (Zanchavex has 6 spare clips).

.30 Rifle: 5D6 S.D.C. per single shot, 15 round magazine (Zanchavex uses this rifle for hunting primarily and has about 200 rounds for it in his gear).

Vibro-Knife: 1D6 M.D.

Armor: Custom Made M.D.C. Hide Armor (75 M.D.C.). Zanchavex owns two extra suits of this.

Skills of Note: Wilderness Survival (95%), Land Navigation (74%), Track Humanoids (80%), Horsemanship: Exotic (85%/75%), Lore: Demons and Monsters (60%), Detect Ambush (65%), Camouflage (55%) Rope Works (65%), Spelunking (90%), Skin and Prepare Animal Hides (65%), Climbing (70%/60%), Lore: Xiticix (45%), W.P. Axe (+3 to strike and parry), W.P. Knife (+3 to strike and parry, +5 to throw), W.P. Energy Pistol (+5 to strike), W.P. Energy Rifle (+5 to strike), W.P. Archery and Targeting (+5 to strike, +1 to parry, rate of fire: 6), W.P. Paired Weapons.

Magic Knowledge: None.

Psionic Abilities: Empathy (4), Telepathy (4), Sixth Sense (2), Mind Block (4), Mind Bond (10), Psionic affinity with animals (as per a Psi-Stalker).

Equipment: Zanchavex has a sizeable collection of wilderness survival and hunter related gear.

Appearance and Disposition: Zanchavex is a matter-of-fact, plain speaking Simvan who will be all too willing to tell the players when they are about to do something stupid. Still, he will let them make their mistakes unless their actions endanger him as well. He appears to be a typical Simvan, though older than most as he has lived far longer than most of his kind given their violent lifestyles.

In classic Simvan style, Zanchavex rides an exotic monster. The beast is a rare creature that originated from the Calgary Rift. Zanchavex calls it a Lake Runner for its unique ability to run with such intense bursts of speed that it can literally run across water for short stretches.

Lake Runner:

Monster from the Rifts and Zanchavex's mount.

Alignment: Animal equivalent of Anarchist.

Attributes: I.Q. 6 (highly cunning animal intelligence), M.E. 5, M.A. 4, P.S. 35 (Supernatural), P.P. 22, P.E. 25, P.B. 9, Spd 220 (can double this for brief periods; see Natural Abilities below).

Size: 12 feet (3.6 m) tall and long with an 18 foot (5.5 m) tail, 850 pounds (382.5 kg).

Horror Factor: 10

M.D.C.: 175

P.P.E.: 27

I.S.P.: 12

Attacks per Melee: 6

Bonuses: +2 on initiative, +4 to strike, +5 to parry, +4 to dodge, +7 to dodge while running, +5 to save versus magic, +5 to save versus poison, +4 to save versus Horror Factor.

Damage: Forelimb Claws (2D6 M.D.), Hind Legs Claws (4D6 M.D.), Kick (6D6 M.D.C.), Bite (1D4 M.D.).

Natural Abilities: Nightvision 3000 feet (914.4 m), Prowl (55%), Wilderness Survival (35%), Natural Climber (65%), Land Navigation (75%), Swim (95%), Natural Leaper: 25 feet (7.6 m) high and 50 feet (15.2 m) across (triple leaping length when running at full supernatural speed).

Supernatural Burst of Speed: Can put on a burst of speed to double its ordinary running speed for 2D6 minutes. This allows it to evade most natural predators and even run across smooth bodies of water for a limited time. When the sprint is over, the beast can not travel any faster than one quarter its normal speed for 1D4 hours.

Magic Knowledge: None.

Psionic Abilities: Sixth Sense (2).

Appearance: At first glance, the Lake Runner resembles any number of bipedal dinosaur-like monsters that have emerged from the Rifts since the Great Cataclysm. However, the entire body seems emaciated, little more than skin and bones with wiry muscles bulging beneath the green and brown mottled skin. A long tail longer than the Lake Runner's body acts as a counterbalance when it is running. While this carnivorous monster usually preys on fish, it will attack most creatures and humanoids smaller than it, though it seems to be perfectly docile when under the influence of the Simvan Monster Rider.

Though Zanchavex will do his best to guide them around the worst of the areas (although he has only been in the region for a couple of years, he knows them well), it will be impossible to avoid trouble entirely. Southern Wisconsin is second only to the Magic Zone in North America with regards to the density of ley lines and nexus points. Supernatural monsters roam the countryside and the Coalition patrols the area.

As with the trek across Lower Michigan, the journey will take several days of slow, steady travel to avoid detection. The region is mainly dense wilderness broken up by numerous small and large lakes, streams, and rivers. Game Masters should feel free to populate the region with as many or as few encounters as they like. The following list can be used for any wilderness encounters from Chapter Four through the beginning of Chapter Eight.

Suggested encounters for the wilderness region of Southern Wisconsin and the edge of Minnesota include:

- Random Ley Line Storm.
- Random ley line. Game Master's discretion as to what might be found along the length of the magical line.
- Random Rift opening.
- Light Coalition patrol. 4 SAMAS (old style) and 2 Sky Cycles (old style) fly overhead. They are only scouting for a larger force some fifty miles (80 km) away and will not engage the players unless they feel that they can easily take them on or unless fired upon first. Unless the players are distracted, they will hear the whine of the Sky Cycle engines long before they are overhead and will have time to hide. If not, then their position will be reported and the players can expect to be attacked by a much larger force later that day.
- The ground shakes as a herd of Rhino-Buffaloes charge by. The players will have 1D4 rounds to make for higher ground or be caught up in the stampede and crushed or attacked by the vicious monsters.
- The players begin to notice that they are suffering from slight hallucinations that are growing increasingly more bizarre. They are being stalked by a young D-Bee Mind Melter who has been enjoying the fun of messing with the players. This kid really has no intention of harming them seriously and is doing it more for the amusement than cruelty. If discovered, he will fight them off and escape. If he is not discovered, he will continue to pick on the players until he grows bored and wanders off in search of someone new to bug.
- A group of 1D4+4 Wild Psi-Stalkers approach the players, demanding that they leave their clan's territory. When they discover that they are being led by a Simvan Monster Rider, they will decide that the players are spies and attack.
- The party spies a small flock of flying creatures in the distance. Anyone using telescopic optics will be able to identify them as Xiticix. What such a large number of these insects are doing so far south of the Hivelands is anyone's guess; however, it cannot be good sign. If the players move along quickly, they will not be spotted.
- Medium Coalition patrol. 6 Striker SAMAS led by 2 Super SAMAS, flying point ahead of a pair of Spider-Skull Walkers, a platoon of Dog Boys and a Psi-Stalker. They are out for blood and are under orders to destroy anyone they find in Lower Minnesota. The players will only have 1D4+2 minutes to hide before the squad finds them. During the day, the use of infrared is limited so as long as the players can get out of the direct path of the patrol, find a hiding place, and power down any vehicles or robots, they should avoid detection. During night, the I.R. signal of any vehicle will light up like a beacon even if they power down, and will draw the flight of SAMAS straight to them.

- While traveling along a ley line, the players are attacked by 20 animated dead dressed in pieced together Coalition Dead Boy armor (remaining M.D.C. is about 40-50) and brandishing Vibro-weapons (2D6 M.D. damage). An insane Necromancer has recently claimed the area and is using the power of a nearby nexus to further his diabolical plans.

- The players enter what at first looks like an artificial clearing, almost perfectly circular, several nearby tree stumps neatly sawed flat, etc. However, the majority of the center of the clearing (about the length of two football fields; 600 feet/ 182.9 m) is nothing more than scorched, barren dirt. After 1D4 minutes in the clearing, any psychic in the party will suddenly become overwhelmed with a nearly palpable sense of anguish, sorrow, rage, fear, and sadness. Furthermore, those who possess psionic Empathy or Telepathy or who are open to the supernatural (Mystics) will be so overwhelmed by the sensations that they will need to save versus psionics or be stunned for 4D6 minutes (-3 to strike, parry, dodge, -20% on skill rolls, and reduce attacks per melee by 2). This is the site of one of CS General Micander Drogue's secret Death Camps. While two of the five camps (Camps Grace and Glory) were successfully liberated (some say that at one of the camps, CS soldiers actually allowed the prisoners to escape), the other three were "misted," the General's euphemistic phrase for burning every last scrap of evidence that the camp or its inmates ever existed, before his superiors in the CS High Command learned of his little projects. This is the site of one of those three "misted" camps. The players will suddenly find themselves surrounded by thousands of D-Bee ghosts (Haunting Entities). All show signs of their horrific deaths - some clearly mutilated or tortured, others experimented upon, but most burned to death in the final misting of the camp. Some will be angry at the players for not coming to help sooner, others will be sad, lamenting their fate. A few will be in a state of confusion, refusing to believe they are dead, still looking for loved ones they think might be held in another part of the camp. Most, however, will simply ask to be put to a proper rest somewhere else far from this horrible scene. If the players simply leave the clearing, they will be hounded by the angriest of the ghosts for the next 1D6 nights (this will attract all manner of unwanted attention in the wilderness, from other supernatural menaces to CS patrols). The only way to put the dead to rest is to locate the mass grave where many of the bodies were disposed of prior to the camp's final destruction, exhume as many bodies as possible (a gruesome task which may require the players make a saving throw versus Horror Factor), and bury them someplace far from the clearing (at least 30 miles/48 km distance).

- As the players are about to exit a cluster of thick woods, anyone with the psionic sensitive power Sixth Sense suddenly receives an intense warning. If the players wait, nothing will happen. However, every time they are about to proceed into the clearing, the warning returns. It will be apparent that something terrible will happen if the players enter the clearing. As long as they go around it, nothing happens and the players may continue. If none of the players possess Sixth Sense, Game Masters may want to have another form of warning occur (perhaps a Haunting Entity or some other mysterious occurrence). If the players do not heed the warnings, there's no telling what will happen.

- A small group of refugees fleeing Coalition occupation. This group has no real information to give the players, but will be an excellent chance for the players to see the horrors of the war as well as to give them a chance to earn some bonus Experience Points by helping them with humanitarian needs (food, water, medical attention).

- A Fade Town of a different sort. One night while traveling near a ley line, the players come across a town that seems to have been untouched by not only violence but the modern era (looks to be about circa 1850 - there is no sign of any modern weapons or equipment). The humans seem friendly enough, though they will be a little guarded towards any D-Bees. If anyone possesses psionic or magic abilities to sense the supernatural, they will detect a faint aura of supernatural magic permeating the entire village (distinct but non-threatening). When asked why they haven't been attacked by any monsters or demons from the Rifts, much less the Coalition, who are known to atomize any settlement they find in southern Wisconsin, they will claim ignorance. Overnight, the players' sleep will be punctuated by dreams of a peaceful village being destroyed in a devastating raid, though they will not see who is attacking. When they awaken, there will be no trace of the village, not even ruins. What the players experienced is a ghostly visitation of a village that was wiped out by a Native American raid centuries ago and whose rest has been disturbed by the coming of the Rifts.

- A small group of 1D4 Daemonix, fleeing from Tolkeen and looking for somebody to kill, attack the party.

- An isolated fishing village of D-Bees resting on the shores of a small lake. Seemingly untouched by violence and the horrors of the war in the neighboring region, what makes this village most unusual is that it has not yet been turned into a smoldering crater by the Coalition. In reality, the village is an unusual form of Fade Town. Instead of phasing randomly in and out of reality, the ley line has psychically bonded with the inhabitants of the village and is able to sense the approach of danger (both mundane and supernatural). When it does, the entire town fades out of existence as if it were never there until the danger passes.

- Brodkil Sub-Demons (actually not from Tolkeen, they just happen to be in the area looking for trouble) attack the party with the intent of stripping them of any valuable technology and leaving them for dead.

- A small lake, one of many, in the middle of the wilderness. It can be deserted, a watering hole for wildlife, the site of a small fishing village, or the home to any number of supernatural creatures (Aquatic demon, freshwater sea monster, Kelpie Faeries, Toad Stool Faeries, Water Elemental, lone Daemonix, etc.).

- Large Coalition patrol. Actually a small company on a seek and destroy mission. They are currently searching for a large group of refugees fleeing from Tolkeen, and if the players do nothing to attract attention to themselves they will be passed by. The company includes about 100 Dead Boy CS Grunts, 200 Skelebots, 4 IAR-2 Abolishers, 10 IAR-Hellraisers, 2 IAR-3 Skull Smashers, 4 CR005 Scorpion Skull Walkers, 2 CTX-20 Grinning Skull Tanks, 2 CTX-52 Sky Sweepers, 4 CS Mark V APCs, 12 Super SAMAS, 24 Smiling Jack Light Assault SAMAS, and 15 Wing Jammer Sky Cycles as well as several support vehicles. The group they are pursuing is well guarded by a large number of magical and supernatural defenders and CS intelligence believes that one or more of Tolkeen's high ranking officials may be traveling with them. If the players learn this, they might be able to move ahead of the company and warn the refugees, though this will prove very dangerous as it will involve evading numerous Coalition Ranger and Psi-Stalker patrols.

- In a small clearing located at the heart of a ley line nexus, the players will see a single small sapling that looks to be no more than a year old (actually, it is much, much younger, only about two weeks old). Psychics will feel an instant calming sensation as they approach the area and it will soon become evident that a large number of Faeries as well as numerous other wilderness folk have been recently drawn to this site and will defend it with their lives. These defenders include not only ordinary wilderness nomads but also several practitioners of magic, a Dragon Hatchling, and a handful of Cyber-Knights, as well as others. It is possible that this might be the site of North America's first and only Millennium Tree (coming into being as a result of the tragic fall of Tolkeen), or something entirely different (Game Master's discretion).

Game Masters, if you do not have the necessary source books for the aforementioned encounters, feel free to adjust them accordingly.

One afternoon, at some point while still well within Wisconsin, the players will see a fairly large group of travelers in the distance. As they approach, it will become obvious that they are most likely refugees from Tolkeen. By the time the players get close, the group will have made camp in a secluded cluster of trees and appear to be settling down for the night before moving on.

If the players decide to approach the encampment, they might realize that the group is not entirely without its protection. Unless the players make a successful Perception Roll of 16+, they will not notice until too late that as they approach the camp, they themselves have been surrounded.

As with most of the groups of refugees fleeing from the CS occupation, this one also has its defenders. Hiding in the woods around the camp, a number of warriors have noticed the players' approach and have quietly surrounded them. So far, they have determined that the players are not members of the Coalition, though this does not mean that they are necessarily friendly. The defenders of this particular refugee camp include a 5th level Forest Runner Dragon Hatchling, a 7th level Cyber-Knight, a 4th level Full Conversion Cyborg, a pair of 5th level Ley Line Walkers, a 3rd level Juicer, and a 6th level Burster. The dragon and one of the Ley Line Walkers have been following the players invisibly for the past few minutes when the Cyber-Knight steps before them and demands they surrender to him and follow him to their camp. If they refuse, the other defenders will attack from their hiding places with the intent of incapacitating the players. If the players comply, they will be asked to surrender their weapons to him but are assured that they will be returned if the leader of the refugees determines that they pose no threat. One way or the other, the players will be escorted to the encampment.

This will be a good chance for the players to see just how horrible it is for the refugees from Tolkeen. As the players enter the camp, anyone of good or Unprincipled alignment will need to successfully save versus a Horror Factor of 12 to not be overcome by the sights they see. Almost all of the refugees (D-Bees and humans) are clearly suffering from malnutrition. Several are missing limbs or have been brutally maimed. A detailed examination of these wounds (requires a successful Crime Scene Investigation, Field Surgery, Forensics, or Medical Doctor skill roll) will reveal that most of them have been caused by modern energy and Vibro-weapons, while some are the result of animal attacks (bites, claws, etc.). Such an examination will also reveal that two or three of them will most likely pass away that evening or in the next few days if they do not get immediate medical attention, food and clean water. **Game Master Note:** This would be a perfect opportunity for players to use their medical or Wilderness Survival skills to help the refugees out. Those who do should be successful and should receive bonus Experience Points.

All of the refugees are dressed in torn and ragged clothing. They are huddled in small groups, either sitting silently gazing into the darkness (there is no fire for fear of drawing attention to their hiding place) or quietly sobbing into one another's arms. All of them wear hollow, shell-shocked expressions on their faces and will not respond if spoken to directly. Any psychic in the party, even without using their powers, can sense the overwhelming sadness and hopelessness emanating from the refugees. A successful skill roll in Psychology will reveal that they are all suffering from severe states of depression and many are in shock. Most of them will shy away in fear if the players approach them. Even the defenders look like they are at the end of their ropes and only hanging on because they know that without them, the refugees will be lost. One of the guards will explain that most of this damage was caused *after* the Kingdom of Tolkeen had actually fallen. These refugees were attacked by Coalition forces as they fled.

The players will be escorted through the suffering survivors to a small cluster of people who seem to be engrossed in a quiet though intense conversation. As the Cyber-Knight announces their arrival, the leader of the refugees will look up and cast her gaze at each of the players. Players from Lazlo may recognize the person seated before them (requires a Perception Roll of 15+) as Arianna Konaras. Arianna Konaras is a Rogue Scholar who is something of a student of Erin Tarn. Though Tarn never formally taught, Arianna became inspired by her earlier works and took it upon herself to follow in her footsteps. However, unlike the famous scholar, Arianna is not a pacifist. When it became evident that Tolkeen and the CS would ultimately clash, she became an outspoken advocate for Tolkeen's stance against Chi-Town. Citing numerous times in history where peaceful nations were forced to take military action in a preemptive effort to defend themselves from an aggressor, Arianna added her voice to the impassioned speeches being made by King Creed and others on the Council of Twelve, the leaders of Tolkeen. When the Kingdom of Lazlo and especially Erin Tarn herself warned against fighting the mighty Coalition army, Arianna was shattered. Feeling betrayed, she left her home and joined the defenders in Tolkeen. Even after the atrocities of the "Sorcerers'

Revenge," something even the outspoken, passionate Konaras could not condone, she still supported Tolkeen's efforts. Now, with her adopted kingdom fallen, she makes her way east, torn between returning home to Lazlo in shame and defeat and heading into the Magic Zone to add her voice to the cries for revenge ringing from several of the factions of the Federation of Magic.

Arianna Konaras:
7th level Rogue Scholar and defender of Tolkeen.

Alignment: Unprincipled with leanings towards Anarchist.

Age: 35

Attributes: I.Q. 20, M.E. 11, M.A. 22, P.S. 10, P.P. 11, P.E. 13, P.B. 12, Spd 15.

Size: 5 feet, 5 inches (1.65 m) tall; 145 pounds (65.3 kg).

Hit Points: 34

S.D.C.: 15

P.P.E.: 11

I.S.P.: 0

Attacks per Melee: 5

Bonuses: +2 to parry, +2 to dodge, +2 to roll with punch, +2 to pull punch.

Weapons: <u>WI-LP3 Pepperbox Holdout Laser Pistol</u>: 1D4 M.D. per round, can fire one, two, three or all four rounds, 4 round payload.

<u>Wilk's 247 Hero Dual Pistol</u>: 2D6 or 3D6 M.D., 32 shots per clip.

<u>Vibro-Knife</u>: 1D6 M.D.

Armor: Huntsman (40 M.D.C.) with helmet (30 M.D.C.) and air filter.

Skills of Note: Recognize Authenticity (82%), Professional Restoration (82%), Literacy: American, (98%), Dragonese (96%), Spanish (96%), Techno-can (96%), Languages: American (98%), Dragonese (94%), French (94%), Demongogian (94%), Appraise Goods (86%), Find Contraband (66%/86%), History: Pre-Rifts (84%/74%), History: Post-Apocalyptic (91%/86%), Public Speaking (86%), Lore: Demons and Monsters (76%), Lore: Magic (76%), Psychology (71%), Anthropology (76%), Computer Operation (96%), Creative Writing (81%), Coalition Tactics (35%/25%), Hand to Hand: Basic (4th level skill), W.P. Energy Pistol (+3 to strike).

Magic Knowledge: Lore knowledge only.

Psionic Abilities: None.

Equipment: While living in Tolkeen, Arianna had all manner of equipment and gear. Now, on the run, she has some basic wilderness survival gear as well as her personal portable computer with her latest writing saved on it.

Appearance and Disposition: Arianna is physically ordinary with dark brown hair and fair skin. What sets her apart is her passion, for both history and justice (the latter specifically related to justice against the Coalition). She genuinely cares about the people of Tolkeen and the refugees who now look to her as their leader. She would lay down her life to defend them, though she will make sure to take as many of her enemies down with her as she can.

Arianna will ask the players who they serve and why they are traveling west towards Coalition occupied Tolkeen. While she will be satisfied with any answer that includes joining the resistance that still tries to drive the occupation from the shattered kingdom, she will wonder what they think they can possibly do when all seems lost. Though not psychic, Arianna is an expert in Psychology and unless the players are skillful in their answers, she will be able to tell if they are deliberately misleading her. If the players come right out and say that they are heading there to find a magical artifact, she will become enraged, calling them looters and grave robbers. At this point, it will take fast talking to prevent her from ordering her defenders from executing them on the spot. Clever role-playing is needed to talk their way out of this volatile situation. Even if they try to convince her that they are seeking a specific item in order to use it against the Coalition and defend New Lazlo, she will only respond that if New Lazlo and Lazlo had entered the war in the first place instead of preaching from their safe distance, the war might have turned out differently (not true, but most of the Tolkeen refugees blame those who stood aside almost as much as they blame the Coalition). Watching most of her friends die and her home crushed by the Coalition has pushed the Rogue Scholar close to the brink of insanity, though she still possesses a keen wit. If the players mention that they are seeking a creation of Galidor Marik, she will pause to consider what they have just revealed. Arianna has no love of the warlord and blames him for his part in the ill-fated, ill-conceived "Sorcerers' Revenge" and would consider any perversion of one of his creations a worthwhile goal. Ultimately, it is up to the Game Master to decide if the players have been able to calm down the edgy, strung out scholar enough to gain their freedom.

If the players offer at any point to help the refugees either with medical skills and equipment, psychic and magical healing, or food and water, this will go a long way toward earning her respect, even if she does not entirely agree with what they are doing. From her, they can learn that the Coalition Army in occupied Minnesota is indeed shooting any and all refugees fleeing from Tolkeen. They will also learn that while so many are fleeing, third parties have already begun to move in to loot the ruins in search of the kingdom's secrets. Though she does not know for certain, she suspects that both the Splugorth and the Federation of Magic have already sent agents into the area in search of magic and Techno-Wizard items and artifacts. Finally, she is able to tell them that some of the warlords and commanders of Tolkeen's defense are still at large, including, she believes, King Creed himself, either fighting in the ruins against the Coalition Army or trying to flee into the wilderness themselves. (She will not mention the king's final speech in which he seemingly repented for his actions that brought his kingdom to war with the Coalition - she is not sure how she feels about the man she admires so much having such a dramatic change of heart.) In return for this information, Arianna will greatly appreciate any information the players might be able to give her about the wilderness to the east as well as how they might cross Lake Michigan. She will be very glad to learn about the location of the Landing.

The next morning, the refugees will head on their way eastward, leaving the players and their Simvan guide to continue west towards the Coalition occupation.

Chapter Five: With Extreme Prejudice!

"So just where are you fellows headed, anyway?"
- Lieutenant McGill (a.k.a. "Mackie")

A few days after the encounter with Arianna's refugees, the party will be camping at night in a cluster of dense woods when a pair of strangers will make their presence known. Identifying themselves from a distance as Mackie and Arnold, a pair of Mercenary Soldiers who had recently become separated from their company during a Coalition attack, the pair ask to be allowed to approach and bunk in their camp for the night, maybe even travel a ways with them before they try to return to their company or whatever remains of them. If the players seem a little hesitant, Mackie, who seems to be the leader or at least more outspoken of the two, will explain that he has spent the past few days in the region before his unit came under attack and can let them in on the lay of the land, including what they know of CS troop activity in the region. Any player attempting to use psychic probes on his mind (Telepathy or Empathy) will get the feeling that Mackie is speaking the truth, though he is being a bit guarded. If all else fails, the pair will ask to at least be allowed to camp in the vicinity as they figure that they have been lucky so far to have traveled alone in the Wisconsin wilderness without being attacked by some supernatural menace or another CS patrol. As a peace offering, Arnold will produce a bottle of very excellent liquor and offer it to the players.

In reality, Mackie and Arnold are a pair of Coalition Special Forces operatives who are part of a CS recon squad operating out of the CS army at Tolkeen. Recent intelligence reports from the ruins of Tolkeen have suggested that numerous factions have begun to sneak into the city in search of whatever magical and Techno-Wizard secrets might have been left behind by the fleeing Tolkeenites. While the CS occupation forces in the city have already dispatched Magic Recovery Teams to find these magical secrets before they fall into the hands of those who might use them against the Coalition Army in some future war, other units have been sent into the wilderness to intercept looters who have not yet arrived at the city. Their plan is to infiltrate those groups who seem to be headed towards the Kingdom of Tolkeen in order to find out what their intentions are. It is hoped that this will give the CS the intelligence to find some of these secrets before others get to them first.

These two soldiers are experts at infiltration and as such, have mentally conditioned themselves to never display any obvious signs of duplicity. This includes the ability to resist mental probes. Mackie and Arnold make sure that no matter how they answer any questions, they never allow their surface thoughts to differ from their spoken words. This is why mental probes do not reveal that they are really Coalition agents.

Their plan is to attempt to learn from the players what they are hoping to find in Tolkeen. They already know that the fallen kingdom is their most likely destination, as their recon squad has been shadowing the movements of the party for the past 24 hours. Game Masters, the players should have no idea that they have been followed unless they have taken measures to watch behind them or disguise their trail. Even then, it will take a successful Surveillance, Tailing, or Detect Ambush skill roll to notice the distant pursuit. Any attempt to confront their pursuers will only result in the recon squad halting at the current distance and taking their own precautions lest the players turn around and attempt to ambush them.

The entire time that Mackie and Arnold are with the players, they will be keeping an open communication channel between their position and the rest of the recon squad via Mackie's cybernetic radio implant. This scrambled, ultra-high frequency, narrow band signal will be very difficult to detect (requiring a successful Electronic Countermeasures skill roll at -20%) and even more difficult to jam (another successful Electronic Countermeasures skill roll at -30%). If asked at some point about the Coalition gear that they are carrying, they will claim that they "won" it during an earlier engagement. The rest of their Coalition gear has been carefully disguised to prevent obvious detection. It would require a detailed examination (and a successful Recognize Weapon Quality skill roll made at -10%) to realize that most of their gear, as well as their body armor, is CS standard issue.

Regardless of whether or not the players reveal the full details of their mission, the decision has already been made to attack at dawn the following morning. The CS strategy is to have Mackie and Arnold remain with the party and seem to fight with them when the attack initially begins. Then, when the party least expects it, the two will turn on the players and attempt to subdue them for further interrogation and ultimately, imprisonment and execution.

Mackie: a.k.a. Lieutenant Raymond McGill, 6th level CS Special Forces Commando O.C.C.

Alignment: Miscreant.

Age: 31

Attributes: I.Q. 15, M.E. 18, M.A. 17, P.S. 20, P.P. 18, P.E. 14, P.B. 15, Spd 20.

Size: 6 feet, 2 inches (1.9 m) tall; 190 pounds (85.5 kg).

Hit Points: 41

S.D.C.: 45

P.P.E.: 8

I.S.P.: 0

Attacks per Melee: 7

Bonuses: +6 on initiative, +6 to strike, +10 to parry, +11 to dodge, +4 to automatic dodge, +5 to roll with punch, +3 to pull punch, +1 to disarm, +1 to body flip/throw, +3 to save versus magic, +3 to save versus poison, +2 to save versus psionics, +2 to save versus insanity, +2 to save versus Horror Factor, 45% to trust and intimidate.

Weapons: Conventional Dagger: 1D6+5 S.D.C.

CP-30 Laser Pulse Pistol: 2D4 M.D. single shot, 4D6 M.D. triple burst, 30 shot long clip (Mackie has 8 spare clips).

NG-IP7 Ion Pulse Rifle: 3D6 M.D. single shot, 1D4x10 M.D. triple burst, 30 shots per clip (Mackie has 8 spare clips).

4 Fragmentation Grenades: 2D6 M.D. to a 20 foot (6 m) area.

4 Heavy Explosive Grenades: 4D6 M.D. to a 6 foot (1.8 m) area.

Vibro-Sword: 2D6 M.D.

Armor: CA-7 Special Forces Heavy Dead Boy Armor EBA (100 M.D.C.) disguised to look like generic heavy EBA body armor. The armor has retractable forearm Vibro-Blades (1D6 M.D.) and a garrote wire concealed in the left wrist. It also has a Mag-5 Jet Pack (60 mph/96 km) for 80 minutes of flight.

Skills of Note: Radio: Basic (85%), Electronic Countermeasures (70%), Land Navigation (66%), Intelligence (62%), Streetwise (56%), Lore: Demons and Monsters (65%), Pilot Jet Pack (72%), Pilot Robots and Power Armor (94%), Power Armor Combat Elite: Special Forces SAMAS, Wilderness Survival (61%), Tracking (66%), Prowl (65%), W.P. Energy Pistol (+4 to strike), W.P. Energy Rifle (+4 to strike), W.P. Heavy M.D. Weapons (+3 to strike).

Magic Knowledge: None.

Psionic Abilities: None.

Equipment: 4 signal flares, pocket computer, air filter and gas mask, short-range radio, climbing cord, plus other items typical of a CS Special Forces Operative (all CS markings and indicators have been removed to make the gear seem generic). Mackie pilots a MI-3000 Firefly Hovercycle: 190 mph (304 km), 72 Main Body M.D.C., Double Barreled Heavy Lasers (2D6 M.D. single shot, 4D6 M.D. double shot, 40 single shots, 20 double shots), 2 mini-missiles (1D4x10, 4 missiles total).

Cybernetics: Amplified Hearing, Oxygen Storage Cell (30 minute supply), Multi-optic Eye, Scrambler Radio Implant, Radar Detector. Cybernetic bonuses have already been factored in.

Appearance and Disposition: Mackie will seem to be friendly and easy going when attempting to infiltrate the group. In reality, he is a cold, calculating killer who despises all enemies of the Coalition. He has short brown hair, a weathered face, and green eyes.

Arnold: a.k.a. Sergeant Arnold Gustafson, 5th level CS Special Forces Commando O.C.C.

Alignment: Miscreant.

Age: 27

Attributes: I.Q. 12, M.E. 14, M.A. 10, P.S. 20, P.P. 15, P.E. 16, P.B. 11, Spd 22.

Size: 6 feet, 6 inches (2 m) tall; 195 pounds (87.8 kg).

Hit Points: 40

S.D.C.: 60

P.P.E.: 4

I.S.P.: 0

Attacks per Melee: 7

Bonuses: +3 on initiative, +3 to strike, +6 to parry, +6 to dodge, +2 to automatic dodge, +5 to roll with punch, +3 to pull punch, +1 to disarm, +1 to body flip/throw, +4 to save versus magic, +4 to save versus poison, +2 to save versus Horror Factor.

Weapons: Conventional Dagger: 1D6+5 S.D.C.

NG-57 Heavy Duty Ion Pistol: 2D4 or 3D6 M.D. single shot, 18 shot long clip (Arnold has 8 spare clips).

TX-42 Laser Pulse Rifle: 2D6 M.D. single shot, 1D4x10 M.D. triple burst, 40 shots per clip (Arnold has 8 spare clips).

C-29 Hellfire Heavy Plasma Cannon: 1D6x10 single shot, 8 shots per canister (Arnold has 4 spare canisters).

4 Fragmentation Grenades: 2D6 M.D. to a 20 foot (6 m) area.

4 Heavy Explosive Grenades: 4D6 M.D. to a 6 foot (1.8 m) area.

Vibro-Sword: 2D6 M.D.

Armor: CA-7 Special Forces Heavy Dead Boy Armor EBA (100 M.D.C.) disguised to look like generic heavy EBA body armor. The armor has retractable forearm Vibro-Blades (1D6 M.D.) and a garrote wire concealed in the left wrist. It also has a Mag-5 Jet Pack (60 mph/96 km) for 80 minutes of flight.

Skills of Note: Radio: Basic (80%), Electronic Countermeasures (65%), Land Navigation (62%), Intelligence (58%), Streetwise (52%), Lore: Demons and Monsters (60%), Pilot Jet Pack (69%), Pilot Robots and Power Armor (91%), Power Armor Combat Elite: Special Forces SAMAS, Wilderness Survival (56%), Prowl (60%), W.P. Energy Pistol (+4 to strike), W.P. Energy Rifle (+3 to strike), W.P. Heavy M.D. Weapons (+3 to strike).

Magic Knowledge: None.

Psionic Abilities: None.

Equipment: 4 signal flares, pocket computer, air filter and gas mask, short-range radio, climbing cord, plus other items typical of a CS Special Forces Operative (all CS markings and indicators have been removed to make the gear seem generic). Arnold pilots an NG-220 Rocket Hovercycle: 340 mph (544 km), 84 Main Body M.D.C., Concealed Ion Guns

(3D6 M.D. single shot, 6D6 M.D. double shot, 60 shots total).

Cybernetics: Oxygen Storage Cell (30 minute supply), Radio Implant, Radar Detector, Targeting Eye. Cybernetic bonuses have already been factored in.

Appearance and Disposition: Arnold seems to be the strong, silent type, saying nothing unless asked first, and then saying little in answer. He has blonde hair, pale skin, and blue eyes.

The remainder of the CS forces in the ambush include the following units:

Coalition Commandos (6):
4th level Coalition Commando O.C.C.

Alignment: Anarchist.

Age: 24

Attributes: I.Q. 11, M.E. 11, M.A. 9, P.S. 18 (27 in armor), P.P. 17, P.E. 13, P.B. 10, Spd 30 (44 in armor).

Size: 6 feet (1.8 m) tall; 180 pounds (81 kg).

Hit Points: 37

S.D.C.: 52

P.P.E.: 9

I.S.P.: 0

Attacks per Melee: 6

Bonuses: +1 on initiative, +2 to strike, +4 to parry, +4 to dodge, +5 to roll with punch, +3 to pull punch, +1 to disarm, +1 to body flip/throw, +2 to save versus Horror Factor.

Weapons: 2 Conventional Daggers: 1D6+15 S.D.C.

CP-40 Laser Pulse Rifle: 2D6 M.D. single shot, 6D6 M.D. triple burst, 30 shot long clip (Commandos have 7 spare clips each).

C-20 Laser Pistol: 2D6 M.D. single shot, 30 shots per clip (Commandos have 7 spare clips each).

CR-1 Rocket Launcher: 1D4x10 M.D. to a 3 foot (0.9 m) area.

Vibro-Saber: 2D4 M.D.

Armor: CA-6EX Heavy Dead Boy Armor EBA (100 M.D.C.), adds 10 feet (3 m) to leaps and reduces fatigue by 50%.

Skills of Note: Detect Ambush (45%), Wilderness Survival (45%), Land Navigation (58%), Detect Concealment (40%), Escape Artist (45%), Tracking (50%), W.P. Energy Pistol (+2 to strike), W.P. Energy Rifle (+2 to strike), W.P. Heavy M.D. Weapons (+2 to strike), W.P. Sword (+2 to strike and parry).

Magic Knowledge: None.

Psionic Abilities: None.

Equipment: 4 signal flares, robot medical kit, short-range radio, compass/inertial mapper.

Appearance: Typical nondescript Coalition foot soldiers with cropped hair.

Coalition Rangers (2):
4th level Coalition Ranger O.C.C.

Alignment: Scrupulous.

Age: 22

Attributes: I.Q. 11, M.E. 12, M.A. 9, P.S. 19, P.P. 12, P.E. 14, P.B. 10, Spd 25.

Size: 6 feet (1.8 m) tall; 180 pounds (81.7 kg).

Hit Points: 35

S.D.C.: 35

P.P.E.: 8

I.S.P.: 0

Attacks per Melee: 5

Bonuses: +4 to strike, +5 to parry, +5 to dodge, +2 to roll with punch, +2 to pull punch.

Weapons: 2 Conventional Daggers: 1D6+15 S.D.C.

CP-50 Dragonfire: 2D6 M.D. single shot, 6D6 M.D. triple burst, Micro-fusion grenades 6D6 M.D. to a 12 foot (3.6 m) area, 30 shot long clip and 12 grenades (Rangers have 5 spare clips each and 24 extra grenades).

CP-40 Laser Pulse Rifle: 2D6 M.D. single shot, 6D6 M.D. triple burst, 30 shot long clip (Rangers have 5 spare clips each).

C-20 Laser Pistol: 2D6 M.D. single shot, 30 shots per clip (Rangers have 6 spare clips each).

4 Heavy Explosive Grenades: 4D6 M.D. to a 6 foot (1.8 m) area.

2 Vibro-Knives: 1D6 M.D.

Vibro-Sword: 2D4 M.D.

Armor: CA-3 Light Dead Boy Armor EBA (80 M.D.C.).

Skills of Note: Prowl (50%), Land Navigation (68%), Wilderness Survival (80%), Track (55%), Trap Construction (50%), Trap/Mine Detection (50%), W.P. Energy Pistol (+2 to strike), W.P. Energy Rifle (+2 to strike), W.P. Heavy M.D. Weapons (+2 to strike), W.P. Knife (+2 to strike, parry, and throw), W.P. Sword (+2 to strike and parry).

Magic Knowledge: None.

Psionic Abilities: None.

Equipment: 4 signal flares, robot medical kit, short-range radio, compass/inertial mapper, laser distancer.

Appearance: Typical nondescript Coalition foot soldiers with cropped hair.

Coalition Psi-Stalker (1): 4th level Psi-Stalker O.C.C.

Alignment: Aberrant.

Age: 26

Attributes: I.Q. 10, M.E. 12, M.A. 9, P.S. 18, P.P. 17, P.E. 15, P.B. 8, Spd 22.

Size: 6 feet, 4 inches (1.93 m) tall; 170 pounds (77 kg).

Hit Points: 32

S.D.C.: 40

P.P.E.: 10, but must consume 50 P.P.E. per week to function without fatigue.

I.S.P.: 70 (needs to roll a 6 or higher to save versus psionics).

Attacks per Melee: 6

Bonuses: +2 on initiative, +3 to strike, +1 to parry, +1 to dodge, +2 to roll with punch, +3 to pull punch, +5 to save versus mind control, +3 to save versus possession, +4 to save versus magic, +6 to save versus Horror Factor.

Weapons: Conventional Daggers: 1D6+7 S.D.C.

CP-40 Laser Pulse Rifle: 2D6 M.D. single shot, 6D6 M.D. triple burst, 30 shot long clip (Psi-Stalker has 8 spare clips).

C-20 Laser Pistol: 2D6 M.D. single shot, 30 shots per clip (Psi-Stalker has 8 spare clips).

3 Heavy Explosive Grenades: 4D6 M.D. to a 6 foot (1.8 m) area.

3 Light Explosive Grenades: 3D6 M.D. to a 6 foot (1.8 m) area.

2 Vibro-Knives: 1D6 M.D.

Armor: CA-4 Dead Boy Armor EBA (100 M.D.C.).

Skills of Note/Natural Abilities: Prowl (50%), W.P. Energy Pistol (+2 to strike), W.P. Energy Rifle (+2 to strike), W.P. Heavy M.D. Weapons (+2 to strike), W.P. Knife (+2 to strike, parry, and throw), Sense Magic and Psychic Energy (80%), Sense Supernatural Beings (60%), Psionic Empathy with animals.

Magic Knowledge: None.

Psionic Abilities: Astral Projection (8), Clairvoyance (6), Sense Evil (2), Telepathy (4), See Aura (6), Object Read (6).

Equipment: 4 signal flares, robot medical kit, short-range radio, compass/inertial mapper, laser distancer.

Appearance: Typical Psi-Stalker with no body hair and tattoos on his head and face.

Coalition Dog Boys (4):
4th level Coalition Dog Boy O.C.C.

Alignment: Scrupulous.

Age: 3

Attributes: I.Q. 13, M.E. 13, M.A. 13, P.S. 24, P.P. 19, P.E. 24, P.B. 13, Spd 45.

Size: 5 feet (1.5 m) tall; 140 pounds (63 kg).

Hit Points: 46

S.D.C.: 37

P.P.E.: 10

I.S.P.: 82 (considered a Master Psionic).

Attacks per Melee: 5

Bonuses: +2 on initiative, +5 to strike, +6 to parry, +6 to dodge, +3 to roll with punch, +3 to pull punch, +2 to save versus disease, +2 to save versus possession, +5 to save versus magic, +1 to save versus psionics.

Weapons: Conventional Daggers: 1D6+7 S.D.C.

CP-40 Laser Pulse Rifle: 2D6 M.D. single shot, 6D6 M.D. triple burst, 30 shot long clip (Dog Boys have 5 spare clips each).

C-18 Laser Pistol: 2D4 M.D. single shot, 10 shots per clip (Dog Boys have 5 spare clips each).

4 Heavy Explosive Grenades: 4D6 M.D. to a 6 foot (1.8 m) area.

4 Light Explosive Grenades: 3D6 M.D. to a 6 foot (1.8 m) area.

2 Vibro-Blade "Cat's Claws" Hand Guards: 3D4 M.D.

Armor: DPM D1 Dog Boy Armor EBA (80 M.D.C.).

Skills of Note/Natural Abilities: Intelligence (50%), Land Navigation (58%), Wilderness Survival (50%), Prowl (40%),

W.P. Energy Pistol (+2 to strike), W.P. Energy Rifle (+2 to strike), W.P. Heavy M.D. Weapons (+2 to strike), W.P. Knife (+2 to strike, parry, and throw), Sense Magic and Psychic Energy (16%/60%), Sense Supernatural Beings (70%/70%/55%/82%), Track by Smell (91%), Identify Smell (62%), Keen Hearing.

Magic Knowledge: None.

Psionic Abilities: Sense Magic (3), Sense Evil (2), Sixth Sense (2), Empathy (4), Telepathy (4).

Equipment: 4 signal flares, robot medical kit, short-range radio, compass/inertial mapper, laser distancer.

Appearance: Generic Dog Boy of no particular breed.

PA-07A Smiling Jack Light Assault SAMAS (4): (Quick Stats)

Pilot: One (1) 4th level CS RPA Elite/SAMAS Pilot O.C.C.

Main Body M.D.C.: 250

Physical Strength: Equivalent to Augmented P.S. of 30.

Speed: Running: 60 mph (96 km). Leaping: 15 feet (4.6 m); jet assist to 100 feet (30.5 m) high and 200 feet (61 m) across. Flying: Hover up to 1000 feet (305 m) or fly up to 300 mph (480 km). Maximum altitude is 6000 feet (1829 m).

Maximum Range: 10 hours of top speed flight before overheating.

Attacks per Melee: 8 (the pilot has 6 attacks per melee round outside of his armor).

Bonuses (including pilot's Hand to Hand skills, W.P., and attribute bonuses): +2 on initiative, +5 to strike hand to hand, +4 to strike with energy weapons, +7 to parry, +8 to dodge, +11 to dodge in flight, +5 to pull punch, +6 to roll with punch.

C-40R SAMAS Rail Gun: Mega-Damage: 1D4 single shot, 1D4x10 burst (40 rounds). Range: 4000 feet (1219 m). Payload: 3000 rounds (75 bursts).

SJ-6 Mini-Missile Launcher: Mega-Damage: 1D4x10 armor piercing mini-missile. Rate of Fire: Single shot or volleys of two, four, or six. Range: One mile (1.6 km). Payload: Six mini-missiles (3 per wing).

CR-004 Scout Spider-Skull Walker (1): (Quick Stats)

Pilot: Two (2) 4th level CS Technical Officer O.C.C.s (one pilot and one gunner).

Main Body M.D.C.: 280

Physical Strength: Equivalent to Augmented P.S. of 40.

Speed: Running: 100 mph (160 km). Leaping: 10 feet (3 m) or 20 feet (6.1 m) across.

Maximum Range: Nuclear (unlimited).

Attacks per Melee: 7 (the crew each have 5 attacks per melee round outside of the vehicle).

Bonuses (including pilot's Hand to Hand skills, W.P., and attribute bonuses): +1 on initiative, +1 to strike hand to hand, +5 to strike with energy weapons, +3 to parry, +3 to dodge, +4 to dodge in motion, +2 to pull punch, +3 to roll with punch.

C-104 Tri-Barrel Rail Guns (2): Mega-Damage: 1D4x10 burst, 2D4x10 double burst. Range: 6000 feet (1829 m). Payload: 10,000 rounds (166 bursts).

CR-2T Laser Turret: Mega-Damage: 5D6. Range: 2000 feet (610 m). Payload: Unlimited.

Other Weapons: Mini-missile launchers (2): 1D4x10 M.D. Armor Piercing mini-missiles, Smoke Dispenser.

IAR-5 Hellfire (1): (Quick Stats)

Pilot: Two (2) CS Technical Officers O.C.C. (one pilot and one gunner; 6th level and 4th level respectively).

Main Body M.D.C.: 480

Physical Strength: Equivalent to Augmented P.S. of 45.

Speed: Running: 120 mph (192 km). Leaping: 30 feet (9.1 m) high or across (double with jet assist).

Maximum Range: Nuclear (unlimited).

Attacks per melee: 8 (the crew each have 5 attacks per melee round outside of the vehicle).

Bonuses (including pilot's Hand to Hand skills, W.P., and attribute bonuses): +4 on initiative, +5 to strike hand to hand, +3 to strike with energy weapons, +5 to parry, +5 to dodge, +8 to dodge in motion, +4 to pull punch, +7 to roll with punch, Critical Strike on a Natural 19-20.

HF-36 Hellfire Rail Guns (2): Mega-Damage: 1D4x10 burst, 2D4x10 double burst. Range: 4000 feet (1219 m). Payload: 10,000 rounds (250 bursts) each.

HF-36 Double-Barreled Plasma Ejector: Mega-Damage: 5D6 single blast, 1D6x10 double blast. Range: 1600 feet (488 m). Payload: Unlimited.

Other Weapons: Mini-missile launchers (2): 1D4x10 M.D. Armor Piercing mini-missiles, HF-12 Laser Turrets (2).

Other Notes: The robot's pilot is the unit's commanding officer. The recon unit is supported in the field by a CS Mark V APC which is currently located some 30 miles (48 km) south of their current position (too far away to take part in the ambush).

This ambush is a perfect example of Coalition overkill. The Coalition military machine tends to overwhelm the opposition with superior numbers and technology instead of superior strategy and tactics. Brutal but effective. In a straight fight, there should be little chance that the players would survive this encounter, much less defeat their opposition (this does not rule out the possibility that the players will be able to hold their own using clever tactics, teamwork, and the thing that the Coalition continues to underestimate in every engagement: magic!).

At a point during which it seems obvious that the players will lose to the Coalition (after the two agents have revealed themselves for who they really are), there will be an unexpected barrage of weapons fire from the north of the battle directed at the CS troops. Suddenly, a small band of warriors (8) will emerge from the forest riding armored hover cycles and rocket bikes and attack the Coalition forces with a vengeance. They will make quick work of any remaining units, making sure that none escape alive. When the smoke clears, the leader of the newcomers will approach the players, introducing himself as Slicer, a Captain in the Juicer Army of Liberation (JAL). He will explain that he and his crew of fellow Juicers have been operating in the region, looking for signs of refugees to protect and Coalition patrols to slaughter. After making sure that the players are alright, he and his team will mount their rides and disappear as quickly as they appeared.

Captain Slicer:
7th level Juicer O.C.C. and a member of the JAL.

Alignment: Anarchist.

Age: 29 (has been a Juicer for 3 years and 5 months).

Attributes: I.Q. 15, M.E. 12, M.A. 10, P.S. 28 (augmented), P.P. 21, P.E. 26, P.B. 12, Spd 32.

Size: 6 feet, 9 inches (2.05 m) tall; 225 pounds (101.3 kg).

Hit Points: 76

S.D.C.: 450

P.P.E.: 7

I.S.P.: 0

Attacks per Melee: 8

Bonuses: +5 on initiative, +5 to strike, +8 to parry, +8 to dodge, +6 to automatic dodge, +7 to roll with punch, +6 to pull punch, +5 to disarm, +2 to entangle, +6 to save versus magic, +6 to save versus poison, Critical Strike on a Natural 18-20.

Weapons: Conventional Dagger: 1D6+13 S.D.C.

FIWS (Forearm Integral Weapon System): *Concealed Vibro-Blades (3):* 3D6 M.D. and *Particle Beam Weapon:* 5D6 M.D. single shot or 1D6x10 double burst, 30 shot long clip (Slicer has 10 spare clips).

JA-12 Laser Rifle: 4D6 M.D. single shot, 1D6x10+10 M.D. triple burst, 30 shot canister plus 30 shots per clip (Slicer has 10 spare clips).

12 Fragmentation Grenades: 2D6 M.D. to a 20 foot (6 m) area.

12 Heavy Explosive Grenades: 4D6 M.D. to a 6 foot (1.8 m) area.

Vibro-Knife: 1D6 M.D.

Armor: Man Killer Juicer Armor EBA (110 M.D.C.) with spikes (2D6+13 S.D.C. body slam or 1 M.D point to M.D.C. materials).

Skills of Note: Pilot Rocket Bike (98%), Land Navigation (65%), Radio: Basic (85%), Electronic Countermeasures (60%), Streetwise (46%), Prowl (75%), Pilot Jet Pack (76%), Intelligence (61%), W.P. Energy Pistol (+4 to strike), W.P. Energy Rifle (+3 to strike), W.P. Heavy M.D. Weapons (+3 to strike), W.P. Sword (+3 to strike and parry), W.P. Knife (+3 to strike, parry, and throw).

Magic Knowledge: None.

Psionic Abilities: None.

Equipment: 4 signal flares, IRMSS Robot Medical kit, air filter and gas mask, short-range radio, climbing cord, optic helmet. Slicer pilots a Wellington AHB-2000 Assault Rocket Bike: 300 mph (480 km), 190 Main Body M.D.C., Particle Beam Guns (2) (5D6 M.D. single shot, 1D6x10 M.D. double shot, unlimited payload), Laser Pods (2) (5D6 M.D. single pod, 1D6x10 M.D. double pods, unlimited payload), 2 mini-missiles (1D4x10 M.D.).

Appearance and Disposition: Slicer has weathered, dark skin with numerous scars (all of which he is immensely proud of, most of which he has earned from Coalition battles). He is fairly silent, saying what he needs to say to the players, waiting to answer their questions and then moving on to find more CS patrols to destroy. Slicer lives to battle and kill CS troops and, although he was never a part of the original Juicer

Uprising against the Coalition, he is a loyal follower of Julian the First.

The stats for the seven other Juicers who attacked with Captain Slicer are comparable to his at 4th and 5th level strength.

Although Slicer and his gang will have thoroughly disabled the CS vehicles and armor, they have left the bodies and all of their equipment behind. This could be a veritable treasure trove of CS gear, ammunition, and supplies. Furthermore, if they track the CS ambush group back about 3 miles (4.8 km) south, they will come across a concealed campsite (this maneuver will require a successful Track Humanoids skill roll at -20% and a successful Detect Concealment skill roll at -15%) with additional ammunition, spare CS Dead Boy armor, and basic CS gear.

Chapter Six: Bug Hunting

"Ew! What did that bug just spray on you?"

- Tanis Lightwing

A couple of days after their near disastrous encounter with the Coalition recon squad, just as they are descending into the Mississippi River Valley towards Minnesota and the city of Tolkeen, the players observe a full scale battle taking place in the valley below. Directly between them and the river stretching for miles, the Coalition Army seems to be engaged with remnants of the Tolkeen Defense Force. It is clear that to attempt to sneak through this chaos would be suicide. Even if they were to somehow magically conceal their entire party, vehicles and all, to avoid complete detection by either side be impossible. Teleporting would certainly be an option, though with the massive discharges of magical energy occurring in and over the battlefield, there is no telling what manner of temporal or spatial distortions are taking place.

Zanchavex will recommend backtracking and then heading north to outflank the battlefield and approach Tolkeen from the northwest as far from the engagement as possible (they should have no idea that this is exactly what General Jericho Holmes himself did in his assault that crippled the city's defenses, unless they asked how Tolkeen's seemingly impregnable defenses were overwhelmed when they were Arianna's captives). He suspects (rightly so) that south, they would only encounter a much stronger Coalition presence while going north will have them skirting close to the Xiticix Hivelands, where the CS occupation should be light if not nonexistent. If the players balk at the idea of going near the Hivelands, Zanchavex will let them know that he is something of an expert on the Xiticix (at least as much as anyone can be).

A day after they begin their maneuver to outflank the battlefield (it will take several more days to backtrack and skirt the entire region), the players will come across the scene of a recent battle. At first, it may appear that a unit from the battle to the south had made a break for it and was intercepted by pursuing troops. However, as the players examine the site it will become evident that this was not a battle between two high tech forces. Though seven bodies of what look like Tolkeen defenders can be found along with damaged TW and conventional weapons, an examination of the bodies will suggest that something liter-

ally ripped them to shreds. Then, the players will find one of the culprits: the body of a Xiticix Warrior.

Before the players can act, three figures will jump out of the nearby brush and demand to know who they are. These newcomers are the survivors of the Xiticix attack and it is immediately obvious that they suffered a losing battle with the insects. Two look to be soldiers of some variety with torn and clawed armor while the third appears to be a magic user nearing the point of exhaustion. When it becomes obvious that the players are not Coalition soldiers or bounty hunters, they will ask them if they can help with their wounded. The three will lead the players back into the brush and after several minutes of tramping through the woods, will guide them to the remainder of their party. Obviously another group of refugees, they appear to be nursing recent wounds from the Xiticix attack. Mostly women

with some older folk, what is most obviously missing from the group are any children. If the players ask what happened, the three will explain that their party was ambushed by the Xiticix as they were escaping Tolkeen with a band of refugees. The bulk of the group's defenders had been drawn into a battle with a pursuing band of Coalition soldiers while the rest of the guard fled with the refugees northward. That was when the bugs attacked. They drew the defenders into an ambush that separated them from the rest of the group and while the defenders fought off the bulk of the Warriors, a smaller group of Xiticix attacked the refugees, abducting fifteen of their children.

Several of the women will come forward at this point and beg the players to help them rescue their children. With their own defenders all but decimated, they cannot hope to pursue the fleeing Xiticix with any chance of survival, much less success. Since the attack only happened 30 minutes ago, they are hoping that somehow the children might still be alive and that the players might be able to rescue them. Zanchavex will agree with that assessment, though he will not explain why he believes that the children are still alive.

One of the survivors will then explain that they are the family members of some of the high ranking officials from the Kingdom of Tolkeen and that, for what it is worth now, the players will forever have a friend and ally in the rulers of Tolkeen, exiled though they might be. Furthermore, whatever they have to offer if the players return with their children they will gladly give, including more recent information on the Coalition occupation of the city.

As the players head north and are well out of earshot of the refugees, Zanchavex will explain that the Xiticix most likely abducted the children for their high amount of P.P.E. in order to make "Sludge." "Sludge" is the concentrated P.P.E. rich nutrient created by Xiticix Nannies and Queens and fed to the insect alien larvae in order to accelerate their growth. Having once been inside a hive, Zanchavex will explain that he has seen cocooned captives that he suspected were to be slain and their life force (P.P.E.) converted into "Sludge." He explains that this should mean that for the moment, the children will be kept alive at least until they get them to the hive. Even then, they may not immediately be slain if there is already an abundant supply of "Sludge" or enough other victims already cocooned and waiting to be slain. However, the Simvan urges that if they are to hope to rescue the children, they will need to try to overtake the insect abductors before they reach the Hivelands, or they will be forced to enter the Xiticix territory teeming with thousands of agitated Warriors. With only a 30 minute head start, he thinks that if they hurry, they might overtake the bugs before they get too far.

The trip north will be fast and furious. At first, there should be no sign of the fleeing Xiticix as the party races on. However, after about an hour, one of the players with superior or enhanced sight may spot a small swarm flying in a "beeline" still heading due north (requires a Perception Roll of 12+). Over the next twenty to thirty minutes, the players will draw steadily closer until they are able to see that the swarm consists of about 18 to 20 Warriors carrying a number of small forms. Although now within range for long-range weapons and missiles, such a tactic would kill the children the Xiticix are bearing. However, the players should be within striking range shortly and Zanchavex

assures them that they should still be just outside of the Hivelands and well outside the territory of the Duluth Hive (which he believes to be the nearest of the six known hives).

At this point, any character with the psionic Sensitive power of Sixth Sense will be warned of imminent danger. Moments later, a single Xiticix will jump out of the nearby brush and attack the party. Even at first glance, this insect clearly does not look like the usual blue-gray Xiticix. It is a Hunter.

Xiticix Hunter: Equivalent to a 6th level R.C.C.

Alignment: Anarchist.

Attributes: I.Q. 15, M.E. 25, M.A. 5, P.S. 28 (supernatural), P.P. 26, P.E. 14, P.B. 5, Spd 28 running, 180 flying.

Size: 7 feet (2.1 m) tall; 400 pounds (180 kg).

M.D.C.: 92 (76 with an additional 16 provided by Resin Augmentation).

P.P.E.: 50

I.S.P.: 73

Horror Factor: 10

Attacks per Melee: 6

Bonuses: +5 on initiative, +9 to strike, +10 to parry, +10 to dodge, +2 to roll with punch, +6 to pull punch, +2 to disarm, +2 to save versus poison, +5 to save versus psionics, +8 to save versus insanity, +4 to save versus Horror Factor.

Damage and Weapons: Punch: 3D6 M.D.

Power Punch: 6D6 M.D. (counts as two attacks).

Sickle Pincer Strike: 4D6 M.D.

Sickle Pincer Power Strike: 1D4x10 M.D. (counts as two attacks).

Xiticix Spear: 4D6+3 M.D. stabbing or 1D4+3D6 M.D. as a thrown weapon.

Xiticix TK Rifle: 4D6 M.D. per blast, 40 shots per 20 P.P.E. or 40 I.S.P.

Natural Abilities and R.C.C. Skills of Note: All natural and chemical abilities common to the Xiticix (see pages 36-43 in *Rifts® World Book 23: Xiticix Invasion*). Specific abilities of note include Nightvision 1000 feet (305 m), Infrared and Ultraviolet vision, Sense Motion in the air: 500 feet (152 m), Feel Vibrations, Ultrasonic Hearing: 2000 feet (610 m), Superior Sense of Smell, Recognize Colony Scent, Chemical Marking (see below), Chemical Alarm (warns other Xiticix of intruders), Death Scent (given off when slain, warns other Xiticix that the person is a Xiticix enemy), Spit Acid (1D4 M.D. for 2D4 rounds, +2 to strike, twice per round), Natural Camouflage (98% undetectable when standing motionless in vegetation), Camouflage (65%), Detect Ambush (75%), Detect Concealment (65%), Prowl (80%), W.P. Paired Weapons, W.P. Spear (+3 to strike and parry, +2 to throw), W.P. Energy Rifle (+3 to strike). Grapple/Wrestle and Strike (holds and pins with hands and strikes with its other arms), Two-Handed Paired Weapon Attack (can attack with paired weapons and still retain its automatic parry).

Magic Knowledge: None.

Psionic Abilities: None.

Equipment: None, other than the weapons listed above.

Appearance: Unlike normal Xiticix Warriors, the Hunter's exoskeleton is dark green in color. While like its brothers, it possesses four arms, two are located on its upper back above its wings and end in scythe-like pincers instead of hands. Apart from some additional differences in the shape of the head, it is still easily recognizable as a Xiticix.

The Hunter has broken from the fleeing captors in an effort to slow down the pursuers. It will do what it can to slow the players down, though it should not take long for the players to overcome this lone Xiticix. However, before it dies, it will spray several of the player characters with its special Chemical Marking Scent. This chemical is odorless to humans (only faintly detectible to Dog Boys and those with an enhanced sense of small) but easily recognizable to other Xiticix. It tells other Warriors and Hunters that the marked targets are either to be captured if they possess a high amount of P.P.E. or slain as a threat to the Hive. Zanchavex will know this and will warn the players about it.

When the players resume their pursuit, they will see that the fleeing swarm has once again gained its lead and is almost out of sight. As they pursue, they will once again begin to gain on the Xiticix (the bugs are flying at less than their normal speed because of the burden they are carrying), but they will suddenly be ambushed by a patrol of Warrior and Leaper Xiticix lead by another Hunter.

Xiticix Hunter (1): See previous description.

Xiticix Warriors (4):
Equivalent to a 4th level R.C.C.

Alignment: Anarchist.

Attributes: I.Q. 12, M.E. 22, M.A. 2, P.S. 30 (Supernatural), P.P. 17, P.E. 16, P.B. 2, Spd 22 running, 150 flying.

Size: 7 feet (2.1 m) tall; 500 pounds (225 kg).

M.D.C.: 104

P.P.E.: 50

I.S.P.: 0

Horror Factor: 10

Attacks per Melee: 6

Bonuses: +4 on initiative, +4 to strike, +5 to parry, +4 to dodge, +2 to roll with punch, +6 to pull punch, +2 to disarm, +2 to save versus poison, +4 to save versus psionics, +5 to save versus insanity, +4 to save versus Horror Factor.

Damage and Weapons: <u>Punch</u>: 3D6 M.D.

  <u>Power Punch</u>: 6D6 M.D. (counts as two attacks).

  <u>Xiticix Spear</u>: 4D6+3 M.D. stabbing or 1D4+3D6 M.D. as a thrown weapon.

  <u>Xiticix Short Sword</u>: 4D6 M.D.

  <u>Xiticix Knife</u>: 1D4+3D6 M.D.

  <u>Xiticix TK Rifle</u>: 4D6 M.D. per blast, 40 shots per 20 P.P.E. or 40 I.S.P.

Natural Abilities and R.C.C. Skills of Note: All natural and chemical abilities common to the Xiticix (see pages 36-43 in *Rifts® World Book 23: Xiticix Invasion*). Specific abilities of note include Nightvision 1000 feet (305 m), Infrared and Ultraviolet vision, Sense Motion in the air: 500 (152 m), Feel Vibrations, Ultrasonic Hearing: 2000 feet (610 m), Superior Sense of Smell, Recognize Colony Scent, Chemical Alarm

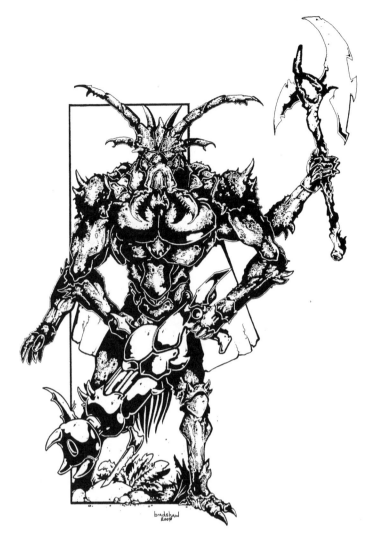

bradshaw 2009

(warns other Xiticix of intruders), Death Scent (given off when slain, warns other Xiticix that the person is a Xiticix enemy), Spit Acid (1D4 M.D. for 2D4 rounds, +2 to strike, twice per round), W.P. Paired Weapons, W.P. Spear (+2 to strike and parry, +1 to throw), W.P. Knife (+2 to strike, parry, and throw), W.P. Sword (+2 to strike and parry), W.P. Energy Rifle (+2 to strike). Grapple/Wrestle and Strike (holds and pins with hands and strikes with its other arms), Two-Handed Paired Weapon Attack (can attack with paired weapons and still retain its automatic parry).

Magic Knowledge: None.

Psionic Abilities: None.

Equipment: None, other than the weapons listed above.

Appearance: A typical Xiticix Warrior with a blue-gray exoskeleton, four arms, and wings.

Xiticix Leapers (2):
Equivalent to a 4th level R.C.C.

Alignment: Anarchist.

Attributes: I.Q. 9, M.E. 13, M.A. 4, P.S. 25 (supernatural), P.P. 21, P.E. 17, P.B. 1, Spd 37 running, 80 full sprint, 90 flying.

Size: 6 feet (1.8 m) tall; 400 pounds (180 kg).

M.D.C.: 116 (88 with an additional 28 provided by Resin Augmentation).

P.P.E.: 60

I.S.P.: 25

Horror Factor: 11

Attacks per Melee: 5

Bonuses: +6 on initiative, +6 to strike, +5 to parry, 10 to dodge, +4 to roll with punch, +4 to pull punch, +2 to disarm, +3 to save versus poison, +1 to save versus magic, +4 to save versus Horror Factor.

Damage and Weapons: <u>Punch:</u> 2D6 M.D.

<u>Power Punch:</u> 4D6 M.D. (counts as two attacks).

<u>Xiticix Long Sword:</u> 4D6 M.D.

<u>Xiticix Spiked Whip:</u> 3D6+4 M.D.

<u>Body Block Ram:</u> 3D6 M.D.

<u>Resin Shoulder Spikes:</u> Adds 1D6 M.D. to ramming attack.

<u>Bite:</u> 3D6 M.D. + poison (save versus lethal poison or inflicts 5D6 S.D.C or 3D6 M.D. to torture victims or 1D4x100 S.D.C. or 4D6 M.D. and 1D6 M.D. for 1D6 rounds to kill).

<u>Rear Power Kick:</u> 1D4x10 M.D.

<u>Leap Kick:</u> 1D6x10+12 M.D. (counts as two attacks).

<u>Foot Strike:</u> 4D6 M.D.

Natural Abilities and R.C.C. Skills of Note: All natural and chemical abilities common to the Xiticix (see pages 36-43 in *Rifts® World Book 23: Xiticix Invasion*). Specific abilities of note include Nightvision 1000 feet (305 m), Infrared and Ultraviolet vision, Sense Motion in the air: 500 (152 m), Feel Vibrations, Ultrasonic Hearing: 2000 feet (610 m), Superior Sense of Smell, Recognize Colony Scent, Chemical Alarm (warns other Xiticix of intruders), W.P. Paired Weapons, W.P. Whip (+2 to strike, disarm or entangle), W.P. Sword (+2 to strike and parry), Leap 20 feet (6 m) high and 40 feet (12 m) across, Power Running Leap 60 feet (18.3 m) high and 120 feet (36.6 m) across, Can parry attacks with its feet.

Magic Knowledge: None.

Psionic Abilities: Considered a Minor Psionic with the following abilities: See the Invisible (4), Sense Magic (3), Impervious to Cold (2), Impervious to Fire (4).

Equipment: None, other than the weapons listed above.

Appearance: Unlike normal Xiticix Warriors, the Leaper has only two arms and a pair of oversized legs. Its wings look more like a moth's and are semi-transparent. The head is a cross between an ordinary Xiticix and a demonic skull with overly large, spider-like pincers.

After the Xiticix are defeated, Zanchavex will not immediately resume the chase, despite the urging of the players. Instead, he will begin slicing into their corpses and carefully removing a small gland-shaped organ from their interiors. He will explain that by the time they are able to catch up with the rest of the Xiticix, they will be within the Hivelands and will most certainly be attacked as a result of both the earlier Chemical Marking from the first Hunter as well as the Death Scents given off by the recently slain Warriors they just killed. He believes that the scent glands from these fallen Xiticix might be strong enough to overwhelm the previous scents and mask them from the rest of the insects, at least the ones from the same colony that spawned their attackers (which he still believes to be the Duluth Hive).

Once the glands are retrieved, the Simvan will apply a liberal amount of the secretions from the organ to everything the party has in their possession, including their armor, weapons, and even themselves. Then the players and Zanchavex can resume their pursuit north into the Hivelands.

Chapter Seven: The New Hive

"Now all we have to do is sneak in past a few hundred bugs, find the nursery, rescue the kids, and make it back out before the whole hive knows were are here."

-Zanchavex

Zanchavex still believes that the Xiticix that abducted the refugee children came from the Duluth Hive and that they are still a few days travel from their destination. As such, he still hopes that they can overtake the bugs before they get too close to the largest Hive City in North America. It therefore comes as a great surprise to him when the party crests the nearest ridge and looks out over a wide plain dominated by a single Hive Tower.

With the sudden defeat of the Kingdom of Tolkeen, the Elder Xiticix Queen in charge of the primary Xiticix Hive at Duluth has sensed the opportunity to expand her hold on the region to the south. Without the magical might of Tolkeen to stand in her way, there will be little organized opposition to the establishment of a new hive just north of the fallen kingdom. With the Coalition Army scattered throughout the region still engaged with remnants of Tolkeen's military, fighting against guerrillas, fending off looters, and hunting down fleeing refugees, there will be little to stand in the way of this new hive until it has grown too strong to eliminate without engaging in a full scale invasion. Not only that, but with so many P.P.E.-rich refugees swarming over the countryside, it gives this new hive a vast amount of power with which to create the "Sludge" that accelerates the growth of the larval Xiticix in the early stages. Essentially, this is the first move in the expansion of the Hivelands southward.

From their vantage point some 2 miles (3.2 km) away, the players can already see signs of activity in the sky around the lone tower. The plain below their position looks to have been recently cleared of any large vegetation that might have concealed any immediate dangers to the hive. At this point, Zanchavex will explain to the players that their odds of success have just decreased dramatically. Overtaking the swarm of Xiticix while still several days from the Duluth Hive City was one thing; infiltrating a Hive Tower swarming with bugs is something completely different. Even for a small hive, there will most likely be hundreds of insects to contend with. And they will be on high alert as such a new hive is in a vulnerable state until its population grows considerably. He will stop here and continue to study the distant structure while the players deliberate about what to do next.

Then again, he will continue after several minutes, a new hive such as this should have only one Young Xiticix Queen and a relatively small nursery. That would make searching the tunnel network beneath relatively easy. He will ultimately leave it up to the players to determine a course of action, though the Simvan will remind them that time is still of the essence as by now the abducted children will have been cocooned somewhere in the tunnels beneath the tower.

Should the players decide to infiltrate the hive, Zanchavex will explain that the only conventional entrance would be through one of the several large openings located about 30 to 40 feet (9 to 12 m) above the ground (since this is a lone tower, there are no bridges to connect to other towers). Once inside (assuming their scent disguise holds), they will need to carefully sneak down the length of the tower into the subterranean levels where the Young Queen and her nursery would be located. He advises them all to reapply the scent gland secretions before heading out and warns them not to attack *any* of the Xiticix they might encounter unless they are attacked first.

Game Masters: Although Zanchavex's assessment of the situation is accurate, do not let the players know that he is right. Though he knows a great deal about the bugs, having spent some time exploring parts of the Hiveland near Duluth, he is by no means a complete expert (Lore: Xiticix: 45%), therefore, when role-playing his explanations and instructions to the players, he should seem not entirely confident that his plans will work. The players should continue to worry that at some point, they will be discovered by the swarm of alien insects and be overwhelmed. The entire situation should generate a Horror Factor of 16+. Still, as long as the players follow Zanchavex's advice, they will be able to penetrate deep into the hive without detection, at least until they begin trying to rescue the refugee children from the nursery. However, the terror of this entire scenario should be taken advantage of to the fullest. In addition to the specific encounters described below, suggested tactics to heighten the tension both on the approach to the tower and within the maze of tunnels can include:

- A group of Warriors (two for every one player) conducts a fly-by of the party, getting close enough for the characters to feel the breeze from their wings.
- The ground before the players collapses and 2D6 Xiticix Diggers emerge from a newly formed tunnel. They pause as if considering the players for a moment before moving on.
- A lone Hunter stops in front of the party and closely scrutinizes each one of them, as if detecting some trace of the original Marker scent left on some of the players earlier. Satisfied (fooled) that they are fellow hive members, it moves on, but not without looking over its shoulder one last time.
- Suddenly, all of the Warriors in the immediate vicinity take flight as if roused by something (if in the tunnels, the party will suddenly find itself overtaken by a swarm of scurrying Warriors). However, after several tense moments, the swarm takes off, heading west for some unknown reason.
- A Xiticix Super-Warrior and 12 Warriors surround the party. The Super-Warrior closely examines each of the players and becomes agitated by one of them (determine randomly or Game Master selected; perhaps one of the players sprayed by the Hunter earlier). However, before anything is done, a Xiticix Nanny approaches and "orders" the Warriors to follow her.
- A pair of Leapers overtakes the party, but passes through them and continues onward.
- A section of tunnel collapses behind the players, effectively sealing off their escape. Have they been found out?
- A section of the tunnel into which the players were headed collapses, blocking their route. If the players remain for 1D6 minutes in the area, they will observe 1D4 Diggers and 3D6 Xiticix Workers arrive from newly excavated tunnels and begin to clear the rubble.

- A Nanny accompanied by 4 Workers and 2 Warriors approaches and attempts to order the players to follow her. Since the Xiticix communicate through chemical scents and ultrasonic chittering and clicking, only those with cybernetic amplified hearing will hear anything at all and no one will understand what the bug is saying (even using the Tongues invocation will only provide a partial translation - effectively 25% as the Xiticix manner of speech is so alien). It will become agitated for a few moments when the players do not respond, but will move on, leaving the party shaken but still undetected.
- The floor (or ground if outside) will suddenly collapse, plummeting the players into a deeper chamber. The players will fall about 20 feet (6 m) into a heap of crumbled resin and rubble. Rattled but relatively unhurt, the players will find themselves in the midst of a Xiticix living chamber occupied by dozens of Xiticix (mainly Workers and Diggers with some Warriors). On the other hand, they have just made it one level deeper into the hive.
- A partially cocooned human suddenly awakens near the party. He sees them and begins to beg for help. If the party does not immediately come to his aid, he will begin screaming for help. Within 1D4 rounds, 3 Warriors will appear and kill the human. If the players have already released him, then when the Warriors arrive, they will attack and kill the prisoner (they will still regard the party as members of the hive unless the players interfere).

Unless the players come across a tunnel that takes them immediately into the lower levels of the hive, they will first need to either scale the outside of the tower or fly to one of the openings. Scaling the tower is extremely difficult as the entire surface is covered with spines of varying lengths (-15% to Climbing skill rolls and reduce speed by 30%). Flying might be quicker, but with the constant stream of Xiticix flying in and out of the openings, it is far more likely that the players will be detected as invaders (at least that is what they should think). Falling while climbing will result in 3D6 S.D.C. damage per 10 foot (3 m) fall. While those inside armor will suffer mainly bruises, if one's skin is cut, the scent of human (or D-Bee) blood will overwhelm that character's scent disguise immediately. The players will have 1D4 melee rounds to reapply a heavy coating from the extracted scent glands before being discovered.

Once inside the tower, the players will find a large vestibule-like hall filled with dozens of flying Warriors both leaving and returning to the hive. Tunnels down consist of nearly vertical shafts that drop 20 to 40 feet (6 to 12.1 m) down to the next level. Since almost all of the Xiticix can fly and all can scale walls with the ease of any ordinary insect, there is no need for ramps, stairs, or ladders. If the players do not have rope or some other means of descent (magic or psionic), then exploring the tunnels will have become that much harder. Zanchavex will warn them that using jet packs or power armor for flight will emit too much exhaust and bring the scent-sensitive Xiticix to investigate. Tunnels, both vertical and horizontal, can vary in width from just a few feet wide (room for no more than one or two to walk abreast) to wide causeways where ten or more can spread out and that hundreds of insects can travel through en masse.

Since all Xiticix possess excellent nightvision, there is little illumination within the hive tunnels once beyond the openings in the tower. However, as the players begin to descend into the maze of tunnels, they will notice a pale green luminescent fungus growing on the walls and ceilings. This moss is actually the insects' food (not even Zanchavex knows this). In addition to the minimal lighting, the atmosphere inside the tunnels will be hot, dry, and stuffy. Even those without the benefit of enhanced smelling abilities will detect a faint musky odor (while those with a powerful sense of smell (e.g. Dog Boys) will be overwhelmed by the odors and will find it nearly impossible to track by scent, -50%). There will be a constant low hum heard throughout the tunnels, both as a result of the whirring of wings that echoes throughout the chambers as well as the hum of Xiticix "conversations" which are so frequent that even at an ultrasonic level, the vibrations can be felt, though only just.

Though new (the hive was only completed a few weeks ago), this hive already has a sizable population consisting of a few hundred Xiticix. Even at the accelerated growth rate made possible by the "Sludge," there is no way this many insects could have been birthed in such a short time. The hive's current population was sent by the Duluth Hive Elder Queen to colonize the territory previously dominated by the Kingdom of Tolkeen. Normally, only a handful of Xiticix are sent with a new Young Queen when a new hive complex is being developed; however, with the lingering threat of the fallen kingdom's warriors as well as the presence of a competing force (the Coalition Army), the Elder Queen wanted to leave nothing to chance and sent an unusually large number with this Young Queen to help secure the new hive as quickly as possible.

A rough layout of the hive levels is present in the following section; however, the tunnel network between each main chamber is essentially an interconnected maze of corridors in which one can very quickly become disoriented and lost (-10% to Spelunking skill rolls). Key chambers and encounters are described below and have been adapted from pages 29-36 of *Rifts® World Book 23: Xiticix Invasion*. Original stats for the Hive Complex have been reduced to account for the relatively small size of this newly formed hive.

The Tower Levels

1. The Cap Chambers (2): Since this hive is relatively new (only a few weeks old) and still fairly small, there are only two main Cap Chambers, massive, hollow rooms buzzing with Warriors. Normally, a typical hive Cap would contain several hundred Warriors; however, the current reduced population only maintains around 50 Warriors in each Cap, each group commanded by a single Super-Warrior. To compare this to a modern air base, these would be the fighters on the ready-line, prepared to take flight and exit the hive at a moment's notice while the bulk of the Warriors and defenders ready themselves deeper within the tower. Several wide tunnels descend 30 feet (9.1 m) from the Cap Chambers to the Transit Halls.

2. Transit Halls (8): Directly beneath the two Cap Chambers, there are eight Transit Halls (four directly beneath the Cap Chambers and four more beneath the first four), large rooms from which Warriors from the Caps can rapidly exit the hive in response to an external threat. Through the large oval openings (one per Transit Hall, 8 total for this tower), 3 to 9 Xiticix War-

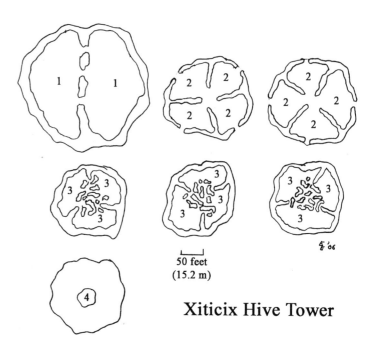

Xiticix Hive Tower

50 feet
(15.2 m)

riors can take flight at once, allowing the tower to disgorge hundreds of insects in a matter of melee rounds. Currently, unless the players have done something to rouse the entire hive, the level of activity is a steady flow of 1D4 bugs either landing or taking flight from the Transit Halls every few melee rounds. Arriving Xiticix either fly upwards into the Cap Chambers or descend to the next level below. In addition to the steady flow in and out, there will be 2D6 Warriors on lookout at each portal at any given time (except when the entire hive is on alert, in which case, the number of guards is tripled). Each Transit Hall has at least two wide vertical shafts that descend deeper into the next level of the tower.

3. Lower Habitats (9): From this point on, the majority of the tower is composed of nine large Habitat Chambers connected by a maze of twisted tunnels (some horizontal, most vertical) and dead-end passageways. Each of the Habitat Chambers will contain anywhere from 10 to 40 (1D4x10) Warriors, 4D6 Workers and a handful of Hunters, Leapers, and Diggers. Connecting these large chambers is a maze of vertical and horizontal tunnels. Each Habitat Chamber has at least one wide tunnel that connects directly to a Transit Hall above for immediate exit in times of emergency. Passageways down, however, are far less direct. (**Note:** Xiticix never get lost in their hive tunnels as a result of scent trails left behind that let each insect "smell" exactly where they are at any given point). It is at this point that the players will begin to notice the luminescent moss.

4. Tunnel Vestibule (1): This chamber represents the base of the tower beneath which lies the bulk of the hive, including the rest of the Xiticix population, the nursery, and the Young Queen's chambers. Although this small chamber (roughly 50 feet/15.2 m in diameter) can be accessed from above by three tunnels (though only after navigating the maze of passages leading from the Lower Habitats), there is only one single vertical drop down into the subterranean parts of the hive. This chamber is currently occupied by 10 Warriors commanded by a Hunter, all of whom are on constant alert. The Hunter will "inspect" anyone other than a Nanny, Super-Warrior, or fellow Hunter (or one who bears their scent) who tries to pass (again, as long as the hive has not already been alerted to their presence, the scent disguise will fool these Warriors, although the players should not immediately know this).

Tunnel Network Level One

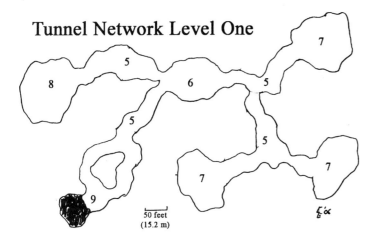

50 feet
(15.2 m)

Tunnel Network Level One

5. Interconnecting Tunnels: Connecting the larger chambers within all four of the Tunnel Network levels is a series of maze-like passages and smaller chambers (too numerous to label or map) that twist and turn, connect with other passages or simply dead-end. These tunnels vary in size and can slope up or down at random. This would be a great place for one or more of the aforementioned "tension" creating encounters to take place. There is a 01-15% chance that the players will encounter a group of 1D6 Workers or Diggers in any given passageway. As long as the players remain scent disguised and do not attack these drones, they will continue to go about their business, creating more tunnels or erecting structures. **Map Note:** The vertical shafts that connect the different levels will most likely be located somewhere in these maze-like passages. Finding them will prove somewhat difficult.

6. Gathering Chamber: Directly beneath the Tunnel Vestibule is a large Gathering Chamber where hundreds of Xiticix can assemble to rapidly ascend into the tower. At present, it is likely to be (01-50%) empty or (51-00%) occupied by four Warriors and a pair of Leapers commanded by a Hunter. Unless the players do something to arouse suspicion, they will be allowed to move through without incident.

7. Living Chambers (3): Three on this level, like the Habitat Chambers in the tower, this chamber could hold hundreds of insects when the hive is at capacity. However, at present, there are only 1D6 Warriors and 1D6 Workers present.

Xiticix Workers: Equivalent to a 3rd level R.C.C.

Alignment: Anarchist.

Attributes: I.Q. 7, M.E. 20, M.A. 5, P.S. 34 (Supernatural), P.P. 13, P.E. 15, P.B. 5, Spd 19 running, 100 flying.

Size: 6 feet (1.8 m) tall; 400 pounds (180 kg).

M.D.C.: 70

P.P.E.: 30

I.S.P.: 0

Horror Factor: 8

Attacks per Melee: 4

Bonuses: +2 on initiative, +1 to strike, +1 to parry, +3 to dodge, +4 to roll with punch, +2 to pull punch, +2 to save versus poison, +3 to save versus psionics, +3 to save versus insanity, +3 to save versus Horror Factor.

Damage and Weapons: Punch: 4D6 M.D.

Power Punch: 1D4x10 M.D. (counts as two attacks).

Pincer/Scissor Claw: 5D6 M.D.

Natural Abilities and R.C.C. Skills of Note: All natural and chemical abilities common to the Xiticix (see pages 36-43 in *Rifts® World Book 23: Xiticix Invasion*). Specific abilities of note include Nightvision 1000 feet (305 m), Infrared and Ultraviolet vision, Sense Motion in the air: 500 (152 m), Feel Vibrations, Ultrasonic Hearing: 2000 feet (610 m), Superior Sense of Smell, Recognize Colony Scent, Chemical Alarm (warns other Xiticix of intruders).

Magic Knowledge: None.

Psionic Abilities: None.

Equipment: None.

Appearance: Similar to Xiticix Warriors with blue-gray exoskeletons, four arms, and wings. The second set of arms, however has a six foot (1.8 m) reach and ends in two massive claws. Workers will never fight except to defend themselves or when ordered to by a Nanny, Super-Warrior, Hunter, or Queen.

8. Storage Chamber: This large, hollow chamber may one day be converted into a Living Chamber; however, at present, it serves as a storage room where discarded materials are dumped. This includes gear and equipment from captured victims. Although most has been smashed beyond repair, there is a 10% chance per 10 minutes spent sifting through the debris of finding some working weapon or salvageable piece of equipment. However, for every five minutes spent in the chamber, there is a 25% chance that 1D6 Workers accompanied by 2 Warriors will arrive to deliver some additional scrap.

9. Small Water Chamber: This part of the network taps into a freshwater spring from which the Xiticix obtain drinking water. 01-10% chance of 1D6 Workers present filling resin buckets to bring water to other parts of the hive.

Tunnel Network Level Two

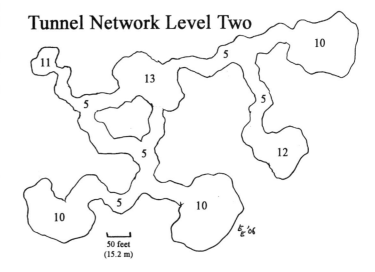

50 feet
(15.2 m)

Tunnel Network Level Two

10. Living Chambers (3): Three on this level, identical to #7 but with 3 times the Xiticix present.

11. Isolated Living Chamber: This small living chamber houses 2D6 Leapers at present. These loners will be hostile to anyone disturbing them, even if scent disguised, though only with the intent of driving off the unwanted hive member and not actually attacking.

12. Small Storage Chamber: Identical to #8, though only a 5% chance of finding something salvageable.

13. Meeting Chamber: Much like #6 only there is a 01-80% chance of being unoccupied. If occupied, there will be 2D6 Workers or 1D6 Warriors present.

Tunnel Network Level Three

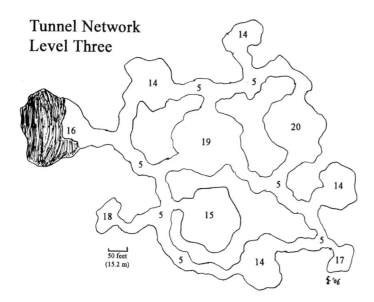

Tunnel Network Level Three

50 feet (15.2 m)

Tunnel Network Level Three

14. Living Chambers (4): Four on this level, identical to #7 only with 10 to 40 Xiticix present, mostly Diggers, Workers, or Nannies. Only 1D4 Warriors present.

15. Large Storage Chamber: This large storage chamber contains not only various pieces of discarded equipment from cocooned victims, but what looks like the remains of several robots, vehicles, and power armor (much of it recognizable as CS hardware). These pieces, all of them damaged well beyond repair, are being salvaged for scrap, their M.D.C. armor being incorporated into the resin that makes walls and structures of the hive to give it added stability. There is a 35% chance that some salvageable components might be found if 10 or more minutes are spent searching (mini-missiles, energy-clips, power cells, etc.); however, 4D6 Workers and Diggers are constantly present at any time with an equal number coming and going, either bringing more junk or taking away scraps to be used elsewhere.

Xiticix Diggers: Equivalent to a 4th level R.C.C.

Alignment: Anarchist.

Attributes: I.Q. 8, M.E. 23, M.A. 3, P.S. 36 (Supernatural), P.P. 14, P.E. 17, P.B. 2, Spd 23 running, 90 flying.

Size: 9 feet (2.7 m) tall when hunched over, 18 feet (5.5 m) tall when standing erect; 2 tons.

M.D.C.: 111

P.P.E.: 30

I.S.P.: 57

Horror Factor: 10

Attacks per Melee: 4

Bonuses: +2 on initiative, +2 to strike, +2 to parry, +3 to dodge, +2 to roll with punch, +3 to pull punch, +3 to save versus

possession, +8 to save versus poison, +1 to save versus magic, +4 to save versus psionics, +6 to save versus insanity.

Damage and Weapons: <u>Punch</u>: 5D6 M.D.

<u>Power Punch</u>: 1D6x10 M.D. (counts as two attacks).

<u>Lunging Attack/Body Slam</u>: 1D6x10 but counts as two melee attacks and must be used as the first attack of the round.

Natural Abilities and R.C.C. Skills of Note: All natural and chemical abilities common to the Xiticix (see pages 36-43 in *Rifts® World Book 23: Xiticix Invasion*). Specific abilities of note include Nightvision 1000 feet (305 m), Infrared and Ultraviolet vision, Sense Motion in the air: 500 (152 m), Feel Vibrations, Ultrasonic Hearing: 2000 feet (610 m), Superior Sense of Smell, Recognize Colony Scent, Chemical Alarm (warns other Xiticix of intruders), Underground Sense of Direction (78%), Digging, Tunneling, and Excavating (84%/86%/86%), Making Traps (78%), Building Hive Structures and Resin Weapons.

<u>Resin Glob Attack</u>: One glob attack per round; the resin is sticky for two rounds (-1 on initiative, -10% to speed) and begins to harden by the third round and is completely stiff and hard after four rounds. Requires 100 M.D.C. of damage to remove.

Magic Knowledge: None.

Psionic Abilities: Considered a Minor Psionic with the following abilities: Ectoplasm (6 or 12), Levitation (varies), Resist Fatigue (4), Telepathy (4), Mind Block (4), and Summon Inner Strength (4).

Equipment: None.

Appearance: This Xiticix looks more like a blue-gray beetle than the typical Xiticix, with a large, bulbous abdomen and thicker fingers instead of claws.

16. Large Water Chamber: This part of the network taps into a large underground aquifer from which the Xiticix obtain drinking water. 01-10% chance of 2D6 Workers present filling resin buckets to bring water to other parts of the hive.

17. Isolated Living Chamber: This small chamber houses 3D6 Hunters. These loners will exhibit hostility to any intruders in order to drive them off.

18. Isolated Living Chamber: Identical to #17 only it houses 4D6 Leapers.

19. Meeting Chamber: This large chamber is used as a meeting chamber for large groups of Xiticix whenever one of the leader types (Nanny, Super-Warrior, or Hunter) needs to issue orders to a large portion of the hive. 01-60% likely to be empty. Otherwise there will be a mixture of 2D6 Workers, 2D6 Diggers, and 1D4 Leapers present at the time.

20. Warrior Living Chamber: This large chamber houses 2D6x10 Warriors and 4 Super-Warriors. In addition to several passages that exit into the current level's corridors, this chamber has several vertical tunnels that lead directly to all upper levels, including a passage directly adjacent to the Tower Tunnel Vestibule in order to allow these Warriors quick access to any level where they might be needed at a moment's notice (within 2D4 melee rounds). As long as the players are still scent disguised, they should be able to avoid attracting attention if they investigate this chamber. However, if they enter this hall, there is a 01-05% chance that one of the Super-Warriors will investigate them and see through their disguise. *Trouble!*

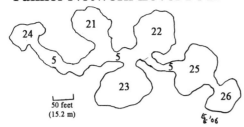

50 feet
(15.2 m)

Tunnel Network Level Four

21. Future Nursery: At present, there are only 4D6 Workers and 4D6 Diggers actively excavating this chamber for the eventual brood of larvae that will hatch in about two months from the adjacent Egg Chamber. There will be 1D4 Nannies present overseeing the work, but as there are presently no larvae in the hive yet (egg gestation takes around 3 months and the hive has only been in place for a few weeks now), this is not considered as a high security chamber as it would otherwise be in any other hive.

22. Future Nursery: Adjacent to the current Egg Chamber, this nursery is identical to #21 with two main differences. **1.** There are currently 4D6 Nannies present overseeing the efforts of 2D6 Diggers. **2.** More importantly, this is the chamber where prisoners are being cocooned for future transformation into "Sludge." Currently the walls are lined with dozens of alcoves occupied by about 50 humanoids. The occupied alcoves are partially closed by a thin wall of M.D.C. resin being secreted by the Diggers working in the chamber (wall strength is a minuscule 15 M.D.C. in order to make it easy for the Nannies to break through it when they are ready to consume a prisoner in order to transform him or her into "Sludge"). An additional hundred of so alcoves are empty, with roughly half partially sealed over by broken resin walls (meaning they were occupied until recently, when their prisoners were removed for "Sludge" creation). Four Workers are working to remove debris from these now vacant alcoves in order to make them ready for new arrivals. Another 12 Nannies are currently ingesting several corpses in a truly disgusting display (save versus Horror Factor 14+ or become overcome by nausea and vomit - an action that will immediately give away their disguises and alert the hive of the intruders) in order to begin the transformation into "Sludge." Every few minutes, 4 Workers appear to gather the regurgitated globs of "Sludge" and remove them for storage on this level. Against the far wall of this chamber, partially cocooned behind fresh resin walls, the players will find the fifteen poisoned but alive refugee children. As long as the players do nothing to interfere with the work or the production of "Sludge," they should remain undetected. However, once they begin breaking into the cocoons to free the children (along with any other prisoners they might try to liberate), they will have 1D4 melee rounds before the confused Workers, Diggers, and Nannies realize that these "drones" are not behaving normally. They will begin to attack, though without initiative and at half strength, bonuses, and number of attacks as they still believe that the scent disguised invaders are really fellow hive members. Within 1D6 melees, however, 2D4 Warriors will appear in response to a chemical warning signal given off by the Nannies. These and any other Warriors will only be caught off guard and confused for a melee round before

overcoming their initial confusion and attacking the intruders with their full strength.

Xiticix Nannies: Equivalent to a 6th level R.C.C.

Alignment: Anarchist.

Attributes: I.Q. 14, M.E. 20, M.A. 10, P.S. 27 (Supernatural), P.P. 12, P.E. 18, P.B. 5, Spd 25.

Size: 12 feet (3.6 m) tall; 1200 lbs (540 kg).

M.D.C.: 165

P.P.E.: 120

I.S.P.: 92

Horror Factor: 10

Attacks per Melee: 4

Bonuses: +3 on initiative, +2 to strike, +1 to parry, +3 to dodge, +4 to roll with punch, +2 to save versus poison, +2 to save versus magic, +3 to save versus psionics, +3 to save versus insanity, +3 to save versus Horror Factor.

Damage and Weapons: Punch: 3D6 M.D.

Power Punch: 6D6 M.D. (counts as two attacks).

Natural Abilities and R.C.C. Skills of Note: All natural and chemical abilities common to the Xiticix (see pages 36-43 in *Rifts® World Book 23: Xiticix Invasion*). Specific abilities of note include Nightvision 1000 feet (305 m), Infrared and Ultraviolet vision, Sense Motion in the air: 500 (152 m), Feel Vibrations, Ultrasonic Hearing: 2000 feet (610 m), Superior Sense of Smell, Recognize Colony Scent, Chemical Alarm (warns other Xiticix of intruders), Spit Acid (1D4 M.D. for 2D4 rounds, +2 to strike, twice per round), Make "Sludge,"

bradshaw
2007

S.D.C. Poison (used to subdue victims in order to make it easier to cocoon them and ultimately feed on them - inflicts 4D6 S.D.C. from the nip plus if the victim does not save versus lethal poison he will suffer 6D6 S.D.C. and reduce attacks per melee and combat bonuses by half).

Magic Knowledge: None.

Psionic Abilities: Considered a Major Psionic with the following abilities: Healing Touch (6), Psychic Surgery (14), Replenish P.P.E. (4+), Suppress Fear (8), Empathy (4), Telepathy (4), See the Invisible (4), Sense Magic (3), Sense Time (2), and Mind Block (4).

Equipment: None.

Appearance: This Xiticix looks similar to the typical Warrior with the following exceptions: a slightly different head style, an enlarged lower abdomen with several oval-shaped organs that glow when she is in the process of converting P.P.E. into "Sludge," and no wings.

23. Sludge Storage Chamber: Connected to both nurseries, this large hall contains numerous piles of recently created sludge. In addition to the 1D4 Warriors present to guard the stockpile, there is a steady flow of Workers carrying armfuls of the disgusting material from the adjacent Nursery (#22).

24. Isolated Living Chamber: Identical to #17 only there will be 1D4 Super-Warriors present. These commanders of the Xiticix hive are extremely hostile to any other Xiticix (or scent disguised person) entering their chamber and will drive them off with aggressive actions. If this happens, there is a 10% chance that their disguise will be penetrated.

Xiticix Super-Warriors:
Equivalent to a 6th level R.C.C.

Alignment: Anarchist.

Attributes: I.Q. 14, M.E. 21, M.A. 8, P.S. 37 (Supernatural), P.P. 24, P.E. 21, P.B. 1, Spd 35 running, 150 flying.

Size: 12 feet (3.6 m) tall; 1000 pounds (450 kg).

M.D.C.: 191

P.P.E.: 80

I.S.P.: 68

Horror Factor: 13

Attacks per Melee: 8

Bonuses: +6 on initiative, +9 to strike, +11 to parry, +9 to dodge, +2 to roll with punch, +6 to pull punch, +3 to disarm, +7 to save versus poison, +3 to save versus magic, +3 to save versus psionics, +4 to save versus insanity, +8 to save versus Horror Factor, +6 to save versus possession, +4 to save versus mind control.

Damage and Weapons: Punch: 5D6 M.D.

Power Punch: 1D6x10 M.D. (counts as two attacks).

Xiticix Spear: 6D6+3 M.D. stabbing or 1D4+5D6 M.D. as a thrown weapon.

Xiticix Short Sword: 6D6 M.D.

Xiticix Knife: 1D4+5D6 M.D.

Xiticix Beheading Axe: 6D6+3 M.D. (one handed) or 1D4x10 M.D. (two handed).

Xiticix TK Rifle: 4D6 M.D. per blast, 40 shots per 20 P.P.E. or 40 I.S.P.

Natural Abilities and R.C.C. Skills of Note: All natural and chemical abilities common to the Xiticix (see pages 36-43 in *Rifts® World Book 23: Xiticix Invasion*). Specific abilities of note include Nightvision 1000 feet (305 m), Infrared and Ultraviolet vision, Sense Motion in the air: 500 (152 m), Feel Vibrations, Ultrasonic Hearing: 2000 feet (610 m), Superior Sense of Smell, Recognize Colony Scent, Chemical Alarm (warns other Xiticix of intruders), Death Scent (given off when slain, warns other Xiticix that the person is a Xiticix enemy), Spit Acid (1D4 M.D. for 2D4 rounds, +2 to strike, twice per round), W.P. Paired Weapons, W.P. Spear (+3 to strike and parry, +2 to throw), W.P. Knife (+2 to strike, +3 to parry, and throw), W.P. Sword (+3 to strike, +2 to parry), W.P. Axe (+2 to strike and parry), W.P. Energy Rifle (+3 to strike). Grapple/Wrestle and Strike (holds and pins with hands and strikes with its other arms), Four-Handed Paired Weapon Attack (can attack with up to four paired weapons and still retain its automatic parry).

Magic Knowledge: None.

Psionic Abilities: Considered a Major Psionic with the following abilities: Deaden Pain (4), See the Invisible (4), Mind Block (4), Electrokinesis (varies).

Equipment: None, other than the weapons listed above.

Appearance: A larger than normal Xiticix Warrior with a blue-gray exoskeleton, *six* arms, and wings.

25. Egg Chamber: This chamber is lined with hundreds of sealed hexagonal alcoves dug straight into the walls. Inside each one, the players will be able to see small, white, translucent eggs, each one occasionally rocking gently in its cocoon as if turning restfully in its sleep. There will be 1D6+6 Nannies present at all times along with 1D6+3 Workers to assist the Nannies. Occasionally, another Worker will emerge from another chamber adjacent to the Egg Chamber bearing a freshly laid egg. One of the Nannies, along with her attendants, will intercept the new arrival. The egg will be transferred from the newcomer to one of the Nanny's attendant Workers who will then be directed to deposit it into a waiting alcove.

26. The Queen's Chamber: Inside this large, oval-shaped hall, the players will see the Young Queen, the matriarch of the newest Hive Complex on Rifts Earth. As the hive is so new, there are no other Queens present and she is the only one laying the eggs that will one day become the foundation of this seventh hive complex. Though young, the Queen is already massive, though most of her bulk is taken up by the egg sac upon which she appears to be seated (actually, the bulk of her frame is resting on a resin pedestal with the egg sac draping off the back and around the side). Large, oval-shaped organs (similar to the ones on the Nanny only far more numerous) glow constantly as she continues to literally pump out one white egg after another to be carted off by a waiting Worker into the adjacent Egg Chamber (there are eleven Workers present at any time, along with two Nannies who see to the Queen's needs). Scattered around the chamber are the Queen's elite guard: eight Warriors, four Hunters, four Leapers, and one Super-Warrior. Players will only have 1D4 melee rounds in this chamber before they are spotted as imposters by the Queen (she will not be fooled by the scent disguise). Her elite guard will jump into action, attacking without mercy while the Workers and Nannies either rush to protect the their Queen or remove any eggs from the chamber before they are damaged. Once the battle is begun, the Queen and all of her Warriors will secrete a chemical alert that will warn the entire hive within moments that their matriarch's chamber has been invaded. Within two melee rounds, another Super-Warrior, 3D6 Warriors and 1D6 Hunters or Leapers will appear. After that, every minute, another 1D10 additional Warriors will appear until the threat is over or driven out of the Queen's Chamber.

bradshaw
2007

Young Xiticix Queen:
Equivalent to a 7th level R.C.C.

Alignment: Anarchist.

Attributes: I.Q. 19, M.E. 25, M.A. 8, P.S. 35 (Supernatural), P.P. 18, P.E. 20, P.B. 3, Spd 29 running, 100 flying.

Size: 25 feet (7.6 m) tall, 15 foot (4.6 m) long egg sac; 2 tons.

M.D.C.: 404

P.P.E.: 180

I.S.P.: 145

Horror Factor: 14

Attacks per Melee: 5

Bonuses: +3 on initiative, +4 to strike, +4 to parry, +5 to dodge, +4 to pull punch, +3 to roll with punch, +5 to save versus poison, +3 to save versus magic, +5 to save versus psionics, +8 to save versus insanity, +5 to save versus Horror Factor, +5 to save versus possession and mind control.

Damage and Weapons: <u>Punch</u>: 4D6 M.D.

<u>Power Punch</u>: 1D4x10 M.D. (counts as two attacks).

<u>Psi-Sword</u>: 1D4x10+8 M.D.

Natural Abilities and R.C.C. Skills of Note: All natural and chemical abilities common to the Xiticix (see pages 36-43 in *Rifts® World Book 23: Xiticix Invasion*). Specific abilities of note include Nightvision 1000 feet (305 m), Infrared and Ultraviolet vision, Sense Motion in the air: 500 (152 m), Feel Vibrations, Ultrasonic Hearing: 2000 feet (610 m), Superior Sense of Smell, Recognize Colony Scent, Chemical Alarm (warns other Xiticix of intruders), Death Scent, Create Sludge, Create TK Weapons, Spit Acid (1D4 M.D. for 2D4 rounds, +2 to strike, twice per round).

Magic Knowledge: None.

Psionic Abilities: Considered a Major Psionic with the following abilities: Empathy (4), Telepathy (4), Empathic Transmission (6), Sixth Sense (2), Sense Magic (3), See the Invisible (4), Impervious to Poison (4), Impervious to Cold (2), Impervious to Fire (4), Levitation (varies), Mind Block (4), Group Mind Block (22), Psi-Sword (8D6 M.D.; 30), Psi-Shield (30), Super Telekinesis (10+).

Equipment: None.

Appearance: This giant Xiticix has a dark gray exoskeleton with black, light gray, and green highlights. Although she possesses the four arms and wings common to most Xiticix, the crown of the Queen possesses exceptionally long antennae. The egg sac extends around and to the side of her body and glows with an eerie green light. It is translucent and one can see some 60 to 70 squirming eggs slowly moving down the length of the sac.

At some point, Zanchavex will make the comment that with only one Queen and such a small egg chamber, it might be possible to eliminate the Queen and her brood before this new hive can truly establish itself. While admitting that the odds of survival once they attack either the egg chamber of the Queen herself will be extremely slim, it will prove far more difficult to root out this hive in a year or so, once thousands of fully mature Xiticix born to this Queen hatch, especially when several more Young Queens hatch and begin to produce their own eggs.

Once the players' presence has been detected within the Hive, the entire complex will become active and alert. As soon as the players have slain their first Warrior, the Death Scent it gives off will taint the players, overcoming their scent disguise. After that, they will not be able to bluff their way past any Xiticix they encounter, though Workers and Diggers will still ignore them unless attacked or ordered to attack by a Super-Warrior, Nanny, or the Queen.

Game Masters: The escape from the Hive should be played as an intense, high speed chase during which players must not only try to break the gauntlet of hundreds of Xiticix attempting to prevent their escape, but also protect the still groggy children they have just rescued. Since the overall population of the hive is relatively small, it should not be impossible to escape, especially with the clever use of magic to help cover their escape.

If the players manage to emerge from the tunnels back to the surface, they will find that the skies above them are swarming with approximately 150 Xiticix Warriors. As the cloud of angry insects begins to descend upon the players, a lone figure will shout to them, calling them towards him. As they approach, the figure will produce a scroll and, in a booming voice that the players will find oddly familiar, he will read a spell that will open a dimensional portal directly in front of them. The mage beckons for the players to escape through the portal. A last glance over their shoulders as they disappear trough the blue Rift will reveal the magic user unleashing a powerful blast of magical flame before stepping through himself. The Rift closes just as the first of the swarm reaches them.

The Hammer of the Forge™

Chapter Forty

Castle Nox

By James M.G. Cannon

The first thing he felt was the steady drip, drip, drip of water upon his brow. But even that faded over time.

Slowly he became aware of his own body: a throbbing pain in his neck; a flare of agony in his shoulders, wrists and ankles that came and went; a dull ache in his joints. He had not felt this way in a long time, he remembered, and with that, it all came back to him.

His friends called him Sol Vyking, and the Cosmic Forge had placed its blessing upon him, empowering him as a living embodiment of universal justice. With Caleb Vulcan and Ariel of Titan, his fellow Knights, Vyking fought against tyranny and evil across the Three Galaxies. Most recently, Vyking had led them and a small contingent of Consortium allies on a raid into Transgalactic Empire space. They hunted a devastating weapon known as the *Shadowstar*, a dreadnought with the ability to generate black holes. When they came upon the ship, the three Cosmo-Knights engaged while their allies dealt with the dreadnought's escort. As the mighty craft powered up its main gun and a black hole began to form in space between the ships, Caleb and Ariel fought a holding action against the legions of Imperial troops while Vyking slipped inside the *Shadowstar* and made his way to the engine room. Blasting the entire engineering section with his powerful energy beams, Vyking crippled the ship. But the black hole was too far along to simply collapse, and it dragged the *Shadowstar* into its implacable maw.

With the *Shadowstar* coming apart around him, and Imperial troops, Kreeghor, human and otherwise, racing about in panic, Vyking expected to die, crushed like a grape within the massive dreadnought as the black hole ground it to nothing.

Instead, he lived. How he survived, he could not say. But Vyking hurt too much for the answer to be otherwise. Strangely, this did not comfort him. As a Cosmo-Knight, he possessed superior bio-regenerative abilities. He could feel pain, certainly, but not over time and not so widespread. His body repaired itself quickly, fueled by the spark of cosmic fire bequeathed him by the Forge.

Cautiously, Vyking opened his eyes. He lay at a sharp angle in a dark room, his arms spread out and his legs straight beneath to form a cross. Metal binders wrapped his wrists, waist, and ankles, and he felt something dig into his throat as well as he craned his neck. There were markings carved into the metal, or perhaps etched there, but they were foreign to his eyes and he could not read them. Vyking tested the restraints, but gave up soon. Either his Forge-enhanced strength had fled him, or the bindings were simply too strong.

He extended his search to the room in which he lay. It was mostly dark, and Vyking could make out only a few humped shapes around him that could have been furniture or statuary or torture devices. He couldn't see well enough to be sure. What little light did enter the room, he discovered, came from a crack in the wall to his left and behind him that might have been a door. He couldn't shift his head far enough to pick up details, but a faint luminescence emanated from that direction, enough for him to make out basic details.

Vyking slumped back against the pallet on which he lay. He could be anywhere. He did not know how long he had been unconscious, nor had he any idea what had transpired within the black hole. It was entirely possible that the Kreeghor had managed to escape, taking him with them, and even now he lay in one of their dungeons somewhere deep within Imperial space.

He reached out tentatively with his cosmic awareness, hoping to sense something of his location, but felt nothing.

A cold sweat broke upon Vyking's pale brow.

Had he Fallen?

He clenched his fists impotently within his cage and felt a deep fear. If he had done something to anger the Cosmic Forge, violated his oath in some way, and been stripped of his powers, then he was utterly lost. If he had failed the Forge, then he did not deserve to go on living. He knew of Knights who had, and there were legends of those who had even redeemed themselves and returned to the order. But Vyking knew that if he had betrayed the Forge's trust and been found wanting, he did not deserve redemption.

The door creaked open, distracting Vyking from his dark thoughts. A massive humanoid creature stepped into the room. It stood nearly three meters tall and wore garments of rough wool, patched and frayed. The creature had a sallow complexion and livid, bone-white scars marred its exposed flesh, particularly at the joints. Eyes, lips, and nails were the same dull black as the shock of dirty hair upon its cumbersome head. The lips parted, revealing yellowed teeth in a jagged smile.

Vyking tried to speak, but his throat constricted and all he could muster was a sickly cough. The creature lurched toward him, and Vyking saw that it held a bucket in its hands. It reached in, withdrew a dripping sponge, and then placed the sponge against Vyking's lips. He sucked at the moisture eagerly, only now realizing how parched he was. The creature nodded at him dumbly, still grinning. There was intelligence in those dark eyes, but Vyking could not fathom how developed it might be. Nor could he be relieved to find another living thing here besides himself. The creature had the look of a reanimated corpse, although its motions were too fluid for it to be a zombie.

The sponge withdrew. Vyking mustered his strength. "More water," he managed to gasp.

The creature nodded and dipped the sponge once more, but before he withdrew it, Vyking said, "Drink." Somehow, the creature understood, for it dropped the sponge and lifted the bucket to Vyking's lips. Gratefully he sipped, and was surprised when the creature regulated the flow carefully, as if it understood that too much water would be a detriment to him.

At last the flow subsided. The creature lowered the bucket and backed away, still grinning that unsettling grin. "Where am I? Who are you? Why am I bound like this?" Vyking asked, coughing, but the creature simply nodded and departed. It closed the door firmly behind it as it left, depriving Vyking completely of light.

Vyking hung his head and resisted the urge to weep.

* * *

Time passed. How long, Vyking could not guess. Minutes could last as long as hours in the dark, mysterious room.

At last the door creaked open again. This time it opened much further, allowing the light from beyond the doorway to fall further into the room. The shapes resolved themselves into instruments of torture, but of an archaic stripe that Vyking had only ever before seen in history trids. They were worn with use, but obviously well cared for. And deeply stained with the blood of their victims. Vyking suppressed a chill.

He expected the creature to return, but the being who stepped into Vyking's line of vision was something else entirely. At first glance, the newcomer appeared to be a man. Tall, spare, and long-limbed, he wore sumptuous clothes of the finest cut, a dark suit slashed with red accents and here and there a glint of metal or precious stone. Pale-skinned and dark-haired like the creature, the man had smooth cheeks and a neatly arranged coif, falling in dark ringlets to his shoulders. His lips were thin, his smile without teeth or warmth, and in his cold, blue eyes there dwelled an ageless evil that Vyking recognized immediately.

"Vampire," he said. His voice sounded hoarse to his own ears.

"Yes," the man said. Vyking was slightly surprised, but realized the man had no real reason to deny the accusation. "I am the Graf Stelbrenich Von Yurgenhacht. You are in the belly of my keep, where you will spend the rest of your days." He paused. The cold eyes examined Vyking. "Your name."

"Sol Vyking. I am a Knight of the Cosmic Forge."

"Cosmic Forge?" Stelbrenich repeated softly, as if unfamiliar with the term. "I do not recognize the order. But I do respect your power, Sol Vyking. You are very dangerous. I should have destroyed you while you slept. Perhaps I will, eventually. But in the meantime, your blood is a rarified delicacy that I do not wish to do without."

Vyking's stomach lurched, and the throbbing pain in his throat took on new meaning. The leech had been feeding on him. It was so obvious, yet the revelation filled him with horror and dread.

"Your arrival in my lands was unconventional," Stelbrenich continued. "We so seldom receive unsolicited visitors these days. You have news to share, I am sure. Begin with the story of your arrival. I wish to know everything."

Vyking said nothing.

Stelbrenich's thin smile faded. He grabbed Vyking's chin with iron fingers and focused his cold eyes on Vyking. "Speak, mortal," the vampire commanded. There was power behind those words, a psychic compulsion to obey. At full power, wrapped in his armor, Vyking might have resisted. Weak, frail, starved and disoriented, without access to his cosmic abilities, he gave in all too easily. He spoke of the *Shadowstar* and the Kreeghor, of Caleb and Ariel, of the Galactic Tracer Sammadar Orak and the Sinestrian scientist Vodal Kee. He spoke of battling Imperial Guardsman in the vacuum of space, of the burning pain of the *Shadowstar's* mighty main guns, and of the suicidal run on the dread ship itself. He spoke of boarding the ship, destroying the engines, and waiting to die, only to awake in Stelbrenich's keep.

When he finished, Vyking slumped, ignoring the pain in his arms and shoulders. The vampire released him and looked away, a strange look on his ageless face. "I have never heard such things," he said, almost whispering. "My lord must be alerted."

For a moment, Stelbrenich looked as though he might leave Vyking then. But before he did, Stelbrenich opened a tiny cut in Vyking's throat and drank deeply from his veins.

This time, Vyking did weep.

* * *

Time passed.

The creature returned at intervals. He brought water and solid food, enough for Vyking to feel some small measure of strength return to him. Yet still he remained bound and locked, and he knew his muscles were atrophying. Occasionally the vampire would visit. He asked Vyking many questions, and no matter how hard Vyking resisted, Stelbrenich got his answers. And he would feed. Not much and not often, but it was enough to wear away at Vyking's spirit and resistance.

He wondered at the loss of his powers, and eventually came to the conclusion that the vampire had done something to him or to the cage that held him in order to cut him off from the Forge. The knowledge that he had not Fallen did little to brighten his mood; the connection was cut, whatever the means, and he feared that the polluting effect of his imprisonment might taint him forever regardless.

Vyking's mind wandered. He wondered if the destruction of the *Shadowstar* had been final. While his survival meant that his friends were probably not dead, it also meant that the Kreeghor probably survived as well. They had lost contact with Sammadar Orak and his craft during the battle. Vyking hoped that the mercenary and the CCW Marines aboard his ship survived.

He thought of Frances Starling, the love of his life, the woman he had left behind years ago to become a Cosmo-Knight. They had reunited recently, briefly, and he was shocked to see her a middle-aged widow on a mining world. He had hoped that by leaving her when they were young, she would be spared the difficulties and dangers of being a Cosmo-Knight's wife. He hoped she would find someone else, hoped she would have a good life. But after seeing her again, he knew he should have stayed with her, whatever might have happened. He loved her then and he loved her still, but she hated him now. With good reason.

If he had stayed with Frances, would they have had a family? Someone to remember him, now that he was gone? Someone to carry on his name, his legacy, his mission? He had led a life of service, but that seemed empty to him now. No one would mourn his passing. No one would miss one more Cosmo-Knight, lost in the line of duty.

Vyking slept for the first time in years, no longer fueled by cosmic fire. He dreamt strange dreams of possible pasts and forgotten futures, and when he woke, he remained bolted to a pallet in a dark dungeon, forgotten and alone.

Time ceased to have any meaning. Stelbrenich and his servant came and went, Vyking brooded and slept. He wasn't sure how long he was there before he heard the girl's voice.

It happened on one of Horst's visits. The creature lumbered into the room with bread and sausage wrapped in cloth and the bucket of water, but paused as strange voice called to it. "Horst – where are you going? Who is in there?"

Vyking froze, shocked. The voice sounded like that of a very young girl, but what was she doing moving about a vampire's keep? While Vyking reeled, Horst clucked his tongue and turned toward the door, where the girl remained out of sight. Something else quite miraculous happened. Horst spoke.

"Not for you, little one," Horst said. "The Graf's special guest." He moved to close the door.

"Hello!" Vyking called out as loudly as he could. "My name is Sol Vyking, and I am a prisoner here! Please –" He would have said more, but Horst's beefy fist slammed into the side of his head. Vyking tasted copper as he bit his tongue and then he felt himself losing consciousness.

When he awoke, Horst was gone and Stelbrenich had taken his place. The vampire loomed over Vyking, staring at him unblinking with eyes of ice. "You will forget the girl," Stelbrenich commanded. Vyking felt his will crumbling under the vampire's psychic assault.

Yet somehow, he held on to the memory of the girl's voice. Some small, almost forgotten part of himself refused to give in to the vampire, refused to let that one moment of hope be quashed. Perhaps it was the fear he sensed in the vampire, somehow linked to the child. Perhaps it was the simple knowledge that someone other than Horst and Stelbrenich and Stelbrenich's "lord" occupied Vyking's new, limited universe. Perhaps it was the steely remnants of a Cosmo-Knight's resolve that allowed him to resist Stelbrenich this once.

Some days later, the door opened and for once it was neither Horst nor the vampire. The girl had come to visit him.

She tiptoed in, a huge, stuffed bear tucked under one arm, and looked up at him with large, blue eyes. Pale and dark-haired like the Graf, she wore a fine dress and shoes, with a silver chain around her neck. She was pretty, but could not have been more than eight or nine years old. "Hello," she said in a whisper.

"Hello," Vyking said.

She stared at him, clutching her bear tightly. "You don't look scary," she said at last.

Vyking laughed weakly. "I am sorry to disappoint."

"It's alright. You're Sol Vyking? My name is Anasophita."

"A pleasure to meet you, Anasophita." Vyking kept his tone light, not wishing to frighten away his only potential friend. "Thank you for visiting me."

"You're welcome," she said primly. She slowly edge towards him, eyeing the bindings that held him fast against the pallet. "Uncle Stel says you're dangerous, that I mustn't speak to you."

"I see." Vyking looked at her. "Then perhaps you should not be here."

"Maybe." She looked over her shoulder, and for a moment Vyking feared Horst or something worse was behind her, but nothing happened. Then she said, "Bye," and disappeared.

Vyking closed his eyes and laid his head back. The girl was alive, the first living thing besides himself that he had seen in this cursed place. She lived, and she was in grave danger. Stelbrenich would feed upon Vyking until he grew bored and then he would probably kill him, but the vampire had a much more sinister purpose in mind for the girl. Vyking could sense it. Whatever had happened to his powers, to his link with the Forge, his instincts remained. Right now they were screaming at him to do something about the girl. He tested his bonds for the first time in days, but found them just as strong as the first time. He pulled again and again, but all he succeeded in doing was to chafe his wrists. There was nothing he could do. He would not be able to help Anasophita. Nor would she return.

But she did. She came to visit him at irregular intervals, always when he was alone. Uncle Graf slept, she claimed, while Horst and the others had chores to do. She had free run of the keep, except down in the dungeons. But she was a curious child, and somewhat willful, and she felt brave violating the Graf's rules. As for Vyking, he found solace in the few conversations he had with the girl, a sense of normalcy began to return to him, a reminder of the things he had fought for and defended all those years. Her presence, her existence, served as a reminder to him that innocent beings remained in the Megaverse. He resolved to do something for her, find some way to get her away from the Stelbrenich. But how?

Inevitably, they were discovered. Horst went looking for Anasophita elsewhere in the keep and eventually found her in Vyking's dungeon. One look at his terrible countenance and the girl burst into tears. She gave no resistance as Horst dragged her away. The creature leveled a terribly joyful grin at Vyking as they left. Vyking yanked at his bonds and shouted at Horst, but to no avail.

Days passed, or near as much as Vyking could estimate, and neither Horst nor Stelbrenich appeared. Hunger and thirst gnawed at Vyking, while the oppressive darkness weighed heavily on his sense. Mostly, he feared for Anasophita and what her terrible guardian might do to her.

Then Stelbrenich appeared. He pushed the door open part way and slid into the room with the preternatural grace of the vampire, his cloak sweeping behind him. His eyes were bright and his cheeks were flushed. He had fed recently. But on whom?

"You have made a grave mistake, my dear friend," Stelbrenich said. His voice was ice. Despite himself, Vyking flinched at the tone. "You have turned my little niece's heart away from me, and fostered rebellion in my own home. I see that even deprived of your formidable abilities, you still present a great danger to me."

Vyking gritted his teeth and forced himself to say, "I will kill you."

The vampire's smile was terrible. "You'll never have the chance." He leaned forward as his mouth parted, his canines lengthened and a red light glimmered in his eyes. His teeth sank into Vyking's throat and tore flesh. He feasted on Vyking's blood for the last time.

* * *

Once more, Vyking awoke, expecting to be dead and feeling a dull surprise that he was not. Perhaps the vampire wasn't through tormenting him.

He felt a tugging at his wrist and turned his head to look. The effort seemed to take a hundred years, but at last he saw Anasophita playing with the manacle around his left arm. She looked even paler than usual, and he saw a bandage around her throat. Her eyes held a haunted look.

"Ana," he said softly.

She looked up at him, terrified for a moment, and stepped back. "You're alive."

Vyking would have nodded if he had the energy, or if his throat didn't feel like it was on fire. "Are you alright? Did he hurt you?"

She touched the bandage at her throat, frowned, and then returned to the manacle.

"You should leave," Vyking said. "If he catches you here again. . ." He left the words unsaid.

But the girl shook her head. "I'm getting you out of here. I should have done it the first day I saw you, but I was afraid." With a screech of metal, the manacle opened up, revealing Vyking's raw and red wrist. He winced, involuntarily flexing his fingers. Anasophita scurried around to the other side and began to tug on the other manacle. She seemed to have figured out the gimmick, because that one came free sooner than the first. Vyking craned his neck towards the door, watching and listening for any sign of Horst or Stelbrenich.

Anasophita moved to Vyking's feet and began to unlock the bindings there. Vyking stretched his arms and rubbed his sore, aching muscles. Then he attacked the bar across his waist, struggling with the strange locking mechanism. Anasophita managed to get his feet unbound and hurried to unlock the clasp around his neck. In moments, he was free.

Vyking felt strength begin to return to his limbs. He levered himself into a sitting position, and just managed to keep from crying out in agony and alarming the girl. With effort, he slid off the pallet and crashed to the floor. She did cry out then, and hurried to his side. "Get up, Vyking, get up," she urged, pushing at his shoulder.

Vyking felt something burning in his chest, as if a match had suddenly been struck within him. The feeling spread through his trunk and into his extremities, becoming a raging fire. The aches and pains flickered and faded. His muscles strengthened. The wound in his throat closed up, healed in moments. Vyking put his hands beneath him and slowly raised himself up. Anasophita watched him with concern and fear. She reached down to the floor to retrieve her stuffed bear and hugged it close.

Vyking stood. He still felt weak, and he could tell that he had lost nearly ten kilograms, but his head was clearer than it had been in ages. He formed fists, reached out with his senses, and tried to use his cosmic awareness to locate his position. An unfamiliar map of stars appeared in his mind's eye; his cosmic awareness was confused, but functioning. He let it lapse.

"Are you alright?" Anasophita asked, only slightly muffled by the bear.

"Yes," Vyking said, his voice stronger. A flash of blue light illuminated the room, and when it faded, Vyking was encased from head to toe in metallic blue plate armor. A pair of curving horns erupted from his helm. From the visor and the gaps in the armor shined the blackness of the void. The armor was the badge of his office, forsaken to a Fallen Knight. The Forge still trusted him.

"We're leaving this place, Anasophita. I want you to stay behind me, and when I tell you not to look, cover your eyes. Okay?"

She nodded, not saying a word. Already, the bear obscured most of her features.

"It's still me in here," Vyking said, "your friend. I will not allow you to be harmed again." He held out his hand. "Do you trust me?"

Anasophita looked at Vyking over her bear for a moment, then took his hand.

* * *

The rest of the keep proved more impressive than the miniscule bit to which Vyking had previously been exposed. The walls, floor, and ceiling were fashioned from irregularly cut stone blocks, fitted together so perfectly that no mortar was needed. Here and there were carved strange glyphs that gave off a warm glow, the only source of light in the halls.

They passed bizarre creatures in the halls, things worse than Horst, with stick-like bodies and pumpkins for heads, doing menial jobs like scrubbing the floors or carrying things from one room to another. Gradually they moved upward, and the utilitarian halls gave way to something a bit more welcoming, almost lived in. Tapestries hung from the walls alongside works of art, and they also passed furniture carved from dark wood and decorated with brass. Yet still Vyking had not seen a single window.

They stumbled across Horst in a large chamber with a number of staircases in it, talking to a hirsute man in stained leather armor. Both of them looked at Vyking and Anasophita with surprise that quickly changed to alarm.

Horst stepped toward them. "Step away from him, little one. You don't want to get hurt."

The other man dropped to all fours on the floor. Fur exploded across his body and his snout began to lengthen and fill with teeth.

"Close your eyes, Anasophita," Vyking said. She obediently raised her bear in front of her face.

Horst lumbered toward them, murder in his eyes. The werewolf bounded across the room, growling. Vyking met them halfway, desperate to keep Anasophita from being hurt.

Horst aimed a right cross at Vyking, but the Cosmo-Knight caught his fist deftly. He'd felt Horst's blows before, when his body wasn't as strong as megasteel, and he did not fear him now. Almost casually, Vyking crushed Horst's hand, then grabbed his wrist and threw him into the werewolf. Horst looked surprised even as he bowled into his companion and knocked him halfway across the room. Vyking was on them in an instant. Forge-enhanced muscles dealt quickly with Horst, who could not stand up to the beating. But the werewolf proved trickier. He shrugged off most of Vyking's punches and pounced with a growl, but himself proved wholly ineffective against the Cosmo-Knight. Deadly as the werewolf's claws and teeth appeared to be, they couldn't even scratch Vyking's armor.

Desperate, the werewolf lunged in Anasophita's direction, and Vyking hammered him with his eyebeams. The energy blasts could punch through starship shields, but all they did was stun the werewolf momentarily. That was enough. Vyking hog-tied the werewolf with some torn tapestries and left him behind. He knew the werewolf would escape quickly, but hoped to be long gone by the time he did.

Vyking hurried to check on Anasophita. She stood where he had left her, clutching her bear desperately. Vyking frowned. She didn't watch, but she heard the entire battle. "It's alright," he said, crouching down beside her. He dispelled his helmet in order to put her at ease.

The bright flash caused her to flinch, but she brightened when she looked up at him over her bear. "Did they hurt you?"

"No." The werewolf snarled and twisted in his bonds, causing both Vyking and the girl to look at him.

"Are they hurt?" she asked.

"A little bit," Vyking said, "but it couldn't be helped."

"How touching," Stelbrenich's voice echoed in the chamber. Despite himself, Vyking felt a chill pass down his spine at the vampire's words. He rose from his crouch and turned to block Anasophita. At the other end of the room, at the base of a set of stairs, a swirling patch of mist was in the midst of forming into Stelbrenich. The vampire snapped his cloak as he achieved full solidity and strode purposely towards Vyking and Anasophita. "It appears that my lord was correct. I should have killed you. But that is a mistake that can readily be amended."

For a moment, Vyking felt terrified. The vampire's voice transported him back to the cage, to the pallet and the iron bars sealing him to it in the dark room. He felt his throat throb as though the vampire was about to feed again. Then the cosmic fire within him swelled, strengthening his resolve, and he straightened as the vampire approached. "I am no longer your plaything, Stelbrenich. I am free, and my power has been returned to me."

"Yes," Stelbrenich said. "I shall deal with her as soon as I am finished with you. I do not appreciate betrayal, and yet she is my brother's daughter. I can't simply destroy her, but I can teach her obedience." The vampire's pale features twisted savagely. His eyes glowed red and his jaw expanded to accommodate his swelling teeth.

"You will not harm her," Vyking said.

Stelbrenich's gaze fell full upon Vyking. Those alien eyes bored into his. "Step aside, Vyking."

The vampire's compulsion was a terrible thing. Vyking felt his body respond, begin to move to the side, shuffling to the right. Behind him, he heard Anasophita whimper.

Forge grant me strength, Vyking prayed. He stopped moving, even as Stelbrenich crept forward. Anasophita backed away, stumbling and uncertain. Vyking seized Stelbrenich as the vampire sprang towards the girl. Stelbrenich was momentarily surprised, but his strength was almost equal to Vyking's and he was twice as slippery. Somehow he twisted out of Vyking's grip, and as soon as he did, he threw a wild punch at Vyking's head which caught him on the chin and knocked him backward.

Either the vampire was very strong, or Vyking was weaker than he had thought. Either could be true, but he did manage to block the next attack. Then he crashed to the ground with a metallic clangor as the vampire swept his feet out from under him. Stelbrenich laughed, a harsh, cruel sound that echoed in the high-ceilinged chamber.

Vyking was on his feet instantly and gave Stelbrenich a taste of his eyebeams, but the vampire shrugged them off with a chuckle. "Your powers are useless here, Cosmo-Knight," Stelbrenich said.

Vyking grimaced. He feared Stelbrenich was right. But he had to try.

He launched himself at the vampire, boosting his charge with a little bit of flight, and slammed bodily into Stelbrenich, throwing him the length of the chamber. But Stelbrenich twisted in the air, caught the wall with his feet and rebounded back on to the floor. Vyking used his eyebeams again; Stelbrenich stood his ground, but Vyking wasn't aiming at him. The stone flagstone beneath Stelbrenich's feet vaporized as the cerulean beams slammed into them. With a surprised sound the vampire dropped from view. But it was only a momentary respite.

Moving with all the speed he could muster, Vyking flew towards Anasophita, scooped her up in his arms, and blasted up a set of stairs and down another hallway. He heard Stelbrenich calling after them, and risked a look behind. The vampire kept pace in the narrow confines of the corridor quite easily, running and jumping, bouncing off walls and ceiling to gain momentum.

Vyking hooked Anasophita under one arm, noticed she was crying but not making a sound, and used his free hand to grab the edge of a massive wooden chest and heave it behind them. Stelbrenich, moving too swiftly to correct in time, slammed into the chest. Hard.

The vampire crashed to the floor and skidded a few meters as the chest exploded into splinters. In the split second before Vyking darted down a side hall, he saw Stelbrenich struggling to get up, the side of his face mashed nearly flat, splinters of wood sticking out of his flesh.

Only moments later Stelbrenich was back in pursuit, seemingly unharmed. But the smile was gone, replaced with a look of cold fury. Vyking heaved a chair at him next, which Stelbrenich nimbly dodged. But as he did so, Vyking unleashed his eyebeams on the ceiling, raking the stone with blue light, and dropped most of the floor above them on top of the vampire with a resounding crash. Vyking hoped that would slow the undead monster down, but Stelbrenich merely turned into smoke, slid through the gaps, and reformed on their tail.

The winding corridors ended, spilling Vyking and Anasophita into a huge, vaulted room with a set of large double doors at the far end – dark wood banded in brass. Vyking flew down the length of the room and deposited Anasophita near the doors. Then he turned to face Stelbrenich.

The vampire stood at the far end of the room, smiling once more. He flicked a lock of jet black hair from his eyes and walked purposely forward. Vyking noticed a few high-backed chairs set against pillars between Stelbrenich and himself, interspersed between baroque suits of armor. A pair of the creatures with pumpkin heads, unperturbed by Vyking's flight through the hall, knelt off to the right, as they scrubbed the flagstones with soap and water.

Stelbrenich paused as he passed one of the suits of armor, and carefully disengaged the great two-handed sword held in its gauntlets. He hefted the sword in one hand and approached once more.

Vyking edged towards the pumpkin-headed creatures. But Stelbrenich nodded at them, and they scooped up their bucket of water and scurried from the room. Vyking frowned. He darted for a chair, but Stelbrenich was there before him, swinging the sword in a deadly arc. Vyking skidded, spun, and a blue line of energy formed in his right hand, coalescing into his chosen weapon, a longsword the same color as his armor. Stelbrenich's sword shattered into a dozen pieces as Vyking's Forge-charged blade connected with it.

The blade spun in Vyking's hand and slapped Stelbrenich across the face. The vampire felt the impact, reeling, but looked unharmed. Vyking took the opportunity to reach the chair and smash it with one blow. Stelbrenich growled and knocked Vyking's sword from his hand. The blade flew upwards, and with superhuman quickness, Stelbrenich snatched it from the air. Vyking managed to grab a shard of wood from the floor, then ducked as his own sword nearly took off his head.

Stelbrenich laughed. "Suffering to the conquered!" he roared and took a mighty swing that Vyking barely evaded. Stelbrenich slashed again and again, and each time Vyking dodged out of the way. But he was slowing. His imprisonment and torture had left their mark, and even the mighty engine of the Forge was taxed by his suffering and the flight and battle. He would not stand against Stelbrenich much longer, and Vyking knew only too well that his blade could cut him easily. Cut him and kill him.

Then it happened. Stelbrenich scored a hit, shearing off a chunk of plate armor and cutting the flesh beneath. Vyking cursed and gripped his side where the sword had bit him. Stelbrenich seized the opportunity and with a cry, drove the sword through Vyking's chest. Blood filled Vyking's mouth. He slumped towards Stelbrenich.

But now, this close, with the blade touching him, he could dispel it. With a flash of blue light the sword dissolved. Even as it did, Vyking's hand thrust forward, driving the shard of wood into Stelbrenich's heart. The vampire looked at him in amazement and then collapsed in a heap. Vyking slid to his knees.

The wound in his chest slowly closed, and when he felt his strength returning, he summoned the sword once more. With one swift blow, he separated Stelbrenich's head from his shoulders. Then he used his eyebeams to burn both parts of the body, now vulnerable to flame.

Only then did he rise and begin to walk down the hall towards where Anasophita huddled. Somewhere along the way they had lost her bear, but Vyking wasn't sure they should bother going back for it.

He approached the doors, threw the massive bar to unlock them, and then pushed them open. It had been too long since Vyking had felt a breeze, tasted fresh air or seen the sky.

But when the doors boomed open, he saw only dark clouds overhead, occasionally lit by flashes of red lightning. Before the keep was a massive square ringed by squat, ugly buildings.

Massed in the square, squeezed tightly together, stood around ten thousand vampires. They all looked towards the keep as the doors opened, and their eyes flickered with red light as they sensed prey.

Hades, Pits of Hell

Official Source Material for Rifts®

The following material was cut from Carl Gleba's **Rifts® Dimension Book 10: Hades,** in large part, due to space restrictions. We present it here as *official* source material for your gaming pleasure.

Notable Exiles Living in the Southern Cliffs

The southern cliff face is a haven for exiled demons, outcasts, the Fallen, and Lesser Demons like Demon Bats, Demon Flies, Labassu, and Gargoyles. Many of the cave openings are small, but a short passage leads to a large chamber or tunnel network and more caves. For outcasts and the lowly, they represent plenty of places to "get lost" when one doesn't want to be found or bothered. Several exiled Baal-Rogs reside among the outcasts of this area. The majority have been defeated in battle by a mortal on some other plane and can't face their fellow demons in their current state. The others are either hiding from Andras or have been exiled by a Demon Lord. Each has his own story, and most prefer to be alone.

Guldon the Mighty, Quick Stats

Guldon was something of a rogue Baal-Rog who spent many years in the Phoenix Empire on Rifts Earth. He was once ruler of a small city-state called Al-Akba, on the western border and, at least in his mind, was second in power only to the Pharaoh and New Phoenix. He ruled the city with an iron fist for many years until a group of warriors defeated and banished him to Hades. The shame was so great that he has taken to hiding in the cliff caves of the Fire Planes, having only recently been reborn. For now he remains in voluntary exile until the stigma of banishment goes away, which could be a long wait for the Baal-Rog. He was quite imposing and powerful during his reign, now he appears pathetic and broken. He wears nothing but a loincloth and is bitter, angry and brutal, killing anyone who bothers him and his brooding.

Race: Baal-Rog.

Alignment: Diabolic.

Alignment: I.Q. 18, M.E. 14, M.A. 14, P.S. 35, P.P. 27, P.E. 22, P.B. 9, Spd 30, 70 flying.

M.D.C.: 225, was 300. (On S.D.C. worlds Guldon has 92 Hit Points, 60 S.D.C., and an A.R. of 13.)

Experience Level: 3rd, was 10th before he died.

Disposition: Bitter and resentful at his sad fate, he lashes out at others and holds a special contempt for mortal heroes from Rifts Earth.

Skills of Note: Was versed in Wizardry, now all that knowledge is gone. He has the basic Baal-Rog skills, all reduced by ½ for the time being.

Weapons and Equipment: Nothing, just a loincloth and a cave to call his own.

Garamone, Quick Stats

Garamone was one of those rare demons to be won over by a *Demon Queller* in Rifts China. For many years he was bound to Khai Nguyen, who taught the Baal-Rog respect and humility. Eventually, the demon renounced his evil ways and pledged to work at being a better person. The last few years the demon and his master accomplished many good and heroic deeds that will be remembered in song and verse for many generations to come. Sadly, their partnership came to a tragic end when he and his master were ambushed and overwhelmed. Both were killed in battle and Garamone was banished back to Hades. While in his discorporation he lacked many of his normal restraints, and mostly on instinct he found a womb for his rebirth. However, he was not able to save the mortal who bore him and now he hides, feeling shame and guilt for having killed an innocent, failing his master, and being sent back to Hades. If Garamone were ever approached by a band of true heroes (not rogues or Anarchists), he could be easily convinced to join them.

Race: Baal-Rog.

Alignment: Scrupulous. (Yes, good!)

Alignment: I.Q. 18, M.E. 14, M.A. 11, P.S. 36, P.P. 17, P.E. 20, P.B. 6, Spd 40, 110 flying.

M.D.C.: 375, was 500. (On S.D.C. worlds Garamone has 110 Hit Points, 80 S.D.C., and an A.R. of 13.)

Experience Level: 2nd, was 7th before he died.

Disposition: He is a kind and gentle giant who can be paternal and overprotective. He is at a point where he is about ready to leave seclusion and fight for justice and goodness, he just needs a cause and a nudge.

Skills of Note: He knew many Domestic skills such as Bonsai and Go, but they are all faded memories and he must relearn many things. He has all the basic Baal-Rog abilities and skills at their normal proficiency for his level.

Weapons and Equipment: He has managed to come across a Demon Bone Screaming Skull Hammer and Bone Knife.

Y'Tal, Quick Stats

Y'Tal is hiding more for fear than the shame of having been banished. He was tricked into revealing his true name and he was used to find out the true names of several other demons. Now he fears that he will receive a horrible punishment from Andras and his fellow Baal-Rogs. He has a very dark bronzed complexion with shriveled bat wings.

Race: Baal-Rog.

Alignment: Miscreant.

Alignment: I.Q. 16, M.E. 16, M.A. 15, P.S. 33, P.P. 18, P.E. 19, P.B. 6, Spd 30, 100 flying.

M.D.C.: 300, was 400. (On S.D.C. worlds Y'Tal has 100 Hit Points, 70 S.D.C., and an A.R. of 13.)

Experience Level: Third, was 6th level before he died.

Disposition: A coward and a fool, in addition to being mean, selfish and suspicious, he now has a wicked paranoid streak and trusts no one.

Skills of Note: He has all the basic Baal-Rog skills at half their normal proficiency.

Weapons and Equipment: He owns nothing of value or interest.

Notable Members of the Brass Guard II

Warlord Thantu

Thantu is the current leader of the Brass Guard II and one of the founding members of the original Brass Guard. He's led many missions and dealt with the failures as well as the successes. Impressed by this combat veteran, Andras made Thantu the foundation around which the Brass Guard II was built. Not only has he proven to be an outstanding and brilliant leader, he is also a good teacher.

As of yet, Thantu has not let his lord down and the team's success rate is impressive at 95%. He knows when he is overmatched and has yet to let his demon ego get in the way of the success of a mission. He has also proven to be patient (something demons are not known for) as well as cunning, resourceful and highly adaptable. He is respected by his teammates, and they never question his orders unless input is specifically requested. Warlord Thantu has come to value the ideas and different points of view from his men and he welcomes constructive

suggestions. However, questioning his orders usually results in immediate discipline and this is something that new recruits learn immediately.

He is your typical large, bronze Baal-Rog. He is often seen in his Brass Guard armor with a huge sword (6D6 M.D.) swung behind. He also wears a black cape with the symbol of the Brass Guard in gold embroidered on it. He wears a ruby colored gauntlet on his right hand when going into combat because it's a unique magic item he won in combat. It has become the unofficial symbol of leadership in the Brass Guard II.

Race: Baal-Rog.

Alignment: Aberrant.

Alignment: I.Q. 18, M.E. 17, M.A. 18, P.S. 35, P.P. 18, P.E. 22, P.B. 8, Spd 40, 100 flying (70 mph/112 km).

M.D.C.: 800. (On S.D.C. worlds like Hades, Thantu has 112 Hit Points, 78 S.D.C., and an A.R. of 14.)

Horror Factor: 14

Size: 14 feet (4.3 m) tall.

Weight: 1000 pounds (450 kg).

P.P.E.: 300

Natural Abilities: Standard for a Baal-Rog.

R.C.C. Skills of Note: Basic and Advanced Math 92%, Literate in Dragonese/Elven, Splugorth, and Demongogian 98%, Intelligence 88%, Forgery 45%, Wilderness Survival 70%, Land Navigation 80%, Swim 70%, Climb 80%/70%, Dance 80%, Streetwise 80%, Lore: Demons & Monsters 80%, Lore: Faeries 60%, W.P. Sword, W.P. Chain, and W.P. Whip.

M.O.S. Skills: Prowl 79%, Surveillance 75%, Use and Recognize Poisons 70%/62%, Track (people) 98%, and Hand to Hand: Assassin at 9th level.

Experience Level: 9th Level Brass Guard II.

Attacks per Melee (Includes those from Hand to Hand: Assassin): 11.

Damage: As per Supernatural P.S.; 5D6+29 S.D.C. for a restrained punch, 4D6 M.D. on a full strength punch, 1D4x10 M.D. on a power punch, 5D6 on a kick, or by weapon or magic.

Bonuses (includes all bonuses): +3 on initiative and Perception Rolls, +7 to strike, +8 to parry and dodge, +7 to roll with impact, +7 to pull punch, knockout/stun on a 17-20, body flip/throw, +3 to disarm, +3 to save vs magic, +12 to save vs Horror Factor, impervious to fire.

Magic: Standard for Baal-Rogs.

Psionics: None.

Vulnerabilities/Penalties: Standard for Baal-Rogs. Also, despite his relatively level-headed nature, his team has had no major defeats to date, and sooner or later, he may underestimate a foe that could cost him dearly.

Rivals and Enemies: Numerous, however in his line of work, no one knows his true name, and even fewer beings outside Hades even know of the Brass Guard II. As far as his enemies are concerned, he is a faceless demon to be exterminated.

Allies: Thantu answers directly to Andras so this has given him a very powerful ally who is used very wisely. His team members are also considered allies, except for Blitz, who covets his position.

Magic Items of Note: Thantu carries as his main weapon a Greater Rune Sword, an *Impaler* from Rifts Atlantis, with fire spells to complement Thantu's existing magic abilities. It is also a *soul drinker* and can do so three times per day. The sword has an I.Q. of 16, is Aberrant in alignment and does 6D6+6 M.D. (S.D.C. in S.D.C. environment) +2D6 when fighting Deevils and Vampires, and double damage against Alien Intelligences! The sword can cast the following fire spells; Fire Bolt (7), Fire Globe (40), Fire Gout (20), and Firequake (160). This particular Impaler has 200 P.P.E., and recovers 10 P.P.E. per hour, double on ley lines and triple on a ley line nexus. All spells are equal to a 6th level caster.

The cape is a Cape of Shadows (from the Palladium World) and allows its owner to *Shadow Meld* as per the spell three times per day for an hour at a time.

The red gauntlet is some sort of a Rune Weapon he calls the Last Blood Demon Claw. Damage is only 4D6 M.D. (S.D.C. in S.D.C. environments), but it does 1D6x10 to good supernatural beings and creatures of magic, like dragons.

Ragnarl, Quick Stats

Ragnarl is second-in-command and the team's Surveillance Specialist. He often scouts out all targets before the team strikes, using his three junior trainees for assistance.

On one mission to Dyval he was attacked by Deevil forces using a new kind of metal that has left him severely scarred.

Race: Baal-Rog.

Alignment: Aberrant.

Alignment: I.Q. 15, M.E. 15, M.A. 15, P.S. 34, P.P. 22, P.E. 23, P.B. 3, Spd 20, 100 flying.

M.D.C.: 700. (On S.D.C. worlds Ragnar has 94 Hit Points, 92 S.D.C., and an A.R. of 14.)

Experience Level: 6th.

Disposition: Ragnar has gone from a wild man on the battlefield to calm and patient. He likes his job as a surveillance expert because he does it so well.

Skills of Note: All those under the Surveillance Specialist M.O.S. and the usual for a Baal-Rog.

Weapons and Equipment: Typical for the Brass Guard II. However, he did come across a Kizh Sensor Gauntlet (see **Rifts® World Book 21: Splynn Dimensional Market** for details), which he finds quite useful.

E'Ell, Quick Stats

E'Ell is the lead Espionage Specialist for the team. She is personally training two junior members in this M.O.S. She is as capable as any male Baal-Rog and merciless in combat.

Race: Baal-Rog.

Alignment: Anarchist.

Alignment: I.Q. 15, M.E. 18, M.A. 12, P.S. 32, P.P. 18, P.E. 20, P.B. 7, Spd 20, 100 flying.

M.D.C.: 700. (On S.D.C. worlds E'Ell has 80 Hit Points and 70 S.D.C. with an A.R. of 14.)

Experience Level: 7th.

Disposition: Quiet and observant, and when she looks at you it's as if she's looking right into your soul.

Skills of Note: All M.O.S. Skills under the Espionage Specialist, and Lore: Magic 75%.

Weapons and Equipment: Your typical Brass Guard II gear. In addition, she has an amulet that gives her the ability of Metamorphosis: Superior (i.e., into anything) twice a day for an hour at a time.

Blitz, Quick Stats

Blitz is the team's senior Military Specialist. He is very vocal in his opinions, mostly because he has come up with many of the plans and strategies that the team has employed over the last year with stunning success. On his bronze physique he has a noticeable crimson hue in his wings when he spreads them, and a few scars.

Race: Baal-Rog.

Alignment: Miscreant.

Alignment: I.Q. 16, M.E. 19, M.A. 15, P.S. 38, P.P. 18, P.E. 22, P.B. 4, Spd 20, 120 flying (82 mph/131 km).

M.D.C.: 500 (On S.D.C. worlds Blitz has 83 Hit Points, 74 S.D.C. and an A.R. of 14.)

Experience Level: 7th.

Disposition: Mean and cruel, despite his conditioning and training, he still covets Thantu's position and can be very jealous when he doesn't get what he wants.

Skills of Note: All those under the Military Specialist O.C.C. and those common to Baal-Rogs. In addition, he has taken it upon himself to learn Demolitions 65%, however this has been a trial by fire learning experience, so he may not be ready to use it for some time.

Weapons and Equipment: A variety of 3D6 conventional M.D. grenades from Phase World and two Type-2 Fusion Blocks.